HOW TO CONQUER AIR POLLUTION
A JAPANESE EXPERIENCE

Other volumes in this series

Studies in Environmental Science 38

HOW TO CONQUER AIR POLLUTION
A JAPANESE EXPERIENCE

Edited by

H. Nishimura

Department of Chemical Engineering, Faculty of Engineering,
University of Tokyo, Bunkyo-ku, Tokyo 113, Japan

ELSEVIER
Amsterdam — Oxford — New York — Tokyo 1989

ELSEVIER SCIENCE PUBLISHERS B.V.
Sara Burgerhartstraat 25
P.O. Box 211, 1000 AE Amsterdam, The Netherlands

Distributors for the United States and Canada:

ELSEVIER SCIENCE PUBLISHING COMPANY INC.
655, Avenue of the Americas
New York, NY 10010, U.S.A.

ISBN 0-444-88537-4

Printed in The Netherlands

Preface

Despite growing concern over global air pollution, urban air pollution still remains in most parts of the world and actually threatens the health of people. Regardless of the vast amount of knowledge on its causes and the tremendous development of control technology, effective countermeasures are slow to be implemented. Sometimes because of economic difficulties and sometimes because of differences in opinion over the measures to be taken.

In this situation, Japan can be praised because of its success in controlling air pollution. Now in Tokyo, one can enjoy "clean air" in spite of the highly concentrated activity and congested traffic. It is difficult to imagine the smog mantle which covered Tokyo twenty years ago, causing immense irritation to the eyes and throat, and bringing a permanent "dusk" to the city.

Until relatively recently, most people in Japan thought that the worsening air quality was an inevitable consequence of industrialization and thought that they should endure it. However, several severe incidents made them recognize the dreadful consequences of air pollution and drove them to demand tighter pollution controls. The strong will of the people first moved the local governments and then influenced national policy which inevitably has changed the attitude of industry, traditionally resistant to tighter controls.

Based on the Japanese experience, this book provides a basic background to help conquer air pollution. It begins with a well documented history of the fight against air pollution, always starting with protests from the victims and ending with the willing cooperation of industry. It tells of the processes and mechanisms of reaching a social consensus on pollution control.

The book describes a successful approach to air pollution control which has integrated well founded scientific knowledge into an effective legal system. The essential steps are the establishment of ambient air quality standards, the introduction of the total allowable mass of emission and the legal control of each emission based on diffusion equations. The scientific background of this approach is fully explained from epidemiology to computer simulations of air quality.

The book presents an up-to-date account of emission control technology. It also deals with the controversial issue of health damage compensation based on actual experience.

An important feature of the book is that it is written by authors who were actually in the forefront of the battle against air pollution in Japan. Two of them (H.K. and M.H.) successively worked as the Director General of the Bureau of Air Quality of the central government and another (H.N.) helped local governments to force the central government to implement the most stringent auto-emission controls in the world.

The book is intended not only for scientists, engineers and administrative planners dealing with air pollution control but also for ordinary citizens concerned about the problem. It may also be of interest to those curious about the Japanese way of reaching a social consensus.

Hajime Nishimura

August, 1989

CONTENTS

X

Chapter 6
THE POLLUTION-RELATED HEALTH DAMAGE COMPENSATION LAW by Michio Hashimoto

CONTRIBUTORS

Michio HASHIMOTO
  Former Director General of Bureau of Air Quality, Environment Agency, Japan

Hitoshi KASUGA
  Professor of Public Health, Tokai University. Former Director General of
  Bureau of Air Quality, Environment Agency, Japan

Saburo KATO
  Director at Bureau of Air Quality, Environment Agency, Japan

Hajime NISHIMURA
  Professor of Chemical Engineering, University of Tokyo

Masayoshi SADAKATA
  Professor of Chemical Engineering, University of Gumma

Yukio YANAGISAWA
  Assistant Professor at Harvard School of Public Health

Chapter 1

HISTORY OF AIR POLLUTION CONTROL IN JAPAN

MICHIO   HASHIMOTO

1.1   INTRODUCTION

The quality of a country's environment depends on complex relationships.
These include the country's economic growth patterns, use of resources, density
of population, geographical formations, political administration, and social
attitudes. Accordingly, this chapter discusses the impact of these and other
factors on the principal events that comprise the history of air pollution
control in Japan.

Japan lies on a 3000 km-long archipelago situated in the western Pacific.
Ragged mountain ranges run down the center of the main island of Honshu and
form the divide between the Pacific Ocean and Japan Sea sides of the country.
Japan is in a temperate climatic zone and has four seasons. It is a small
country, consisting of about 370,000 km^2, of which only a quarter is flat.
Nearly 60% of the population lives in 2.6% of the total land area. Japan's
population was 34 million in 1868, 73 million in 1946, and 120 million in 1984.
In 1983, life expectancy was 74.20 years for men and 79.78 years for women. In
1984, the birth rate was 12.5 per 1000, the crude death rate was 6.2 per 1000,
and the natural increase rate was 6.3 per 1000. At present, 9.8% of the
population is over 65 years old.

The Meiji Restoration of 1868 marks the end of the rule of feudal shoguns
and the emergence of the modern Japanese state. The arrival of Commodore
Perry's canon-bearing black ships ten years earlier and the subsequent realization that Japan was far behind the West in technological development convinced the Meiji leaders that Japan urgently needed rapid economic development.

Economic growth was especially swift during the 1950s and 1960s. The economic growth during this period amplified the factors which formed the basis of
Japan's air pollution problem. Population, GNP, assets, and energy consumption
per unit of habitable land increased dramatically. Table 1.1 shows that in
Japan in 1983 these variables were much higher than in West Germany, France,
Great Britain, and the United States. In addition, the size of Japanese
industrial sectors which consumed energy and raw materials expanded in relation

to all industrial sectors. Between 1935 and 1983, primary energy consumption in Japan increased 10.9 times, and electric power generation increased 25.0 times. In the late 1950s, hydropower began to supplement coal, which was Japan's primary energy source. In the mid-1960s, petroleum largely replaced coal, and in 1965 nuclear power began to be used increasingly. In accordance with policies adopted to deal with the first and second oil shocks, petroleum consumption has declined and coal and nuclear energy consumption have increased. In 1969, liquid natural gas was introduced as an alternative, clean fuel. In the past two decades, the energy demand structure has also changed. The mining and manufacturing sectors consume less energy due to conservation programs, and the transportation and consumer sectors consume more. The latter is due to a shift in the mode of transportation from railroads to automobiles and in the increased use of air conditioning in homes and offices.

Six principal factors had an impact on the management of air pollution control in Japan. These are: (i) relevant clauses in the Meiji Constitution and the current constitution; (ii) the role and effectiveness of the central and local governments; (iii) the court decisions in the pollution trials; (iv) legislation, economic incentives, and technology related to air pollution control; (v) growth, development, energy, and transportation policy; and (vi) international pollution-related events. Table 1.2 presents a chronological overview of pollution-related events from 1868-1984.

1.2 THE PREWAR PERIOD

The Meiji Restoration of 1868 ended the rule of the Tokugawa Shogunate and Japan's 300-year-old, closed-door policy. The new, Meiji leaders restored the seat of sovereignty to the emperor and created a modern, central government. They moved the capital from Kyoto to Edo, newly named Tokyo. In 1868, the two

TABLE 1.1

Population, GNP, assets, and energy consumption per km^2 of habitable land

	Japan	W.Germany	France	Britain	U.S.A.
Population	1,452	386	158	357	55
GNP (10^6 YEN)	2,989	1,161	436	648	130
Total Fixed Assets (10^6 YEN)	952	265	94	137	20
as percentage of DNA	31.9%	22.8%	21.6%	20.3%	15.7%
Energy Consumption (Coal Equivalent; ton)	5,230	2,240	700	1,750	520

Source: National Land Agency, Annual Report 1983

largest cities were Tokyo and Osaka, and the population of Tokyo was already over one million. Urbanization and industrialization in Tokyo, Osaka, and other cities began to cause environmental degradation. The worst problems were cholera, urban filth, black smoke, and offensive odours from animal processing plants. This section describes some of the most famous cases of air pollution in the prewar period.

The Ashio copper mine case. Copper had been mined at Ashio along the banks of the Watarase River since the early 1600s. By 1880, air and water pollution from the mine began to take its toll on the lives of the area's farmers and fishermen. Emissions from the mine's smelter contained a high concentration of SO_2, which devastated about 5000 ha of forest in the vicinity.[1] The mine's effluent contained sulfuric acid, ammonia, aluminum oxide, magnesia, iron, copper, chlorine, arsenic, nitric acid, and phosphoric acid. The effluent drained into the Watarase River, which irrigated the land, and ruined the farmers' crops.[2]

In 1891, Ashio's farmers and fishermen began to demand that the government order the mine to take pollution control measures or to shut down completely. In the following years, they gained the support of prominent Meiji scholars, writers, and statesmen. M.P. Shozo Tanaka called on the government to protect the people's constitutional rights and to revoke the mine's concession. The government responded by forming the Ashio Mining Hazards Study Committee under direct control of the Cabinet, but little concrete action was taken. On 23 March 1897, 800 farmers marched to Tokyo to demand action. They were intercepted by police and a violent skirmish broke out. Faced with a peasant uprising, the government had no recourse but to take action. On 27 May 1897, the Minister of Agriculture and Commerce issued a schedule for preventive construction. Accordingly, in 1898 the Ashio mine built precipitation and filtration ponds and installed desulfurization equipment. However, these measures proved largely ineffective and air pollution from the mine continued to devastate the forest and farmland in the area.

The Besshi copper mine case. Records indicate that residents who lived near the Besshi mine in Shikoku were already lodging complaints against the mine during the Tokugawa era in the 1600s. In 1885, the government approved the installation of a new blast furnace in the village of Niihama on the sea coast, despite the protest of farmers' unions in the surrounding area. The new furnace discharged smoke with a high concentration of SO_2, and farmers began to notice crop damage, as they had warned would happen. The farmers appealed to the prefectural government to take relief measures and remove the blast furnace from Niihama. The Osaka Mine Safety Bureau and the agricultural laboratory of the Ministry of Agriculture, Trade and Industry confirmed the existence of crop damage from smoke. Nevertheless, the operators of the mine continued to deny

Table 1.2

A chronological overview of pollution-related events from 1868-1984

Year	Age Character & Population	Economic, Social & Political Remarks
1868	Meiji Restoration	Open to foreigners, Catch up with West, Modern state, Urbanization
1888	34×10^6 1872	
1889	Imperial Congress	Strong nation, Wealthy state, Social movement Wars, Heavy industry
1930	39×10^6 1889	
1931	Mobilization for War, Militarism	Economic panic, Rural decline, Suppression
1945	65×10^6 1931	
1946	Post War Chaos, New Constitution	SCAP order, War-devasted cities, Poverty, Hunger, Disorganization of old power
1949	73×10^6 1946	
1950	Economic Recovery, Peace Treaty, Korean War	National Comprehensive Development Law; (Food, Energy, Disaster)
1954	83×10^6 1950	
1955	Economic Growth	Urbanization, Industrialization, Energy Shift (Coal to Petroleum
1959	89×10^6 1955	
1960	Regional Industrial Development	Mass production, Consumption, Organized anti-pollution action
1964	93×10^6 1960	
1965	Adverse Side Effects of High Economic Growth	Socialist power locally, Archipelago reform plan
1969	98×10^6 1965	
1970	Special Congress, Court Decisions, Social Crisis	Social & political crisis, $ shock, Oil shock, Stockholm Conference, PPP
1974	111×10^6 1970	
1975	Crisis is Over, World Recession	Economic recession, International Issues
1979	120×10^6 1975	
1980	Administrative Reform, Global issues	New, high technology, Structural change of industry, International issues, Responsibility
1984	120×10^6 1984	

Environmental Issues

Epidemics, Urban filth,
Black smoke, Offensive
odours, National heritage
protection, Police control

Mining hazard disputes,
(Ashio, Besshi, Hitachi)
Industrial pollution, Mining Law,
Factory Law, City Planning Law etc.

Urban hygiene (air, noise),
National park, Rural sanitation,
Strict liability

Epidemics, DDT spray, Special city
plan for reconstruction,
Industrial Pollution Control
Ordinance (Tokyo)

Public Ceasing Law, Ube City
approach to air pollution,
MHW survey on pollution, Atomic
bomb test at Bikini

Smoke Control Law, Public
investment for sewage, Incinerator
nightsoil digestion plant

Basic Law for EP Control Measures,
MHW conclusion of itai-itai
disease, Low sulfur fuel supply
plan by MITI

Drastic policy changes,
Environment Agency, Compensation
Law, Strict liability, Total Mass
Regulation, EIA etc.

Amenity, Habitat, Energy & resource
saving, Stringent autoexhaust
control

Lake eutrophication, Transport &
Environment, Terminal disposal of
wastes, Green conservation, Cabinet
Resolution of EIA, Global
Environment

any connection between the smoke from its plant and the farmers' crop damage.

In 1898, the Osaka Bureau of Mines issued an order based on the Mining Law of 1890 directing the mine to move its operations to Shisaka Island in the Inland Sea. The company moved the mine in 1905, but this resulted in an expanded zone of smoke damage in the new area.[4]

In 1923, the mine installed new stacks, but they proved ineffective in reducing air pollution. In 1925, the mine installed a Petersen-type, sulfuric acid recovery system and increased the height of its stacks to 48 m.[5]

These measures at last succeeded in reducing smoke damage.

The Hitachi copper mine case. In 1905, the new owners of the Hitachi mine in Ibaraki prefecture greatly expanded the mine's operations. Heavy smoke poured from the smelting works and caused damage to the forest and farmland near the plants. By 1912, the damage extended to over twenty surrounding towns and villages. The village of Irishima was especially hard hit, and the village farmers' union lodged many protests. In 1909, the central government established the Committee for Prevention of Mining Hazards, which undertook an investigation of the matter. On the advice of the committee, the mine established a meteorological observatory and built a low, thick stack in 1913. However, the new stack only aggravated the smoke pollution problem. Angry farmers countered by establishing an anti-pollution organization which took daily recordings of the smoke level. The mine's meteorological work resulted in the discovery of high altitude air currents flowing towards the sea. The mine then built a high stack of 150 m to discharge its emissions into this air current. Thereafter, smoke damage gradually decreased.[6]

Other cases. Numerous instances of pollution damage occurred near other mines as well. Some of these included the Toroku, Saganoseki, Kosaka, Kamioka, and Annaka mines. After the 1940s, aluminum smelter plants caused air pollution damage to the areas in their vicinity. The most famous of these is Nippon Keikinzoku in Kambara, Shizuoka prefecture. In addition, pharmaceutical companies emitted Cl_2 gas which caused extensive air pollution. An especially notable episode occurred in Kanagawa prefecture in 1910.[7]

The Asano Cement Company case. In 1883, the government transferred a cement plant that it owned and operated in Tokyo to the Asano Cement Company. Especially after 1903, dust from the plant began to cover the surrounding neighborhood. Citizens became angry and demanded the removal of the plant. After years of inaction by the government, Asano introduced an electric dust collector in 1917. The so-called Cottrell's precipitator turned the dust into potash fertilizer. This advance in technology solved the dust problem and the citizens dropped their complaints.[8]

The Osaka Alkali Company case. In 1906-7, Osaka Alkali, a copper refinery, discharged high concentrations of SO_2 and H_2SO_4, which caused damage to crops

in the surrounding farmland. Thirty-six landlords and tenants sued Osaka
Alkali in the Osaka District Court for negligence. The court held the defendant liable, and the decision was upheld on appeal in the Osaka High Court.
However, the Supreme Court ruled that the use of the best available, pollution-
control technology would shield the defendant from liability and remanded to
the High Court. On December 27th, 1919, the Osaka High Court held that Osaka
Alkali had never used the best available technology because its stacks were
only 100-120 shaku (30-40 meters) high whereas the stacks of the Hitachi mine
and foreign smelters were much higher.[9]

The Yahata iron and steel works case. The government set up a large iron
and steel works in Yahata in Fukuoka prefecture to provide iron and steel for
the army and navy. Almost the entire community was directly or indirectly
dependent on the industry for their livelihood. The works belched a dense,
colorful smoke visible from anywhere in the town. Yet, there is no record of
complaints by the citizens. This is because the smoke was seen as a symbol of
the town's prosperity.[10]

The early legislative and administrative efforts at pollution control were
primitive. In 1877, the Tokyo police started regulating boilers. Also in
1877, the Osaka police began to regulate factories under a new ordinance
entitled Regulations on the Control of Manufacturing Plants. The law
prohibited locating an animal processing plant in the metropolitan district. In
1882, Osaka amended this regulation and made the control of environmental
pollution and other public hazards one of the aims of factory regulation. The
new rule required the selection of industrial sites so as to minimize pollution. The ordinance used the term "kōgai" (environmental pollution) and
created a basis in law for air pollution-related legal action. In 1888, the
Osaka police prohibited locating a factory with a stack in the central part of
the city. In 1913, the Osaka prefecture established the Smoke Abatement
Committee in the Institute of Industrial Technology. The committee attempted
to enact the proposed Regulation on Smoke Abatement, but business interests put
up a strong challenge and the measure failed that year. It was finally passed
in 1932. In 1912, the government passed the Factory Law after many years of
lobbying. The law permitted government personnel to make inspections of
factories. The law did not expressly list pollution control as one of the aims
of the inspections, but this was done under the rubric of protecting public
security. Business and industrial groups opposed the new law and managed to
delay its implementation for three years.[11]

In 1913, the Osaka Municipal Hygiene Institute began to monitor air pollution in Osaka by measuring deposited matter. In addition, Osaka began to monitor CO in 1928, and SO_2 by the PbO_2 method in 1933.[12]

In 1927, Tokyo began an air pollution monitoring program similar to the

Osaka program. The Tokyo Metropolitan Police recorded a sharp increase in the number of pollution-related complaints around 1932.[13]

In 1928 the Sanitation Bureau sponsored an official meeting of prefectural health officers in which the problems of air pollution control were discussed.[14]

These early efforts at pollution control were largely ineffective. Pollution levels in the large cities continued to increase. However, certain developments quietly took place during the prewar period that would enable the formulation and implementation of strong, pollution-control policies two decades later. This was the development of the prefectural and municipal government system. Irate victims of a factory's pollution invariably turned first to local government for redress. Local initiatives provided the first programs of pollution control and compensation upon which later national programs were modeled. In addition, the prewar period saw the establishment of a network of national and local hygiene laboratories. Finally, the compulsory education system raised the general level of competency and produced a pool of talented bureaucrats and technicians equipped to deal with the many complex issues of pollution control.

1.3 LOCAL INITIATIVES IN THE POSTWAR PERIOD

The legal basis of local autonomy. The central government organized the system of local government in 1871, and established cities, towns, and villages in 1881, and prefectures in 1890. Although the Imperial Constitution of 1889 did not grant autonomy to local governments, the ministry of the Interior in fact permitted a measure of local autonomy. However, the Ministry maintained considerable authority by appointing the prefectural governors, who also served as the director-generals of the prefectural police. The administration of public health matters came under the jurisdiction of the police.

In 1946-7, the Supreme Commander of the Allied Powers abolished the Imperial Constitution, disbanded the Ministry of the Interior, and assisted in drafting the new constitution. The new constitution provided for local autonomy, and the central government passed the Local Autonomy Law in 1947. The Local Autonomy Law provided for the election of prefectural governors and municipal mayors, and authorized local governments to enact ordinances which did not conflict with national laws. Thus, prefectures, cities, towns, and villages now had the legislative authority to regulate pollution.

Tokyo. In 1949, the metropolitan government of Tokyo passed the Factory Pollution Prevention Ordinance in response to complaints by the citizens about industrial pollution. The ordinance authorized the metropolitan government to stop or limit a factory's operations where the community was harmed by dust, offensive odours, poisonous gases, steams, liquid wastes, noise, or vibrations.

The specific devices used were notifications, permits, and orders to install pollution-control equipment. In addition, the ordinance required new factories to apply for permits, the issue of which was linked to building permits and city planning.

The ordinance was of limited value in achieving air pollution control. For example, it did not set quantitative emission standards, and the standards for factory operations were absent or unclear. Moreover, there were no penalties for violations. From a regulatory perspective, the ordinance was virtually ineffective.[15]

Kanagawa, Osaka, and Fukuoka. U.S. military spending during the Korean War helped to accelerate economic growth in Japan during the 1950s. This in turn led to pollution in many of Japan's industrial centers. In 1951, 1954, and 1955, the Kanagawa, Osaka, and Fukuoka prefectures each passed ordinances modeled on the Tokyo ordinance.

Ube. The three main industries in the city of Ube in Yamaguchi prefecture were coal mining, cement making, and chemical manufacturing. Ube's approach to the control of air pollution from these industries was unique. Instead of the local government unilaterally setting mandates for pollution control to which industry was required to comply, Ube's city government, industry, and local university cooperated. Ube formed a committee comprised of representatives from city government, local industry, the university, and interested citizens to jointly develop a pollution control program. Professor Y. Nose, a professor of public health at Yamaguchi University Medical School, conducted an epidemio-logical study of the health effects of air pollution. In 1951, the city council passed a resolution recommending that local industries install dust collectors, and that the city purchase a water spray truck and expand urban greenery. In 1954, K. Nakayasu, vice president of Ube Kosan, visited the United States and was deeply impressed with the progress in air pollution control in Pittsburgh, Pennslyvania since his last visit. Nakayasu decided to adopt business policies which would help make Ube an attractive, clean industrial city. The joint committee commissioned technical and economic feasibility studies and finally decided to adopt voluntary quantitative emission standards for dust. The standard was set at 1.2 g/m^3 with 97% dedusting efficiency to be achieved by FY 1960. From 1951-63, industry invested nearly ¥1.2 billion for more than 40 dedusting facilities. This resulted in a reduction in dust to one-seventh of the former level.[16]

The central government was impressed with the success of the Ube program, and it adopted the Ube emission standard for the Smoke and Soot Regulation Law of 1962.

Yokkaichi. In 1959, a huge complex of oil refineries and petrochemical and power plants began operations in the city of Yokkaichi in Mie prefecture. Soon afterwards, animals and plants in the area began to die, and the fish emitted a strong, oily smell. More serious evidence of environmental degradation began to appear in 1961. Local doctors reported a sharp increase in the incidence of asthma, emphysema, bronchitis, and other respiratory ailments among residents of Isozu a village near the factories. The Smoke and Soot Regulation Law of 1962 was ineffective against the new type of pollution emitted by the petro-chemical complex. Gases from the complex contained SO_x, not the visible, black smoke or heavy deposits targeted by the Smoke and Soot Regulation Law. More-over, desulfurization technology was still not available.

Residents of the area lodged protests against the complex, but the operators largely ignored their pleas. Thereafter, the Mie prefecture health center in Yokkaichi and the Yokkaichi city government began an investigation of the health effects of the pollution. They systematically and continuously monitored air pollution levels and meteorological conditions. They were assisted in this, and in the analysis of the collected data, by Professor K. Yoshida of the public health department of the Medical School of Mie Pre-fectural University and the prefectural health department. Also, they developed a simulation model of the air flow of the pollutants in the area.

Later, the Ministry of Health and Welfare (MHW) and the Ministry of Inter-national Trade and Industry (MITI) established the Kurokawa Investigation Task Force to investigate the air pollution problem at Yokkaichi and make recom-mendations. In accordance with the Kurokawa recommendations, the complex installed higher stacks in 1963. This resulted in greater emission diffusion and lowered the peak concentrations of SO_2, which had been as high as 2.5 ppm/hr. However, it also had the effect of expanding the pollution zone.[17]

In 1965, Yokkaichi city began a Special Medical Relief Program for Pollu-tion-Related Diseases, financed by Mie prefecture. The program was based on the pollution and health effect studies carried out by Mie prefecture, Mie University, and the Ministry of Health and Welfare. The program provided free medical examinations for the sick and financial relief for a few officially certified victims. Despite the remedial measures which had been taken, the pollution worsened from 1965-67. In 1967, twelve victims filed suit against the petrochemical complex for damage to their health. The press provided extensive coverage of the trial. In 1972, the court issued a decision solidly upholding the plaintiffs' claims. The decision broke new doctrinal ground on several fronts. In response to the decision, Mie prefecture enacted the Environmental Pollution Control Ordinance. The new ordinance regulated total SO_2 mass emissions such that an air quality standard of 0.017 ppm/year would be met. According to Professor Yoshida, the total mass emission regulation was very effective.[18]

Later, the central government modeled national legislation on the Yokkaichi project.

The pre-siting studies conducted by Osaka and Nishinomiya were crude, early examples of environmental impact assessments. Osaka and Nishinomiya devised and carried out these pre-siting assessments entirely on their own, local initiative, without the assistance or involvement of the central government. [19]

Mishima-Numazu. In 1963, the central government designated the Mishima-Numazu area in Shizuoka prefecture as a "special industrial development zone" under the National Comprehensive Development Plan of 1962. In 1963, Shizuoka prefecture announced plans for the construction of the nation's largest petro-chemical complex on the site. The plans called for an electric power station, a petroleum refinery, and several petrochemical plants. At that time, the municipal governments of Mishima and Numazu supported the designation, but the citizens organized anti-pollution and anti-development campaigns under the slogan "No More Yokkaichi". Mishima residents persuaded local landowners not to sell their land to the advancing industries, and Numazu residents held mass demonstrations against the complex. In addition, they organized study sessions on the problems of air pollution and invited scientists to attend. Also, they made observation trips to Yokkaichi. The groups opposing the petrochemical complex claimed over 10,000 supporters, and they set the social and political climate of the time.

In accordance with Shizuoka prefecture's request, MITI and MHW recom-missioned the Kurokawa Investigation Task Force, which had earlier investigated medical relief program and the total mass emission ordinance.

Osaka and Nishinomiya: Environmental impact assessments. The problems at Yokkaichi alerted local governments elsewhere to the need for environmental impact assessments of proposed industrial complex projects. In 1960, Osaka prefecture planned to build a huge industrial complex on reclaimed land in Osaka Bay. The Department of Commerce and Industry of Osaka prefecture estab-lished an expert committee to conduct pre-siting reviews of the environmental protection plans of companies planning to locate plants on the reclaimed land. The expert committee solicited data on the companies' pollution abatement plans and extracted written commitments for pollution-control measures. These mea-sures were taken prior to the final siting decision. The expert committee conducted the reviews in secret, and did not disclose any information submitted by the companies to the public.

Similarly, the city of Nishinomiya in Hyogo prefecture planned to build an industrial complex in another land-reclamation project in Osaka Bay. Nishi-nomiya city and an anti-development group comprised of traditional brewers independently organized pre-siting study teams. Nishinomiya city built a meteorological observation post with an automatic air pollution monitor. In the end, however, the governor of Hyogo prefecture cancelled the proposed

Yokkaichi. The Kurokawa team made an in-depth assessment of the impact of the proposed plants on the area's environment. At one point, it met with representatives from the anti-pollution and anti-development campaigns, but the groups could not reach a consensus. Under intense pressure from local residents, the city councils of Mishima, Numazu, and neighboring Shimizu each voted to cancel the project. The central and prefectural governments and the participating industries capitulated and withdrew their proposals.

The forced cancellation of the Mishima-Numazu project shocked industrial and economic organizations. It threatened to disrupt Japan's heretofore single-minded pursuit of economic growth. Even more upsetting, the initiative and energy for the cancellation came from local sources.[20]

Isogo and the routine use of environmental impact assessments and anti-pollution agreements. In 1964, the Tokyo Electric Power Company sought to purchase reclaimed land in Isogo from Yokohama city and Kanagawa prefecture in order to build a coal-fired power station. The electric company presented a master plan of the proposed project to the National Electricity Power Source Development Council of the Economic Planning Agency, a unit of the central government. Residents of Yokohama adamantly opposed the proposed construction, and they elected Mr. Asukada, a Socialist Party candidate who campaigned in favor of strict pollution control, as mayor of Yokohama. However, the headquarters of the Socialist Party in Tokyo urged Asukada to accept the coal-fired power station because the coal miners' union was an important constituent of the Socialist Party. In any event, Yokohama established an independent team of experts to conduct an environmental impact assessment of the proposed power plant. The team carried out their work on a scale and at a level of sophistication similar to that carried out by the Kurokawa Investigation Task Force at Mishima-Numazu. The Yokohama team developed detailed pollution control measures which it recommended that the city require the power station to implement.

Yokohama and Kanagawa entered into negotiations with the Tokyo Electric Power Company on the terms of an anti-pollution agreement. The proposed agreement set strict standards for dust, SO_x, and noise for the plant, required it to install stipulated pollution control equipment, use low sulfur oil and coal, permit city officials to inspect its facilities, and to observe all future municipal instructions for pollution prevention.[21]

The emission standards required in the agreement were far stricter than those required by law. Asukada declared that Yokohama would permit the construction of the power plant only if it agreed to the terms of the proposed antipollution agreement. The approval of the master plan required the central government to solicit the opinion of the governor of Kanagawa, but he did not express his opinion in view of the delicate social and political situation.

Fearing another cancellation like that at Mishima-Numazu, both MITI and MHW urged the power plant to accept the anti-pollution agreement. Finally, Tokyo Electric conceded to the local demands, and construction of the plant began.[22]

The procedures taken at Isogo -an environmental impact assessment and an anti-pollution agreement between the local government and the power company- became a standard part of the National Electricity Power Source Development Council's review of the basic plans for power stations. This development was hastened by the election of socialist governors in Tokyo and Osaka, although soon pollution control became a top priority of all political parties.

After the enactment of the Basic Law for Environmental Pollution Control Measures in 1967, the practice of signing anti-pollution agreements became standard for all polluting enterprises. Occasionally, residents' groups them- selves negotiated these agreements directly with the applicant industries, while at other times the agreements were tripartite arrangements among local citizens, municipal or prefectural governments, and industry. The terms of some agreements granted procedural rights, such as the right to inspect factories while others established special trust funds to compensate indi- viduals injured by pollution. Most agreements set additional standards and imposed other obligations on the applicant industries beyond those already established by law.[23]

For example, Osaka prefecture set up a pollution control center consisting of a modern laboratory, mobile units, monitoring equipment, and a telemeter system. It then negotiated with individual industries to set up a direct tele- meter link between emission sources and the pollution control center. In addition, prior to the implementation of MITI's desulfurization plan in 1969, Osaka formulated a Blue Sky Plan in which individual industries agreed to implement agreed-upon desulfurization measures.

The cumulated experience of negotiating anti-pollution agreements with dif- ferent types of industries served to increase the technical expertise of local government personnel. Whereas early agreements were abstract because local government lacked the knowledge to negotiate and draft more specific provi- sions, recent agreements have been precise and rich in content. In fact, today local governments are a storehouse of information on pollution control techno- logy and finance. In addition, there is an active, regional exchange of moni- tored data, pollution impact assessment analysis, and control-technology infor- mation. The central government subsidizes a regional telemeter system in the Osaka and Tokyo Bay areas.[24]

Sapporo. More recently, the city of Sapporo and Miyagi prefecture have regulated the use of spiked tires on vehicles during the snow season. Spiked tires puncture the road surface, and create dust pollution in the spring.[25]

Summary. A number of reasons can be cited for the success of local initia-

tives in pollution control. In Japan, local government has been more immediately responsive to the concerns of citizens than the central government
bureaucrats in Tokyo. Since the Local Autonomy Law provided for the election
of prefectural governors and municipal mayors in 1947, these officials have
been highly susceptible to public appeal. From 1964-73, pollution control was
the central issue in the campaigns of conservative, liberal, and far left
candidates. In addition, local government found itself in a good bargaining
position vis-a-vis private industry. Available land for new plants was scarce,
and in the intensely competitive world of Japanese business, industries had to
concede to tough local demands in order to find suitable sites for their
industrial plants. Also, Japan is a society where harmony and consensus are
valued, and industries wanted good relations with the local communities. Thus,
they were apt to concede to strict terms during the negotiation of anti-
pollution agreements.

1.4 THE ROLE OF THE CENTRAL BUREAUCRACY IN REGIONAL INDUSTRIAL DEVELOPMENT AND THE SMOKE AND SOOT REGULATION LAW OF 1962

   The central bureaucracy. The different ministries of the executive branch
of government rarely acted in concert in the management of air pollution. The
health- and development-oriented ministries each had their own, often conflicting, agenda. In 1953, the Bureau of Sanitation of MHW conducted a nationwide survey of environmental pollution by polling all the prefectural governments on the status of pollution-related illnesses in their respective jurisdictions. The survey found that 10,044,241 persons living in 43 prefectures
had pollution-related illnesses resulting from 102,290 pollution cases. In the
category of air pollution, the survey showed that the worst problems were dust,[26]
offensive odours, gases, and smoke, in descending order of severity.

   In 1954, MHW requested that the Japan Public Health Association investigate
the tolerance limits to smoke and noxious gases. Using this and other data,
MHW drafted pollution-control legislation in 1955.

   MITI and other development-oriented ministries strongly opposed MHW's proposed, pollution-control legislation, and they eventually forced MHW to with-
draw it.[27]

   MITI's relentless goal during the 1950s and 1960s was to oversee the economic rehabilitation and growth of Japan. The other main, pro-development
agencies were the Ministry of Construction and the Economic Planning Agency.
MOC was in charge of actual physical construction and EPA's functions included
medium- and long-term economic planning and the formulation of a national
comprehensive development plan. In 1960, Prime Minister H. Ikeda proposed an
ambitious, ten-year, income-doubling plan. Also in 1960, the Diet passed the
New Industrial City Development Law. Communities everywhere welcomed industry,

and the idea of the supremacy of the economy prevailed all over Japan.

In this pro-development milieu, MHW lacked the political leverage to push its pollution-control programs. Other ministries considered MHW a threat to the all-important regional industrial development projects they were pushing. Moreover, there were structural limitations on MHW's ability to act. Its budget for environmental pollution control studies, for example, was only ¥350,000. Also, it did not have any enforcement powers for pollution violations. However, the other ministries began to listen more to MHW after the occurrence of several severe pollution episodes. The mass citizen protests at Yokkaichi and the horrible suffering of Minamata disease and itai-itai disease victims began to generate more sympathy for MHW's pollution control agenda. In addition, MHW's influence expanded because it had jurisdiction over the national health center network and the sanitation administration at the prefectural and municipal levels. Local public health laboratories fulfilled an important function in pollution measurement and analysis. Over the years, MHW benefitted from the cumulated experience of the many local programs and the joint efforts between MHW and local government.

The Smoke and Soot Regulation Law of 1962. The provisions of the government's first attempt at comprehensive anti-pollution legislation in 1962 reflected the relative strength and weakness of MITI and MHW. The Smoke and Soot Regulation Law of 1962 regulated smoke, soot, dust, and SO_x emissions generated by combustion, heating, and melting processes. The law was a piecemeal effort in that it applied only to these types of emissions, and then only in designated air pollution control districts. The law did not apply to mines, power stations, and gas works, which were regulated by other, existing laws under the jurisdiction of MITI. The 1962 law set quantitative emission standards for designated pollutants classified by the type of emission source. For soot and dust, the standard ranged between 0.6 g/m^3 and 2.0 g/m^3. For example, the standard for soot and dust emissions from a pervilized coal combustion boiler was 1.2 g/m^3. The standard for SO_x emissions ranged from 0.18% to 0.22% by volume of maximum stack output. The law required factories to notify the prefectural governor of new or modified smoke-emitting facilities. However, the government's only recourse in the event of emission violations was to issue a clean-up or desist order. In addition, the law required prefectural governments to monitor air quality routinely and to issue alerts if the pollution level posed a danger to health.

The Smoke and Soot Regulation Law was effective in controlling the traditional types of pollutants--dense, visible smoke and heavy deposits--but it did not help to curtail SO_x emissions. This was because the SO_x emission standards were set in terms of the concentration of the pollutant at the stack. A factory could easily circumvent the intent of the law, while still complying

with its specific terms, by increasing the number of stacks, using larger
stacks, or diluting concentrations with fresh air. Moreover, the SO_x emission
limitations were not strict enough to do any good. SO_x emissions from the
worst pollutors in Yokkaichi were only 0.17% when the strictest standard was
0.18% [28]

During the preparation of the Smoke and Soot Regulation Law, MHW made an
extensive study of existing programs in Great Britain, the United States, West
Germany, and other countries. Great Britain's smokeless coal program was
impressive for its integration of anti-pollution and energy supply policies.
However, the Great Britain example was not transferable to Japan due to differences in the availability of coal and the stage of industrial development in
Japan. Despite MHW's efforts to include strict anti-pollution provisions, in
the end the shape of the bill showed MITI's stronger influence. Pollution
control was still a halfhearted policy in Japan in the early 1960s. [29]

But perhaps the most important contribution of the 1962 law for future
pollution control was the monitoring provisions. The issue of alerts under the
law was the first time that the government disclosed data on pollution levels
to the public. The disclosures increased public awareness of the worsening air
quality situation, and this created the information basis for later demands by
the citizens for the enactment of strict pollution control programs.

Kurokawa Investigation Task Force. The interests of MITI and MHW were not
always at odds, however, and they cooperated in pollution control when their
interests overlapped. After the petrochemical complex at Yokkaichi commenced
operations in 1959, and doctors reported an increase in the incidence of asthma
and other respiratory diseases, MHW began to worry that the case would develop
into a serious pollution episode with many casualties. After consulting with
the governor of Mie prefecture, MHW proposed that it and MITI commission an
interdisciplinary team of experts to study the pollution situation at Yokkaichi
and make recommendations for pollution control. MITI agreed, and the Kurokawa
Investigation Task Force was established. Dr. M. Kurokawa was the director-
general of MITI's Institute of Industrial Technology and an expert on fuel
science and technology. The other members of the task force included top
scholars and practitioners in the fields of emissions, the environment,
meteorology, public health, city planning, and industrial siting. After a six-
month investigation, the Kurokawa team submitted its report to MITI and MHW in
1964. [30]

The Kurokawa report contained 13 main recommendations. (i) Establish
special emission standards for SO_2 at Yokkaichi. (ii) Develop and utilize
desulfurization technology for the petroleum refinery plant. (iii) Construct
higher stacks for better emission diffusion. (iv) Improve the air pollution
control measures in the sulfuric acid, carbide, and titanium plants. (v)

Institute better practices with respect to fuel use and combustion at the small, Banko ceramic plant. (vi) Design a redevelopment plan. (vii) Provide medical care for victims of pollution-related diseases. (viii) Establish air monitoring and meteorological observation stations. (ix) Improve procedures for plant operation, maintenance, and safety. (x) Develop mechanisms that maximize plant utilization and minimize emissions, effluents, and other wastes. (xi) Encourage the different plants at the petrochemical complex to install joint pollution abatement equipment. (xii) Improve community relations. (xiii) Consider the costs of the recommended programs. The government carefully reviewed the Kurokawa report, and in time the companies at the petrochemical complex instituted all of the recommendations.

In 1964, MITI and MHW recommissioned the Kurokawa Investigation Task Force to conduct an environmental impact assessment of the Mishima-Numazu petro-chemical complex and to recommend preventive, anti-pollution measures. The task force studied all aspects of the proposed complex, including developing a simulation model and conducting wind-tunnel experiments. The team formulated recommendations for fuel, combustion, stacks, emissions, and other aspects of the complex's operation. This was the first sophisticated, large-scale environmental impact assessment conducted in Japan.[31]

In view of the Kurokawa recommendations, MHW proposed that Yokkaichi and Mishima-Numazu be designated under the Smoke and Soot Regulation Law. However, MITI and industrial and economic groups opposed the proposed designation. They succeeded in stalling the Yokkaichi designation until 1966, by which time the city had certified 355 patients of air pollution-induced pulmonary disease. MITI was successful in preventing the designation of other areas as well. In fact, during the five years of the law's existence, the government designated only 20 areas.[32]

However, environmental impact assessments became a standard part of the pre-siting approval process for regional development projects. Beginning in 1965, the government provided a budget for the assessment program jointly conducted by MHW, MITI, and local government. The program did not include public hearings where citizens could express their views, however. The environmental impact assessments were technical in nature and only the results were disclosed to the public. They did serve to increase the sophistication of government officials on pollution control matters.

1.5 THE 1967 BASIC LAW, THE 1968 AIR POLLUTION CONTROL LAW, AND THE AAQS FOR SO_2

The Basic Law. In 1965, the government began to see the need for a compre-hensive approach to pollution control. Pollution awareness had increased in

all sectors. It was the main topic of political campaigns, where politicians
described industrial pollution as a threat to human health, even to life
itself. The public became infuriated by the events in Yokkaichi and Minamata
Bay.

In 1965, both houses of the Diet established Special Standing Committees for
Industrial Pollution Control. This signaled the start of an intensive debate
among the political parties and the ministries on the shape of general pollution policy that was to result in the 1967 Basic Law for Environmental Pollution Control Measures. The main issues centered on whether government or
industry should be responsible for pollution control, and whether anti-pollution considerations should be harmonized with the need for economic growth.

The first piece of legislation considered by the Special Standing Committees
was a bill chartering the Environmental Pollution Control Service Corporation.
The brainchild of the MHW, the service corporation was a government-owned and
operated entity which selected environmentally sensible sites, purchased land,
established green belts, installed pollution control and abatement equipment,
and thereafter conveyed title to the property of the concerned enterprise. It
also made loans to small- and medium-size enterprises for the installation of
pollution control equipment and waste-treatment plants.[33]

The government used excess funds from the national pension fund to finance
the service corporation. MITI supported the MHW-initiated chartering legislation, and the bill was passed in 1965.

MHW sponsored other pollution-related projects as well. With the assistance
of the Ministry of Construction, it built a health and welfare community facility in Ichihara, Chiba prefecture. The community facility was built as a
buffer zone between the industrial and residential areas of Ichihara. The idea
for a buffer zone in Ichihara had come from the mistakes in city planning made
at Yokkaichi. In 1964, the Kurokawa Investigation Task Force recommended that
a similar community facility be built at the perimeter of the petrochemical
plant in Yokkaichi, and the buffer zone project was later carried out.[34]

In 1964-65, MHW and MITI added new divisions which made them better equipped
to deal with policy-making in the pollution area. In 1964, MHW established the
Division of Environmental Pollution Control, and in 1965 MITI established the
Division of Industrial Pollution Control. Also in 1965, MHW established the
Pollution Commission, a forty-member advisory body to MHW which played a criti-
cal role in determining many of the important policies embodied in the Basic
Law. In 1967, after the enactment of the Basic Law, the government transferred
the functions of the Pollution Commission to the Central Advisory Council on
Environmental Pollution Control Measures, initially located within the Prime
Minister's Office. With the establishment of the Environment Agency in 1971,
the Central Advisory Council was reorganized as the principal advisory organ to

the new agency's director-general.[35]

In 1965, the MHW instructed the Pollution Commission to draft a report which would provide basic policy recommendations for future legislation. In August 1966, the Pollution Commission submitted its Interim Report to the Minister of Health and Welfare. The report assigned responsibility for pollution control to industry and urged that industry be held strictly liable for pollution damage. In addition, it noted the inadequacy of existing pollution legislation and recommended that new, comprehensive measures be adopted which give explicit priority to health over industrial development. All pollution programs, it said, should be designed with the purpose of achieving ambient air quality standards.

The Interim Report met with intense controversy, especially from the Keidanren. The Keidanren and other economic and business groups argued that pollution control should in no way harm industry's development. Nevertheless, the Pollution Commission's Final Report retained the original, hard-line stance, and on October 7th 1966 it was submitted to the Minister of Health and Welfare and the Cabinet.

The Prime Minister then requested MHW to prepare draft legislation for the Basic Law. At this point, a serious jurisdictional dispute broke out among the 14 ministries and agencies which claimed responsibility for aspects of pollution control policy. For example, MITI possessed regulatory powers over the factories which were the sources of pollution; the Ministry of Agriculture and Fisheries had an interest in the protection of farming and fisheries; and the Ministry of Local Autonomy represented the interests of local government, which wanted the authority to enact stricter pollution standards than the national laws required.[36]

In view of the need for a referee, the government decided that the Liaison Council for Pollution Control Promotion, an interministerial coordinating body, would oversee the preparation of the draft legislation. Within the Liaison Council, MITI and the Economic Planning Agency attacked MHW's emphasis on public health and environmental concerns. They asserted that these policies should be harmonized with the need for sound economic development. Under pressure from the pro-development ministries, the Liaison Council weakened or eliminated many of MHW's recommendations. For example, it eliminated proposals for strict liability for industry, the establishment of an administrative compensation fund, and the creation of an independent administrative body for pollution control. The public was especially dissatisfied over the harmonization clause and the elimination of the principle of strict liability. But the Special Standing Committees for Industrial Pollution Control urged the government to submit a bill as soon as possible.

On February 24th, 1967, the Cabinet directed MHW to incorporate the proposals agreed upon in the Liaison Council into a bill. After a few amendments and more review by the concerned ministries, the Cabinet submitted the bill to the Diet on May 16th, 1967. The Diet debated the provisions of the bill and enacted the Basic Law on August 3th, 1967.

The Basic Law was essentially a long-range charter for pollution control. It set broad policy and identified the respective responsibilities of government and industry, but left many of its specific applications to later legislation. The law defined environmental pollution as air, water, and soil pollution, noise, vibration, ground subsidence, and offensive odours. The controversial harmony principle appeared in the purpose clause. Article 1 stated that the law's purpose was to protect the health of nationals and conserve their living environment. However, article 2 explicitly stated that with respect to the conservation of the living environment (but not human health), "harmony with sound economic development should be considered." Article 9 required the government to establish ambient quality standards for air, water, and noise. However, the law made these standards administrative targets rather than rigid limitations. Again, with respect to the ambient standards for the protection of the living environment, the harmony principle applied. Article 10 required the government to establish emission standards for air, water, and soil pollutants. In other provisions, the law reflected the government's recognition of the responsibility to plan. Article 11 mandated land use controls for environmentally degradated areas; article 13 exhorted the government to set up monitoring and measurement systems; and article 17-1 stressed the need to include environmental protection provisions in the planning and implementation of regional industrial development. In addition, the Basic Law helped to consolidate the administration of pollution control. It established an interministerial Environmental Pollution Control Council that replaced the Liaison Council for Pollution Control Promotion, and also established several local Environmental Pollution Control Councils. Article 21-1 required the government to establish a mediation or arbitration board to resolve pollution disputes, and article 21-2 required the government to set up a pollution-related health damage compensation system. Finally, article 22 required private industry to pay for all or part of government pollution control programs.[37]

Critics complained that the Basic Law did not contain a strict liability provision. However, article 3-2 set forth a new principle of indirect enterprise responsibility. It stated that companies "shall endeavor to take precautionary measures to prevent environmental pollution which might otherwise be caused by the use of the products which it manufactures or processes." In any event, Prime Minister Sato pledged to make efforts to enact strict liability legislation in the near future.

The 1968 Air Pollution Control Law. The Basic Law directly influenced the

passage of the 1968 Air Pollution Control Law. The most important achievement
of the 1968 law was that it set an emission standard for SO_2 discharges.
Generally, an emission standard is a cap on the quantity or concentration of
a pollutant that may be discharged from a specific source per unit of time. It
is binding and enforceable. In contrast, an ambient standard is a targeted
ceiling on the concentration of a pollutant in a receptor medium, such as air
or water. It does not, by itself, impose a constraint upon an individual
polluting facility, and the facility is not liable simply because an ambient
standard is not met.

The 1968 Air Pollution Control Law was a major advance beyond the Soot and
Smoke Regulation Law, which it replaced. First, it applied to all areas, even
areas not yet polluted. Thus, it applied to the new industrial development
projects. Second, it set stricter emission standards for new emission
sources.[38]

Third, it replaced the ineffective earlier approach to emission controls
with the k-value system. Under the new system, SO_2 emissions from an individual emission source were limited by a complex formula ($Q = k \times 10-3He2$). The
standard is defined in terms of a quantity of pollutant, but it is (partly) a
function of the volume of exhaust gas, which means that it is possible to
increase the quantity of pollutant discharged by means of dilution. However,
this possibility is limited by the fact that the speed and temperature of
exhaust gas (which would be modified by an increase in volume) are taken into
account in the calculation of the standard.[39]

The k-value was calculated as $584 \ C_{max}$/hr (maximum ground level concentration ppm). At first, there were eight k-value classifications, depending on
local air pollution levels. Later, the government added three additional,
stricter k-value classifications for areas which exceeded the ambient air
quality standard.

To meet the k-value standards, many industries began to construct higher
stacks. This improved peak SO_2 concentrations, but it also resulted in greater
diffusion and thus a wider polluted area. Mie prefecture tested and confirmed
this phenomenon in Yokkaichi.[40]

Beginning in 1969, the electric power stations in the Tokyo Bay area started
importing ING to help meet the new emission standards.

AAQS for SO_2. In addition to emission standards in the Air Pollution Control
Law, the 1967 Basic Law spawned ambient air quality standards for SO_2. Soon
after the enactment of the Basic Law, the Central Advisory Council on Environmental Pollution Control Measures established an expert committee on ambient
quality standards for SO_2 and requested it to review the existing data and to
offer its opinion on the appropriate standard. The expert committee relied on
the epidemiological and clinical studies from Yokkaichi as well as other

domestic and foreign data. In 1968, the expert committee recommended a very strict AAQS for SO_2: 0.1 ppm/hr (0.1 ppm for 1 hr average) and 0.05 ppm/24hr (0.05 ppm for 24 hrs average).[41]

Immediately, the petrochemical, power, and other industries mounted a fierce attack against the proposed standards. They argued that achieving the standards would require desulfurization both in the refinery and the stack, that this was too costly, and that it would disadvantage Japanese business internationally. They also argued that the proposed standard was unwarranted scientifically.[42]

In FY 1966, MITI began working on a large-scale project to develop desulfurization technology. MITI's goal was to lower the cost of desulfurizing petroleum to either ¥500/kl or ¥1000/kl. The price of crude oil in 1967 was about ¥6000/kl. In a study done in 1967, MITI calculated that the impact of these targeted desulfurization costs would not significantly burden total production costs, although the impact would be detectable. See Table 1.3.

Despite MITI's data showing that desulfurization was affordable, industry groups succeeded in lowering the proposed AAQS for SO_2. In February 1969, the Cabinet adopted standards which were lower by a factor of three. Also, the government extended the period for the standard's attainment, and exempted their application to areas exclusively for industrial use.[43]

The adopted AAQS for SO_2 was as follows: (i) More than 99% of the total number of hours of a year to be below 0.2 ppm/hr; (ii) More than 70% of the total days number of a year to be below 0.05 ppm/24hr; (iii) More than 88% of the total number of hours of a year to be below 0.1 ppm/hr; (iv) The annual average hourly value not to exceed 0.05 ppm/yr; (v) The total number of days

TABLE 1.3

Economic impact of fuel desulfurization on production costs

Industry		500 Yen/kl	1,000 Yen/kl
Agriculture, Forestry, Fishery		0.09%	0.19%
	Average;	0.19%	0.39%
Mining & Manufacturing Industry	Chemical Industry;	0.24%	0.49%
	Ceramic Industry;	0.67%	1.33%
	Iron & Steel Industry;	0.41%	0.81%
	Electricity, Gas;	0.94%	1.89%
Transportation & Traffic Service;		0.05%	0.11%

Source: Economic Monthly Report, Economic Planning Agency   September 1967

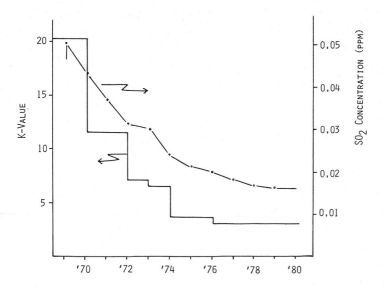

Fig. 1.1. Changes in K-values and SO$_2$ concentrations

with an incidence of an alert condition not to exceed 3% of the total days in a
year, and no incidence of an alert condition should last for more than 3 consecutive days.[44] Although it was not disclosed in 1969, achieving these
standards was equivalent to about 0.03 ppm/yr.

By the late 1960s, it was apparent that the government needed a long-term,
comprehensive desulfurization policy. In December 1969, MITI requested its
advisory organ, the Comprehensive Energy Investigation Committee, to submit a

TABLE 1.4

Sulfur fuel demand to achieve AAQS of SO$_2$

Fiscal Year	1967			1973			1978		
	Fuel	Fuel	Air	Fuel	Fuel	Air	Fuel	Fuel	Air
Area Classification	10^4 kl	S wt%	SO$_2$ ppm	10^4 kl	S wt%	SO$_2$ ppm	10^4 kl	S wt%	SO$_2$ ppm
Congested	2,297	2.41	0.38	3,920	1.00	0.27	5,500	0.55	0.20
Polluted	1,037	2.51	0.24	2,880	1.30	0.20	4,600	0.80	0.20
Preventive	–	–	–	2,560	1.55	0.20	5,400	1.00	0.20
Other	3,604	2.45	–	9,360	1.25	–	15,500	0.80	–

Source: Ministry of International Trade & Industry; December 1969

24

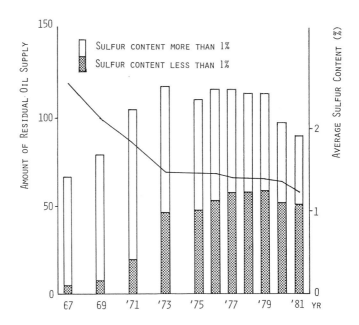

Fig. 1.2. Annual trends in residual oil supply and sulfur content

recommendation on a national energy supply program designed to meet the AAQS
for SO_2. The energy committee's plan set FY 1973 as the interim target for
achieving the standard and FY 1978 as the final target[45]

See Table 1.4. The implementation of the ten-year desulfurization plan took
into account the expansion of Japan's petroleum refining capability and investment plan formulated by MITI's Industrial Structure Council. By 1970, five
plants had installed stack gas desulfurization equipment. Between 1970 and
1976, the government issued stricter k-values step by step in accordance with
Japan's capacity to supply low-sulfur oil. See Fig. 1.1. The expansion of
nuclear power stations also helped to cut SO_2 pollution in the Tokyo and Osaka
Bay areas. Fig. 1.2 shows a clear improvement of SO_2 levels since 1968.

In May 1973, the government tightened the AAQS for SO_2. The 1969 standard
was equivalent to 0.03 ppm/year and the new 1973 standard was equivalent to
0.017 ppm/year. By 1973, before the oil crisis, Japan's refinery desulfurization capacity had expanded to the point where it could meet the demand for low-
sulfur fuel. As a result of the oil crisis and the increase in the cost of
oil, stack gas desulfurization became more economical than low-sulfur fuel.
Fig. 1.3 shows the increase in the installation of stack gas desulfurization
equipment.

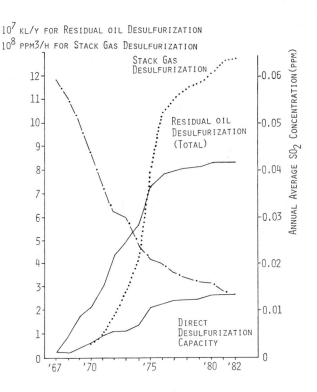

10^7 KL/Y FOR RESIDUAL OIL DESULFURIZATION
10^8 PPM3/H FOR STACK GAS DESULFURIZATION

Fig. 1.3.   Annual trends in desulfurization capacity

Monitoring programs.   In order to assess its pollution programs, the
government continued environmental impact assessments and air monitoring
programs.   MHW and MITI, in cooperation with local government, conducted
surveys of regional development projects modeled on the pre-siting survey done
at Mishima-Numazu.   The surveys included tracer experiments, topographical and
meteorological studies, and evaluations of appropriate stack heights.   The data
collected from the surveys provided a scientific basis for the implementation
of pollution controls and evaluation of the appropriate air monitoring systems.
The government also conducted follow-up surveys to determine the effectiveness
of the pollution controls.   These were often done in the worst seasonal conditions from the standpoint of pollution levels.   The surveys helped scientists
to gain an understanding of the topographic features of diffusion and the
meteorological parameters at each site.   Finally, they helped in the construc-[46]
tion of a computer-assisted simulation model.

   In addition, central government provided more funds to expand the local air
monitoring networks and to install a telemeter system to connect the local
stations with the central air pollution headquarters.   Several prefectures and

cities set up electronic demonstration panels which showed real-time pollution trends as part of a public education program. The government's policy was to disclose publicly all air monitoring data, except source telemeter data.[47]

In the fall of 1965, the government disclosed the results of its air pollution and health effect studies done at Yokkaichi and Osaka.[48]

See Table 1.5 and Fig. 1.1.

1.6 1970-74: THE PACE OF CHANGE QUICKENS

Catalysts for change. Beginning in 1970, a number of events took place in rapid succession that drew attention to the government's procrastination and inadequacy in combating pollution, and roused the public to demand immediate, effective action. A national survey of environmental pollution caused by mercury and cadmium discharges showed that these heavy metals were widely distributed in the nation's waterways. In May 1970, newspapers reported that residents of Yanagimachi in Shinjuku Ward, Tokyo were being poisoned by lead. The Tokyo Metropolitan Government disproved the reports two years later in a comprehensive study undertaken by a team of experts.[49]

But other adverse publicity continued. In July 1970, Tokyo experienced episodes of photochemical smog that reportedly induced partial suffocation and hospitalized a number of school children. The smog also caused acute damage to vegetation. The Institute of Environmental Pollution of the Tokyo Metropolitan Government announced that these reactions were due to a high concentration of photochemical oxidant and sulfuric acid mist.[50]

Also, news reports on the phenomenon of cross-media pollution in the air, water, soil, and biosphere shocked the public. In 1967 and 1968, the victims of Minamata disease in Niigata prefecture, itai-itai disease in Toyama prefecture, and air pollution in Yokkaichi filed lawsuits for damage to their health. The suits attracted intensive press coverage, and spawned the formation of several support groups. Also, other anti-pollution and anti-development

TABLE 1.5

Standardized prevalence rate of chronic bronchitis symptoms in Osaka and Yokkaichi, 1964 (Standardized by age and smoking)

	Osaka		Yokkaichi	
	Male	Female	Male	Female
High Pollution Area	6.8%	3.8%	15.1%	11.3%
Low Pollution Area	5.2%	1.0%	5.5%	2.8%

Source: Ministry of Health & Welfare, Division of Environmental pollution 1966.

interest groups formed and accused government and industry of inadequate or misguided environmental policies.

These domestic events coincided with rising international concern over pollution. In 1970, President Nixon issued a provocative statement on the importance of environmental protection. In his remarks, Nixon indirectly criticized Japan for taking an unfair trade advantage by neglecting the environment and thereby not incurring the costs of domestic pollution controls. For its part, the United States passed the National Environmental Policy Act and established the Environmental Protection Agency. In 1970, the Organisation for Economic Co-Operation and Development established an Environmental Committee, which generated many reports on the problems of modern society. In 1972, the United Nations held an international conference on the human environment in Stockholm and issued a widely-read final report.

At home, scientists noted that exhaust from automobiles was chiefly responsible for the increase in NO_x and hydrocarbon levels in recent years. In response to calls to control this pollution, MITI adopted a lead-free gasoline plan in June 1970, and the Ministry of Transportation set a target date of 1975 for the control of automobile exhaust.

The central and local governments often disagreed on the shape of pollution-control measures. In general, local governments, controlled by the Socialist or Communist Parties, demanded more far-reaching measures than the central government, controlled by the Liberal Democratic Party, was willing to allow. In the Diet, members of the special standing committees of both houses began to question government officials, and both committees passed resolutions calling for more aggressive government action. It was felt that a new, unifying body was needed in order to coordinate the views of government agencies with an interest in pollution control.

The 1970 special Diet session. In July 1970, Prime Minister Sato ordered the establishment of the Central Headquarters of Environmental Pollution Control to accelerate the formulation of new policies and measures. The Prime Minister himself directed the new body, and it was staffed by 15 senior administrators (at the deputy director-general and director level) and 19 assistant administrators (at the deputy director level). In addition, the Cabinet organized a special Ministers Conference for Pollution Control, which met seven times in a three-month period to consider 14 pieces of legislation for submission to the special Diet session in November 1970. Also, the three, main opposition parties submitted proposals to the government and the Liberal Democratic Party. All four political parties reached consensus on emergency policy measures on eight major subjects.

The special Diet session, held from the end of November to the end of December 1970, was a productive one. The Diet passed all 14 pieces of pollu-

tion legislation during the short, hectic session. In connection with air
pollution control, five major laws were passed. (i) One law repealed the
harmony clause of the Basic Law. In the 1967 Basic Law, measures to conserve
the living environment were to be balanced, or harmonized, with the need for
"sound economic development." This harmony clause had in fact been used to
justify tilting all pollution policies in favor of economic growth, and was
thus repealed. (ii) The 1968 Air Pollution Control Law was amended to abolish
the system of designated districts. Under the 1970 amendments, the law applied
to all of Japan, not just the former designated districts. In addition, the
amendments created a national minimum emission standard, and authorized local
governments to set more stringent emission standards. Finally, the law provided
emission standards for specific hazardous substances and strengthened penalty
provisions. (iii) The Soil Pollution Abatement Law was newly enacted. The law
empowered prefectural governors to set strict enforcement standards in order to
control soil pollution. (iv) The Environmental Pollution Crime Law was newly
enacted. This special criminal law defined a pollution crime as the discharge
of pollution which causes health damage. In prosecuting a pollutor, the law
permitted the government to rely on a rebuttable presumption of causation when
proving the pollutant-disease nexus. The presumption was based on the bitter
experiences with the Minamata disease in Kumamoto and Niigata prefectures. (v)
The Law for Cost Bearing by Enterprises for Public Pollution Abatement Work was
newly enacted in accordance with article 22-2 of the Basic law. The law
required pollutors to contribute to the costs of government pollution control
programs.[51]

In 1971, the Diet passed the Offensive Odour Abatement Law. The Law provided for district designation, odorous substance designation, a range of
ambient standards, and a step-by-step schedule of odour abatement. Offensive
odours in urban settings had been a problem since early Meiji days. However,
abatement efforts were hindered by the fact that most sources of offensive
odours were small- and medium-scale companies in the agricultural and fishery
fields, and the Air Pollution Control Law was not designed for these types of
pollution sources. A second problem was the difficulty of scientifically
detecting and identifying low concentrations of odorous pollutants in spite of
strong complaints from residents. This was a case of the human nose being more
sensitive than measuring instruments.

The Environment Agency. On July 1st 1971, the government established the
Environment Agency within the Prime Minister's Office. The agency is headed by
a director-general who is a member of the Cabinet and holds the rank of state
minister. It performs the functions of coordination and planning in regard to
pollution control and environmental conservation. The agency's charter autho-
rizes the director-general to collect information from other agencies and

advise them regarding the formulation of environmental policies. The new agency took over jurisdiction of the Air Pollution Control Law from MHW and MITI, and established an Air Conservation Bureau to administer it.

The Environment Agency succeeded in raising a number of pollution standards. The new standard cut the emission ceiling by two-thirds of the former ceiling for existing sources, and by one-third for new sources. The emission standard for SO_2 was raised in accordance with progress in the desulfurization program. In September 1971, the agency began to address the top-priority photochemical oxidant problem. It established an Expert Committee for Long-Term Approaches to Automobile Emission Control within its advisory organ, the Central Advisory Council on Environmental Pollution Control Measures. In January 1972, the Environment Agency set ambient standards for suspended particulates.

The anti-pollution arsenal. The social and political crisis generated by the pollution problem continued throughout 1974. The episodes of photochemical oxidant pollution reached a peak in 1973, causing thousands of people to experience throat and eye irritation. From 1971-73, the courts decided strongly in favor of the victims in the four major pollution trials. The passage of the U.S. Clean Air Act of 1970 stimulated demands for automobile exhaust control. In 1972, the OECD announced the pollutors-pay-principle, which had a significant domestic impact.

These factors contributed to the passage of new environmental policies. This occurred despite the adverse economic and trade impact of the devaluation of the dollar in 1971 and the energy crisis of 1973 when oil supplies dwindled and prices jumped. In 1972, the Diet passed strict liability legislation, which removed the difficult issue of negligence from pollution lawsuits. Also in 1972, the Cabinet by resolution required environmental impact assessments on all public works. In 1973, the government enacted the Pollution-Related Health Damage Compensation Law. Also in 1973, the government set stringent ambient air quality standards for SO_2, NO_2, and oxidant. In 1974, it passed total mass emission regulations for SO_2-pollution control, a law regulating plant sitings, and a law instituting a factory pollution-control manager system. Finally, the second National Comprehensive Development Plan of 1969, the so-called Japanese Archipelago Reform, met with nationwide opposition from anti-pollution and anti-development groups. The pace of these developments, coming one after the other in the span of a few years, was unique in Japanese history.

From the Meiji Restoration until Mishima-Numazu in 1964, Japan was a pollutor's heaven. From 1965-69, the government took some anti-pollution measures in response to growing public protest, but these were largely ineffective. The turning point was the pandemic episodes of severe, photochemical smog and the news reports of ambient lead poisoning. They ignited the fighting spirit of the people, and thereafter change was not long in coming. From 1970-74, Japan

completed its arsenal of this time effective anti-pollution legislation. Japan
had plunged into a pollutor's hell.

1.7 THE POLLUTION TRIALS

There were four major pollution cases: the Niigata Minamata disease case
(decided September 29th 1971), the Yokkaichi air pollution case (decided July
24th 1972), the Toyama itai-itai disease case (decided August 9th 1972), and
the Kumamoto Minamata disease case (decided March 20th 1973).   In all four
cases, the courts ruled in favor of the victims, and the decisions made bold
new law and set high standards of care for the pollutors. Of the four cases,
the Yokkaichi air pollution case was the most far-reaching; it immediately
influenced the passage of the Pollution-Related Health Damage Compensation Law
and the government's stricter administration of the air pollution laws.

The Yokkaichi air pollution case. On September 1st 1967, twelve residents
of Isozu in Yokkaichi sued six companies in the petrochemical complex for
health damage from obstructive pulmonary disease allegedly caused by the defendant's SO_2 discharges. The case rested on a theory of negligence based upon
article 709 (torts) and article 719 (joint torts) of the Civil Law. The
plaintiffs invoked the joint tort statute because the discharges of some of the
defendants by themselves were insufficient to cause the plaintiffs' damage.

The court's decision in favor of the plaintiffs centered on four issues:
joint tort, causation, negligence, and damage. The case presented daunting
evidentiary issues. In order to prove the defendants' production, emission,
and transmission of pollutants, the plaintiffs submitted the following evidence. (i) Data showing a reasonable time sequence between the start-up of the
petrochemical complex and the development of increased air pollution in the
community. (ii) Data showing that the SO_2 levels at Isozu exceeded the
relevant ambient air quality standard. (iii) Data showing a correlation
between a seasonal SO_2 downwash phenomenon causing a high SO_2 peak and certain
wind direction and velocity conditions. This was simulated by a diffusion
model and contour patterns. (iv) Data showing a correlation between the trends
in annual ambient SO_2 levels at Isozu and trends in annual SO_x emissions from
the petrochemical plant. (v) Data showing a correlation between the incidence
of high concentrations of SO_2 and the occurrence of a certain wind direction.

In order to show the causal nexus between pollutant and disease, the plaintiffs submitted the following evidence. (i) Data showing that high levels of
SO_2 occurred before the incidence of obstructive pulmonary disease. (ii) Data
showing a correlation between high pollutant levels and high disease
prevalence. (iii) Data showing higher morbidity and mortality in polluted
areas than in the unpolluted, control areas. (iv) Data showing a higher
frequency of asthma-like attacks once the SO_2 level reached 0.2 ppm/week, and

a correlation between the frequency of disease onsets and level of SO_2 pollution. (v) Data showing an exacerbation of clinical symptoms resulting from the controlled exposure to air pollution, such as by relocation or air conditioning in a hospital ward. The plaintiffs here relied on epidemiological, clinical, and air pollution measurement data. (vi) Data showing that such factors as allergies, smoking, or aging in the plaintiffs' medical histories, while not negligible, did not detract from the role of air pollution in disease etiology. (vii) Data showing that experiments on animals corroborated the real observations.

Based on the evidence submitted, the court ruled that the defendants were negligent in siting and operating the complex, and that the harm caused was forseeable. The court said that the defendants had a duty to use the best available technology to control emissions. It also criticized the government in its verdict. The decision was a very strict application of the joint tort statute in an air pollution case.[52]

The strict verdicts in the pollution trials prompted the government to pass a number of environmental laws. On June 22nd, 1972, it passed a law which added strict liability provisions to the Air and Water Pollution Control Laws. In 1973, it enacted the Pollution-Related Health Damage Compensation Law. The Compensation Law adopted the use of standard scales used in the Yokkaichi case for calculating the amount of disability benefits to be awarded victims. In addition, the Yokkaichi court's discussion of foreseeability of harm prompted the Cabinet to pass a resolution requiring the government to make an environmental impact assessment of public works projects. Also, between 1973 and 1974, the government enacted other laws requiring sectoral environmental impact assessments. Directly in response to the Yokkaichi case, the director-general of the Environment Agency made a commitment to strengthen the enforcement of the nation's environmental laws.

In 1972, Mie prefecture enacted the Environmental Pollution Control Ordinance, which regulated total mass emissions of SO_2. In May 1973, the central government established stringent ambient air quality standards for NO_2 and oxidant, and raised the ambient standards for SO_2. In 1974, the government followed Mie prefecture's lead and amended the Air Pollution Control Law, providing total SO_2 mass emission regulations. Also in 1974, the Diet passed the Industrial Siting Law, requiring environmental impact assessments; the Industrial Pollution Factory Manager Law; and the National Land Use Planning Law, which set the rules for land use, development and conservation for the future. With these new laws and the decisions in the pollution trials, Japan had in a hurried five years put in place the basic policy instruments to deal with air pollution.

1.8 POLLUTION MANAGEMENT AND TOTAL MASS EMISSION REGULATION

Pollution-control investment. After 1970, Japanese industry began to take the business of pollution-control more seriously. This new attitude is reflected in the size of pollution-control investments between 1970 and 1975, as reported by the OECD.[53] See Table 1.6.

The size of pollution-control investments began to increase markedly starting in FY 1971, when the air and water pollution control regulations were tightened. In FYs 1971 and 72 and again in FYs 1974 and 75, total private-sector investment declined. The 1971-72 decline coincided with the devaluation of the dollar, leading to export constriction, and the 1974-75 decline coincided with the energy crisis, when the price of oil quadrupled. Also, in FY 1974, Japan experienced high inflation and negative GNP growth. Despite these economic hard times, Japanese industry increased its pollution-control investment during FYs 1971 and 1972 and FYs 1974 and 1975.

On February 28th, 1973, MITI issued a report analyzing Japanese anti-pollution investment. The report found that in 1973 air pollution control investment comprised 58.2% of total pollution control investment. In addition, the report found that in 1973 the ratio of total, pollution-control investment to total investment broken down by the industrial sector was as follows: electric power generation--24.8%; mining--20.4%; pulp and paper--18.5%; petroleum refining--14.8%; and iron and steel--12.9%.

Econometric studies. In October 1971, the Environment Agency's Central Advisory Coucil on Environmental Pollution Control Measures began working on a long-term environmental conservation plan for Japan. The Advisory Council formed an Expert Committee for Econometrics which issued an interim report in 1974. In 1973, the Economic Planning Agency published an economic white paper

Table 1.6

Estimates of anti-pollution investments in the private sector, direct method, 1970-75

	Total investment in private sector (billion Yen)	Anti-pollution investment in private sector (billion Yen)	Share of Anti-pollution Investment in private sector (%)
1970	14,494	232	1.6
1971	14,908	403	2.7
1972	14,723	559	3.8
1973	22,304	839	3.8
1974	22,929	1,333	5.8
1975	21,072	1,783	8.5

Source: OECD, Environmental Policies in Japan

TABLE 1.7

Changes in macro-economic variables generated over time by a soft environmental policy. As estimated by Murakami and Tsukui

	After 5 Years	After 10 Years	After 15 Years
Output	-2.8%	-0.5%	-3.0%
Consumption	-1.4%	-0.2%	-3.1%
Gross Investment	+26.9%	+1.8%	-12.9%
Productive Investment	+11.5%	-3.2%	-16.1%
Housing Construction	+11.5%	-2.5%	-16.1%
Resources Import	-16.8%	-2.0%	-3.7%
Export	+1.8%	+8.2%	+10.7%

Source: OECD Environmental policies in Japan

which included an econometric impact study of environmental expenditures. In addition, economists from different theoretical schools carried out research projects to assess the impact of pollution controls. See Table 1.7.

In 1973, the OECD Environment Committee also began an econometric impact assessment on Japan. In its study, the OECD integrated data on the impact of total mass emission regulation for SO_2 and NO_x into its assumptions for long-term environmental conservation and planning. The Environment Agency included these OECD econometric models for environmental conservation when it developed medium-term social and economic development plans for the late 1970s.[54]

See Table 1.8. In May 1977, the Environment Agency published its long-term environmental conservation plan.[55]

See Table 1.9. In FY 1975, Japan spent 2% of GNP on pollution control. In 1977, the OECD Environment Committee reviewed all the econometric models and impact assessments. It concluded that the economic impact of the high environ-

TABLE 1.8

Changes in macro-economic variables generated over time by stricter environmental policy, as estimated by The Economic Planning Agency

	After 5 Years	After 10 Years
GNP	-0.3%	-2.8%
Productive Investment	-0.4%	-7.7%
Prices (GNP Deflation)	+3.1%	+2.9%

Source: OECD Environmental policies in Japan

TABLE 1.9

Effects of pollution abatement costs on the national economy in FY 1985

	A Case 2 x 10^{13} Yen Pollution Abatement Investment	B Case Without Special Reinforcement of Enforcement	A - B
Real GNP (Average Anrrugi Growth; '75-'85)	6.12%	6.13%	-0.01%
Whole Sale Price (ibd)	4.77%	4.57%	0.20%
Consumers Price (ibd)	6.05%	5.96%	0.09%
Real Export (ibd)	6.15%	6.22%	-0.07%

Source: Long Term Plan of Environment Conservation, Environment Agency 1977

mental costs during the 1970s was detectable in macroeconomic indicators and that there were sectoral differences in the impact. However, it said that the impact was manageable with appropriate implementation and that there were no adverse economic trade effects on the Japanese economy.[56]

Total mass emission regulation. In 1974, the government introduced total mass emission regulation to assist in attaining the ambient air quality standards. The idea was to remedy the defects of the k-value system by restricting the total emission of pollutants in a given area. Mass emission regulation is not per se binding on pollutors; it is a policy objective which is translated into a set of emission standards. The limit on total emissions has the advantage of imposing controls on individual firms. Under the system, a company may allocate pollution discharges within its factories and choose the most economical method of limiting discharges. Thus, it encourages efficient resource allocation.[57]

The government designated 24 districts for total mass emission regulation in November 1974, December 1975, and September 1976.

1.9 AUTOMOBILE EXHAUST CONTROL, 1965-83

As early as 1928, Japanese scientists began to note the problem of urban air pollution caused by carbon monoxide from automobile exhaust. In 1955, air pollution generated by rapid urbanization and motorization began to be a serious problem. A number of factors contributed to this development. In 1955, MITI began to provide administrative guidance to foster the development of the automobile industry and promoted the idea of the "National Car." The large-scale construction projects for the 1964 Olympic Games in Tokyo also contributed to increased air pollution. In 1965, the government commenced a five-year road-construction plan.

When the Diet passed the Smoke and Soot Regulation Law in 1962, it requested the government to study options for automobile exhaust control. Accordingly, MHW commenced a project to develop automatic automobile exhaust monitoring instruments in 1963 with research funds provided by the Science and Technology Agency. Also, MITI and the Ministry of Transportation (MOT) began to conduct similar research and development projects in 1963. In 1964, MHW constructed three roadside automobile exhaust monitoring stations in the Tokyo metropolitan area.

At a meeting of the Liberal Democratic Party, a Diet member complained bitterly about being personally subject to exhaust fumes during his campaign for office. He had campaigned all day in an open car but got caught behind a large, diesel truck belching thick, black smoke. This apparently was a common problem for candidates running for office. A few older candidates had even died soon after the campaign was over. The Diet member advised the police to arrest the driver of the offending truck for operating his vehicle in violation of the Road Transport Vehicle Law. A few days later, the police spotted the truck with the aid of the license plate number provided by the Diet member, and took the driver into custody. He promised to repair his truck's exhaust system immediately. This personal exposure to the automobile exhaust problem had made the politician keenly aware of the growing problem.

In 1964, the government held an interministerial meeting at the vice-minister level to discuss automobile exhaust control. In 1965-66, MHW conducted a two-year study of automobile exhaust air pollution and its health effects. It organised a questionnaire survey, a pulmonary function test, and a CO-Hemoglobin test for roadside residents and traffic police working on congested streets. The study recorded complaints from annoyed residents and a significant increase in CO-Hemoglobin levels.[58]

In the mid-1960s, Los Angeles, New York, and Paris were experiencing automobile exhaust pollution problems similar to those experienced by Tokyo. In Los Angeles, buildups of automobile exhaust caused photochemical smog to settle over the city. In 1963, the Los Angeles Pollution Control District enacted ordinances regulating hydrocarbon emissions from the automobile crankcase and planned future regulations of hydrocarbon emission from the tailpipe. Also in 1963, New York initiated crankcase emission control, and the U.S. federal government announced automobile exhaust emission limits for cars used by the federal government. In Paris, the police authority introduced idling adjustments to regulate carbon monoxide (CO) emissions.

In 1963, Japanese car makers modified their export models to meet the crankcase emission standards set by New York and California. However, they did not comply with an MHW request in 1963 to build domestic models with lower emissions. The car makers claimed that there was no evidence linking automobile exhaust and illness and that Tokyo did not have a photochemical smog problem. The industry's denials were what led MHW to install air quality monitoring equipment at roadsides. In August 1967, the U.S. Public Health Service officially informed MHW that, of 35 automobile companies from all over the world, five companies had passed the U.S. automobile exhaust control standards. Toyota and Nissan were among the five passing companies. This development was good for Japanese exports, but many people were puzzled because the Japanese government had not conducted similar tests for domestic models.

Professor T. Kitagawa urged that the government first concentrate on controlling CO emissions. CO was the main pollutant in automobile exhaust emissions. Accordingly, in 1967 MOT instituted regulations to control CO emissions by making an idling adjustment. In addition, Tokyo, Osaka, and Kanagawa prefectures each announced that they would implement measures on their own initiative to control CO. Osaka prefecture reported that its automatic monitoring station had recorded a maximum CO concentration of 48 ppm/hr at a highway tollgate and 38 ppm/hr in front of the Adult Disease Center.

Dr. J. Middleton, Director of the Air Pollution Control Division of the U.S. Public Health Service and a member of the Air Pollution Control Board of the Los Angeles Air Pollution Control District, came to Tokyo to attend the Pacific Academic Assembly. While in Tokyo, he tested the photochemical oxidant pollution by using gum paper at the window of his hotel room. He observed the same cracking as happened with gum paper in Los Angeles. MHW learned of Dr. Middleton's experiment and asked him for advice on improving Japan's air measurement technology. Tokyo already had an automatic oxidant monitoring station as part of the national air-sampling network. However, the monitoring station recorded lower than expected levels of oxidant despite objective and subjective evidence of high photochemical oxidant concentrations. Dr. Middleton advised MHW to install a device in the monitoring station which would eliminate the interference caused by sulfuric acid mist.[59]

MHW took Dr. Middleton's advice and remodeled its monitoring station. The station then recorded CO at the expected higher levels. The instant peak was 0.35 ppm and the hourly peak was 0.17 ppm.

MHW again urged Japanese car makers to reduce hydrocarbon emissions for domestic models as they had done in their export models. But the Japan Automobile Industry Association was recalcitrant. It questioned the accuracy of the air monitoring stations and sent a team to the U.S. to study the treatment of oxidant there.

On July 18th, 1970, newspapers reported incidents of lead poisoning among roadside residents in Yanagimachi. Several patients were hospitalized, and many experienced adverse medical reactions.[60]

The public exploded in anger and demanded the immediate institution of stringent automobile exhaust controls.

The government responded to the crisis quickly. In July 1970, MITI cut the alkyl-lead content in premium gasoline by 1/2 and planned to implement a lead-free gasoline program within five years. MITI based these measures on its past research on automobile exhaust control technology and on the fact that alkyl lead in gasoline shortened the life of the catalyzer. At first, the lead-free gasoline program experienced problems with valve recession. The process was helped by the introduction of electronically controlled fuel injection.

MOT responded to the 1970 smog incidents by issuing target dates for auto-mobile exhaust emission controls. MOT's 1974 target was 7 g/km for hydrocarbon and 0.6 g/km for NO_x. Japanese car makers accelerated their research and development programs to meet these targets.[61]

Developments in the U.S. had an impact on automobile exhaust control efforts in Japan. In July 1970, Congress passed the Clean Air Act, which set stiff standards for automobile exhaust emissions. The U.S. Environmental Protection Agency was responsible for enforcing the Clean Air Act. However, in February 1972, the U.S. Office of Science and Technology issued a report entitled "Cumulative Regulatory Effects on the Cost of Automotive Transport." The report recommended a flexible attitude in the enforcement of the tough Clean Air Act standards, claiming that such strict regulation unacceptably increased transportation costs.[62]

U.S. automobile makers joined the attack on the Clean Air Act. They filed suit against the Environmental Protection Agency to stop the emission standards planned for 1975 and 1976.

After the government established the Environment Agency in 1970, it became responsible for setting automobile exhaust emission standards under the Air Pollution Control Law. The MOT was responsible for enforcing the emission standards under the Road Transport Vehicle Law. It did this by reviewing applications for type specifications for the production of new cars.

T. Sakakibara, director of the Automobile Pollution Control Division of the Environment Agency, managed difficult and complex negotiations involving MOT, MITI, car makers, and other interested groups. In February 1972, he left his office and did not return. An extensive search did not locate him and it is assumed that he committed suicide. This was a tragic result of the difficult manoeuvers in formulating a policy on automobile exhaust control.

In August 1972, the expert committee of the Central Advisory Council for Environmental Pollution Control Measures published its interim report on the proposed automobile exhaust emission standards for 1975 and 1976. The expert committee adopted proposed standards equivalent to those in the U.S. Clean Air Act. There were technical differences between the U.S. and Japanese testing procedures for automobile type approval. The U.S. standard is expressed as a mean value while the Japanese standard is a maximum permissible limit. Also, the driving mode is different due to differences in traffic patterns between the U.S. and Japan.

When the expert committee issued its proposed standards, MITI did not comment in view of the charged social and political situation in Japan. The public was angry and demanded tough laws. The automobile companies also kept a low profile. They knew that a change was pending in U.S. policy toward the enforcement of the Clean Air Act, yet they worked hard to meet the 1975 and 1976 standards while claiming that there was not enough time to meet them.[63]

In September 1972, the Air Management Section of the OECD held a meeting in Tokyo. At this time, newspapers reported that Honda and Mazda had met the 1975 emission standards. The U.S. delegates were shocked that the standards could be met so quickly and asked Honda and Mazda to confirm the reports, which they did. In October 1972, the Environment Agency formally issued the 1975 and 1976 standards, which were equivalent to the U.S. 1976 standards. In December 1972, MOT issued the emission standards for 1973.

In November 1972, the Tokyo metropolitan government published Professor K. Tsuchiya's report on biological responses to ambient lead exposure in Tokyo residents. The report concluded that there was no significant increase of delta ALA in Tokyo residents, which is the initial biological response to ambient lead exposure. Furthermore, it stated that the accumulation of lead in the human body was distributed within the range of measurement error. However, the report cautioned that there could be significant differences between residents in the concentration of lead in the blood and noted that further research was needed.

In February 1973, the U.S. Environmental Protection Agency revealed that Honda and Mazda had passed the 1975 standards under the Clean Air Act. However, in April 1973, the Environmental Protection Agency decided to postpone the effective date of the 1975 standards to 1976.

Immediately after the dramatic U.S. decision, Japanese automobile makers lobbied the Environment Agency to delay the implementation of the Japanese standards. Honda and Mazda were confident that they could meet the standards but the other automobile makers expressed difficulty. The Environment Agency held a hearing for each automobile maker to collect the following information: (i) the status of research and development for pollution control; (ii) estimates of the cost of meeting the 1975 and 1976 standards; (iii) progress of past research and current problems; (iv) forecast of future production; and (v) forecast of production after 1975. As a result of the hearings, the government concluded that Honda and Mazda could meet the standards, and other car makers could meet the standards for some, but not all, of their models.[64]

The Environment Agency decided to keep the timetable for the enforcement of

the 1975 emission standards. It advised car makers with models which could not
meet the standards to stop production of those models. However, the Environment
Agency was convinced that the 1976 standards could not be met, given the then
state of research and development.

On June 5th, 1973, Environment Day, Senator Muskie was invited to Japan
to give a lecture. The Environment Agency provided him with a car which
already met the 1975 emission standards. This was an impressive achievement,
although the car's fuel efficiency was low. The government encouraged people
to purchase cars meeting the 1975 emission standards and provided a special
tax benefit for such purchases in FY 1974.

The next year, the Environment Agency held another round of hearings with
each car maker to review progress on compliance with the 1976 emission
standards. All the car makers stated that they were unable to meet the 1976
standards on schedule and requested a postponement of their implementation.
The Environment Agency agreed with them that it would be impossible to meet the
deadline. Prime Minister K. Tanaka gave his consent to the postponement, and
the Environment Agency requested the Central Advisory Council to reconsider the
implementation schedule for the 1976 standards.

Many local governments, led by Tokyo, Yokohama, and Osaka, and pro-environment citizens' organizations criticized the reluctant automobile makers' attitude. They demanded that the Environment Agency enforce the 1976 standards on
schedule. The press supported the efforts of the local governments and
citizens. In August 1974, seven large cities jointly organized a study team to
review the 1976 standards. These cities were Tokyo, Kawasaki, Nagoya, Kyoto,
Osaka, and Kobe. In September 1974, the joint study team issued an interim
report. The report claimed that the proposed 1976 standards could be achieved
given the state of current technology. The report criticized the automobile
makers for not trying hard enough to achieve the standards and the government
for giving in to industry's requests. The seven cities demanded the enforcement of the 1976 standards on schedule.

MITI, however, advised that the 1976 standards for NO_x emissions be postponed. In September 1974, the Diet held a hearing for automobile industry
representatives to review the 1976 standards. Toyota and Nissan stated that a
standard of 0.9 g/km for NO_x emissions would be feasible in 1976; Honda and
Mazda stated that 0.6 g/km was feasible. In July 1970, MOT set an emission
standard of 0.6 g/km for NO_x to be implemented in 1975. The Central Advisory
Council held a meeting with representatives from the seven-city group, but no
consensus was reached. All members of the expert committee of the Central
Advisory Council concluded that the 1976 standards could not be achieved given
the then state of technology. The expert committee discussed proposals for a
two- and three-year delay, but could not reach agreement. In December 1974,

the expert committee recommended the implementation of provisional emission
standards for NO_x in 1976 and a postponement of the original 1976 standards to
1978. The proposed provisional standard was 0.6 g/km for small cars and 0.85
g/km for large cars.

The expert committee presented its proposals at a plenary session of the
Central Advisory Council. However, the plenary session could not reach agreement and it was decided to convene the Comprehensive Committee of the Advisory
Council. The Comprehensive Committee discussed the proposals exhaustively, but
could not reach agreement. Finally, Dr. R. Wadachi, president of the Central
Advisory Council, offered to make a decision based on the discussions which had
taken place. All members concurred with Dr. Wadachi's offer. Dr. Wadachi
decided to adopt the original recommendation of the expert committee, with a
few amendments adding stricter language. The Advisory Council accepted Dr.
Wadachi's recommendation.

In January 1975, M.P. T. Fuha, secretary-general of the Communist Party,
criticized Prime Minister Miki and the director-general of the Environment
Agency regarding a leak of matters discussed at a meeting of the expert committee of the Central Advisory Council. Fuha claimed that a member of the expert
committee, who was a representative of the automobile industry, had leaked
information to car makers. The meetings of the expert committee were supposed
to be secret and closed to the press and public. In view of the incident, the
government decided that representatives from the automobile industry could not
be members of the expert committee and that, if the expert committee needed to
hear the views of the automobile industry, it would hold a hearing for that
purpose. This issue became very controversial in the budget committee of the
Diet.

To avoid repeating such a fiasco, the Environment Agency set up a Technology
Review Council (TRC) comprised of four university professors who were experts
in the field of internal combustion engines. The TRC's function was to review
the state of technology development for the control of NO_x emissions from
automobiles. This was a purely scientific task. The TRC invited representatives from automobile manufacturers to give candid explanations of the state of
their technology. The TRC promised to keep all trade secrets confidential.
The idea was to publish the state of technological advance of each company in
order to stimulate competition.

The TRC held its first meeting in August 1975. It requested each automobile
company, with which it met separately, to present all information and data on
their technology. The Environment Agency attended the meetings as observers.

TRC and Environment Agency members also visited each company to view
research in their laboratories and to see driving tests on their test fields.
The TRC drafted its first report without outside assistance. Then each company

deleted portions which it considered confidential. It was agreed not to identify the automobile companies individually. In December 1975, the Environment
Agency released the report to the public and the TRC members held a press
conference to allow questions from journalists. The report was widely read by
members of the Diet, other ministries, local governments, citizen groups, and
concerned industries.

The report enabled people to understand the state of automobile exhaust
control and helped in the process of setting a date for the implementation of
the emission standards. For example, it helped consumer groups to better
understand the problems of the car makers in meeting the deadlines. The report
also stimulated intense competition among the automobile makers to be the first
to achieve the standards. Some companies used portions of the report for
public relations and advertising. Automobile dealers promoted cars which were
clean and fuel efficient. At the request of the Environment Agency, the Japan
Automobile Association funded the translation of the full text of the report
into English and distributed it all over the world in the spring of 1976. This
was done because the automobile is an international commodity, and trade
considerations were important for the development of further, pollution-control
programs.[65]

The automobile makers could not meet the 1975 hydrocarbon emission standards
for two-cycle passenger cars in time for the April 1975 deadline, and were
forced to stop production. Suzuki was the biggest maker of two-cycle cars and
so the failure had the most impact on it. According to the TRC, NO_x emissions
from Suzuki's two-cycle engine were lower than the 1978 NO_x emission standards,
but hydrocarbon emissions were high due to the nature of combustion in the
engine. Suzuki's engines in fact had better fuel efficiency than other types of
engines. Although Suzuki continued research on its engines to try to meet the
hydrocarbon standard, the TRC concluded that the 1975 hydrocarbon emission
standard could not be met in the near future.

In its December 1975 report, the TRC recommended that the government adopt
provisional hydrocarbon emission standards for two-cycle engines. Accordingly,
the Environment Agency organized an interministerial meeting to consider an
exemption for the 1975 hydrocarbon emission standards. The other ministries
were consulted because pollution policy on the hydrocarbon matter had a great
potential impact on employment, energy, and trade policy, given the factory
shut-down of two-cycle engine cars. The MOT and the Ministry of Labor were in
favor of the exemption. In the end, the government adopted a 1976 provisional
hydrocarbon emission standard exclusively for two-cycle engine cars.

In May 1976, the Environment Agency held a meeting with foreign automobile
manufacturers to inform them of the Japanese automobile exhaust control regulations. The foreign car makers were well informed about the state of automobile

42

exhaust control technology in Japan, and the Environment Agency and the TRC
were also aware of foreign automobile exhaust control technology. At the
second meeting for foreign car makers, also held in May 1976, all the companies
announced that they had developed pilot cars meeting the 1978 emission standards. The companies reported that the key to their achievements had to do
with the fact that they put their research into developing better combustion.
They also reported that fuel efficiency had improved as compared to cars built
prior to the 1973 standards. By the final meeting in August 1976, all companies had moved into the mass production stage for cars that met the NO_x
emission standards.

The TRC published its second report on the state of automobile exhaust
control technology in Japan in May 1976, and its third in October 1976. For
the third report, all car makers agreed to have the report identify the names
of the car makers with their technology. The Japan Automobile Association also
translated and distributed the second and third reports worldwide.

In November 1976, the OECD Environment Committee held a special session in
Tokyo to review Japanese environmental policies. The OECD report praised
Japan's success in automobile exhaust control. Also, the OECD report commented
that Japan's stringent automobile exhaust standard was not a trade barrier
against foreign imports. It noted that the standard was necessary to achieve
the desired air quality and that the domestic automobile industry had opposed
the standards.[66]

In 1976, Japan held a ministerial-level meeting to discuss ways to encourage
people to buy cars meeting the 1978 standards rather than the old emission
standards. MOT published test data on emission levels and fuel efficiency of
new cars approved for production. This helped to promote sales of clean,

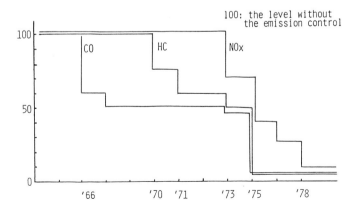

Fig. 1.4. Autoexaust emission controls for passenger cars

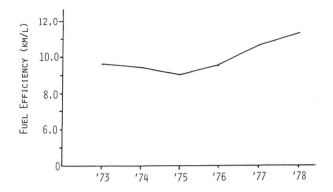

Source : Japan Automobile Manufacturing Association '79

Fig. 1.5. Trends in fuel efficiency of passenger cars

efficient cars. Also, the government provided a tax incentive to encourage
people to buy cars meeting the 1978 NO$_x$ standard prior to the enforcement date
in April 1978.

In addition, the ministers discussed whether to grant a grace period for
compliance with the 1978 standards for U.S. and European automobile imports.
U.S. officials requested a two-year grace period, and European Community officials met with their Japanese counterparts to request a similar grace period.
As a result of the European meeting, Japan decided to offer a three-year grace
period for foreign automobile imports, and the U.S. and European Community
agreed. The Environment Agency then set up a program to visit foreign automobile manufacturers to explain Japanese emission standards.

Fig. 1.4 shows Japanese emission control standards for passenger cars.
Fig. 1.5 shows trends in fuel efficiency of Japanese cars. Fuel efficiency
declined from 1973-75, and increased again in 1978. These charts show the
progress of the automobile makers in meeting the emissions standards of 1975,
1976, and 1978. Developing clean cars had the unexpected side effect of improving combustion. It shows that stringent pollution control standards sometimes
lead to technological innovation. It also improved the international competi-
tiveness of Japanese cars. However, without the strong public demand for
automobile exhaust control, the government and automobile makers probably would
not have achieved the success they did.

1.10 TRUCK AND BUS EXHAUST CONTROL

In the 1970s, a change occurred in the mode of cargo transport in Japan--
railways were used less and less and trucks were used more and more. Noise and

Table 1.10

Reports of the vehicle pollution control technology review
council and enforcement schedule, 1978-1985

Report	Time of Evaluation	Published Year	Notification Year
1st Report	1978 August	1979 May	1979 September
2nd Report	1979 August	1980 May	1980 September
3rd Report	1980 August	1981 May	1981 August
4th Report	1981 August	1982 May	1982 September
5th Report	1982 August	1983 May	1983 September
6th Report	1983 August	1984 May	1984 October
7th Report	1984 Oct. Nov. (Air) 1984 August (Noise)	1985 May	Not Yet

Note: Vehicle means heavy duty car (truck, bus, trailer
Source: Environment Agency, Bureau of Air Conservation,

Enforcement Schedule	
Implementa- tion Year	Vehicle Classification
1981 Standard	Light Gasoline Vehicle (NOx) Middle Weight Gasoline Vehicle (NOx)
1982 Standard	Heavy Weight Gasoline (NOx) Light (NOx) Indirect Injection Diesel (NOx) Passenger Car (Noise)
1983 Standard	Direct Injection Diesel (NOx) Middle Size (Noise)
1984 Standard	Big Size Bus (Noise) Small Size (Noise) Except 4 WD Motorbike; Less than 50cc (Noise)
1985 Standard	Large Size Truck (Noise) Except 4 WD, Tractor, Trailer, Light Autobicycle (Noise)
1986 Standard	Large Size 4 WD, Tractor, Crane (Noise) Motorbike; More than 50cc (Noise) Manual Speed Gear Diesel Passenger Car (NOx)

Not Yet

etc.) unless stated as passenger car.
Division of Automobile Pollution Control, 1985

black smoke from heavy, diesel trucks and bus traffic became a major nuisance. Since the 1960s, the Vehicle Safety Law and the Road Traffic Law had set qualitative controls on visible smoke without setting definite emission standards. In 1972, the government set a black smoke concentration standard of 50% based on the Bosch smoke scale. In 1974, it set CO, hydrocarbon, and NO_x emission standards for diesel trucks and buses. In 1976, it set noise limits for trucks and buses, and in 1977 it set long-term NO_x emission standards for trucks and buses. These regulatory statutes were to an extent contradictory, especially with respect to black smoke, NO_x, and noise. By 1980, the truck and bus manufacturers had developed the technology to meet the NO_x emission standards, and they incorporated it in 1983 models.

In 1978, in view of the success of the TRC in evaluating emission control technology for passenger cars, the Environment Agency commissioned the Vehicle Pollution Control Technology Review Council (VPCTRC) to evaluate control technology for trucks and buses. The VPCTRC had air and noise control subcommittees, and issued reports annually. In 1984, it set emission standards for trucks and buses to be enforced in 1986. See Table 1.10.

The implementation of emission controls for trucks and buses was different from that for cars in two important respects. There is much less competition among truck and bus manufacturers than there is among car manufacturers. Thus, there was no incentive to be the first to meet the standards and thereby increase market share. Also, buyers of trucks and buses, as opposed to cars, are usually businesses rather than individuals. Private companies generally purchase trucks for transporting cargo and public corporations generally purchase buses for transporting people. More than individuals, businesses are concerned about keeping costs down in their purchases of capital equipment.

Transportation and urban air pollution. By the middle of the 1970s, there was a remarkable improvement in the urban air pollution of SO_2, CO, suspended particulates, and photochemical oxidants. This was largely due to emission controls on stationary sources and passenger cars. However, roadside zones of large metropolitan areas have experienced almost horizontal trends in NO_2 and noise levels. This was due, in part, to the fact that truck cargo transport increased steadily by about 2% a year.

In 1980, the Diet passed the Law for Environmental Development in Roadside Zones. However, the designation of roadside zones under the law did not progress very rapidly because of the difficulty of obtaining consensus among roadside residents. In 1983, the Central Advisory Council formulated recommendations to deal with pollution in roadside zones. The proposals included land use, building siting, and truck traffic flow. The Cabinet had required environmental impact assessments for new roads since 1972, and the Ministry of Construction had implemented a number of environmental measures in road con-

TABLE 1.11

Trends in the NOx emission structure during FYs 1983-88

— Tokyo Capital Area —

		1983 FY		1988 FY		
		Amount of Emission 1000 t/year	Share (%)	Amount of Emission 1000 t/year	Share (%)	$\frac{88}{83}$
Stationary Sources	Factory, Business Office	11.6	20	11.6	23	1.00
	Mass of Small Sources	3.7	6	3.7	7	1.00
	Sub-total	15.3	26	15.3	30	1.00
Mobile Sources	Automobile	40.3	69	33.1	65	0.82
	Other Mobile Sources	2.6	5	2.6	5	1.00
	Sub-total	42.9	74	35.7	70	0.83
Grand Total		58.2	100	51.0	100	0.88

Source: The Medium Term Perspective of NOx Control Measures in Large Metropolitan Area, December 1985

struction. However, environmental impact assessments were lacking for regional highway construction projects.

The Environment Agency devised several programs to control NO_x automobile exhaust. In 1978, the environmental quality standard for NO_2 was revised from 0.06 ppm/24hr to 0.04 ppm/24hr at the 98 percentile value. The program called for achieving this standard by 1985. In 1982, the government implemented total mass emission regulation by designating districts. In addition, the Environment Agency set emission standards for passenger cars in 1978 and heavy-duty trucks in 1983. The MOT enforces the emission standards at the time it gives type approval.

Despite these efforts at NO_x emission control from stationary and mobile sources, Japan failed to meet the AAQS for NO_2 by May 1985, the date set for its achievement. The Environment Agency responded by developing a medium-term plan of NO_x control measures for implementation in metropolitan areas. It analyzed emission and pollution data to identify reasons for the failure to meet the 1985 standard and tried to predict future emission and pollution trends from current data.[67]

The agency's report identified four reasons for the failure: (i) The increase in traffic flow due to the marked increase in cargo transport by trucks. (ii) The increase in the size of trucks for cargo transport, and the increase in the number of diesel trucks with direct fuel injection engines. (iii) The extension of car life from seven to ten years, which has slowed the shift from old cars to new cars meeting emission standards. (iv) The failure for the simulation model to properly account for NO to NO_2 conversion.

The Environment Agency concluded that the May 1985 NO_x AAQS could not be achieved before 1988. In FY 1986, it started a research project to develop a better simulation model that accounted for the conversion of NO to NO_2. In addition, it implemented a new policy to encourage turnover from old trucks and buses to new ones meeting the emission standards. Table 1.11 presents trends in the NO_x emission structure in FYs 1983 and 1988.

1.11 AAQS FOR NO_2 AND THE NO_x CONTROL PLAN

The Smoke and Soot Regulation Law of 1962 first designated NO_2 as a specific noxious substance. The government based this designation on a past pollution dispute arising from a chemical plant. Also, research conducted in Los Angeles in the late 1950s on the photochemical oxidation process indicated that NO_2 was a precursor to photochemical oxidant formation. The drafters of the Smoke and Soot Regulation Law foresaw the increase in NO_2 pollution and the subsequent appearance of photochemical smog as Japan entered a period of fast growth and high energy consumption.

In 1962, MHW developed automatic air monitoring instruments for NO, NO_2, and oxidant. Three automatic air monitoring stations were placed at roadsides in the Tokyo metropolitan area, and they recorded a steady increase in the concentration of NO_x, beginning in 1967. During the same period, a National Air Sampling Network Station in Tokyo recorded high peaks of oxidant. In 1965, MHW began to fund an experiment conducted on animals on the chronic effects of long-term exposure to NO_2. A study conducted under contract by Y. Nakajima found that pulmonary laveoral cells developed structural changes after thirty days' exposure to NO_2 at a concentration of 0.7-0.8 ppm.[68]

In view of the results of this study, MHW focused its research on the health effects of long-term exposure to low-level NO_2. The photochemical smog episodes in 1970 further increased the interest in studies showing the health effects of oxidant and NO_2.

In the fall of 1970, the Central Advisory Council formed an expert committee to study proposals for an AAQS for NO_2 and oxidant. Soon after that, the Environment Agency began a continuous, five-year study of the community health effects of air pollution in six cities. It issued an interim report in 1970 on results obtained during the winter of 1970-71.[69]

The NO$_2$ expert committee adopted the report as a reference to be consulted for the formulation of NO$_2$ criteria and guides.

In June 1972, the expert committee recommended an AAQS for NO$_2$ of "less than 0.02 ppm for 24hr average in a community environment". In selecting this standard, the expert committee noted the possible adverse health effects of chronic bronchitis and the synergic effects of SO$_2$. The expert committee did not have the accumulated pollution measurement data when it developed this standard. It had to rely on studies conducted on animals and a few epidemiological studies conducted in Japan and overseas. The foreign material which the expert committee consulted included a document prepared by the U.S. Environmental Protection Agency in January 1971 on NO$_2$ criteria and a conference report of the World Health Organization expert meeting in April 1972.

The expert committee arrived at the 0.02 ppm/24hr (equivalent to 0.01 ppm/year) standard by twice applying a safety factor of 0.5 to a standard of 0.04 ppm/year. The 0.04 ppm/year NO$_2$ standard corresponds to a 5% prevalence rate of chronic bronchitis symptoms in adult male workers in the Tokyo metropolitan area when simultaneously exposed to SO$_2$ at the 0.05 ppm/year level. This is nearly twice the background prevalence rate. This accounts for the first safety factor. The second safety factor is due to the risk of cancer suggested by the abnormal structural changes reported in the experiments on animals. This was the thinking of the expert committee in a period of intense social concern about the quality of the air.

The 0.02 ppm/24hr standard was very strict. By comparison, the U.S. Clean Air Act set an NO$_2$ AAQS of 0.05 ppm/year in April 1971. The U.S. automobile industry attacked even this comparatively lax standard as too strict in September 1971.[70]

In Japan, economic and industrial organizations, led by the Iron and Steel Federation, criticized the proposed 0.02 ppm/24hr standard. But the critics met strong resistance. The social and political climate surrounding pollution control was different in the U.S. and Japan. In the U.S., the devaluation of the dollar in August 1971 had cooled the resolve for environmentalism, but in Japan the Yokkaichi trial had strengthened the environmental movement. The government had empowered the Environment Agency to establish environmental quality standards by agency notification rather than by Cabinet resolution.

In May 1973, the Environment Agency finally decided to accept the recommendation of its expert committee, despite the protests, and issued a notification setting an NO$_2$ AAQS of 0.02 ppm/24hr. It set ten years as the target date to achieve the standard, with an interim target of 0.04 ppm/24hr. At the same time, it set a photochemical oxidant AAQS of 0.06 ppm/hr and raised the SO$_2$ AAQS from 0.05 ppm/24hr to 0.04 ppm/24hr. The Environment Agency based the stricter SO$_2$ standard on morbidity data at Yokkaichi.[71]

The Environment Agency's new NO_2 AAQS prompted related anti-pollution developments. In September 1973, Osaka prefecture responded to the new, strict NO_2 AAQS by formulating a major plan for environmental conservation. The Osaka plan included Japan's first total mass emission regulation, enacted one year in advance of the national regulation. In addition, the new NO_2 AAQS served as a guide for environmental impact assessments. The Environment Agency applied a guide of 98 percentile value of one-year monitoring data. Local governments reviewed the siting and expansion plans of electric power plants, petrochemical complexes, and iron and steel plants. The Environment Agency instituted a strict policy on plant sitings and expansions in order to help meet the NO_2 AAQS. In July 1973, the Sumitomo Chemical Company introduced the first dry denitrification process at its plant in Chiba. In December 1973, the Tokyo Electric Power Company installed the first wet denitrification process at its Minami-Yokohama works. In Hokkaido, the prefectural government took the new NO_2 AAQS into account while conducting an environmental impact assessment on a giant industrial development project that was part of the 1969 Japanese Archipelago Reform. As a result of the assessment, in August 1974 the Hokkaido government and the electric power company agreed that the power company would install denitrification equipment at its coal-fired power station.

The Kawasaki Iron and Steel Company case shows an example of intervention by the Environment Agency to ensure the construction of clean plants. Chiba prefecture entered into negotiations for a pollution control agreement with Kawasaki Iron and Steel regarding Kawasaki's plans to expand a furnace. As a result of the negotiations, Chiba prefecture agreed to lenient terms of pollution control. At the same time, Chiba requested that the government designate the area surrounding the iron and steel plant under the Pollution-Related Health Damage Compensation Law, which had been enacted in 1973. At this point, the Environment Agency entered the picture. It argued that Chiba's policy was contradictory: on the one hand it had conceded to lenient terms of pollution-control, and on the other, it had requested designation for compensation purposes. The Environment Agency stated that it would oppose Kawasaki's expansion plans unless it instituted stricter pollution control. Under pressure, Kawasaki agreed to install denitrification and desulfurization equipment and to build a high stack for the furnace. The Iron and Steel Federation strongly criticized Kawasaki's pollution control measures because it had set a precedent which in time other iron and steel companies would have to meet.

In 1975, the Environment Agency intervened in another iron and steel company's expansion plans. It required the Nippon Kokan Company to install state-of-the-art denitrification and desulfurization equipment at its Oogishima plant. Nippon Kokan and the local government strongly criticized the Environment Agency for requiring costly anti-pollution measures. The U.S. Environ-

mental Protection Agency took an interest in the pollution control facilities
at Oogishima and requested permission to study the facilities in detail.
However, at the request of the U.S. Iron and Steel Industry Association, Nippon
Kokan denied the Environmental Protection Agency's request. The U.S. iron and
steel companies were afraid that the Environmental Protection Agency would be
impressed with the Oogishima facilities and require U.S. plants to install
similarly advanced, pollution-control equipment.

In April 1974, Professor S. Shishido of Tsukuba University conducted a study
on the macroeconomic impact of pollution-control expenditures for the Japan
Economic Study Federation and the OECD Environment Committee. His study
examined the period from FYs 1972-77 and analyzed the macroeconomic impact of
maintaining current pollution-control standards and of raising the standards.
Professor Shishido's study concluded that the macroeconomic impact was
detectable, but not significant.[72]

Japanese industry had always been critical of the NO_2 AAQS, but the criticism reached a peak in FY 1975. In FY 1974, the Japanese economy shrank in
terms of GNP. In addition, the devaluation of the dollar and the energy crisis
helped to bring about a new social climate. The attack on the NO_2 standard was
carried out at a technical level, rather than an emotional or political level.
A famous scholar of chemical engineering specializing in air pollution control
and one of the five major Japanese daily newspapers supported the attack on the
NO_2 standard. In some respects, the attack was similar to the U.S. Environmental Protection Agency's criticism of the epidemiological studies supporting the
U.S. NO_2 ambient standard.   Japanese industry distributed the report of the
hearings held by the U.S. Congress's Senate Committee of Public Works on
November 5th and 6th, 1973.[73]

The Environment Agency commenced a study of the health effects of exposure
to high levels of NO_2 and low levels of particulates and SO_2. In 1974, it
estimated it would cost a total of ¥2000 billion to achieve the NO_2 ambient
standard. In addition, it estimated that NO_x emissions would have to be cut by
more than 90%. In FY 1975, two expert committees began a three-year review of
NO_x emission control technology--one for automobile exhaust emissions and the
other for stationary source emissions. The stationary source committee held
hearings and made site visits to emission control equipment manufacturers and
users. The committee reviewed both combustion and denitrification technology to
find ways to reduce NO_x in fuel and in the air.

The Environment Agency took the position that it should listen closely to
industry's arguments against the NO_2 ambient standard. But it also felt the
review should center on a re-evaluation of the June 1972 Central Advisory
Council expert committee report which formed the basis for the NO_2 standard.
The review was difficult. Experts offered conflicting testimony; the interests

of diverse groups clashed. In the process, the administration was guided by article 9-3 of the Basic Law for Environmental Pollution Control Measures. Article 9-3 stated that environmental quality standards should be reappraised periodically, and revised if necessary.

At this time, MITI and the Environment Agency agreed to conduct separate, independent reviews of the NO_x ambient standard without any cooperation or interference. The reviews were scheduled for completion by May 1978.

To benefit from an international perspective in its reconsideration of the NO_2 standard, in 1976 Japan asked two organizations to conduct a review of its environmental policies--the Joint Expert Committee of the World Health Organization and the UNEP, and the Environment Committee of the OECD. Japan agreed to have the results of the review made public. The WHO-UNEP Joint Expert Committee, which included members on the expert committee of the Central Advisory Council in 1972, released its report in 1977. The Joint Committee concluded that the epidemiological studies upon which the NO_2 ambient standard was based could not, by themselves, provide a quantitative basis for evaluating the health risks of exposure to NO_2. Specifically, the Joint Committee said that the NO_2 concentrations for given periods did not correspond conclusively to the health effects reported in the epidemiological studies. This is because the epidemiological studies estimated the amount of NO_2 exposure when increases in the prevalence of chronic respiratory disease were reported. Accordingly, the Joint Committee noted the need for more in-depth studies of populations exposed to changing concentrations of air pollutants. The Joint Committee recommended a maximum, short-term exposure standard of 0.10-0.17 ppm/hr. It derived this standard by applying a safety factor of 3-5 to 0.5 ppm/hr, the threshold for hazardous health effects on animals. A standard of 0.10-0.17 ppm/hr is equivalent to 0.065-0.125 ppm/24hrs and 0.018-0.035 ppm/yr.

The OECD report made the following conclusions:

It seems true that the available epidemiological studies on which [the NO_2 AAQS] is based are not very convincing. But the contrary (namely that such concentrations would not constitute health hazards) is not rigorously proven either. More generally, the notion of a 'scientifically-based' standard must be viewed with some skepticism. Epidemiological studies can only provide dose-effect relationships. In the best case, such relationships will exhibit thresholds that can suggest quality standards. In all cases, they only provide information to be taken into account in the selection of standards. But the selection is made by men, not by science.[74]

In January 1977, the Environment Agency summarized its community health study of housewives in six cities. The results were translated into English

and distributed to the World Health Organization, the U.S. Environmental Protection Agency, and interested scholars and organizations. The report was
inconclusive with respect to the relationship between air pollution and the
prevalence rate of respiratory symptoms in residents living along roads with
heavy traffic. However, residents of polluted roadside areas lodged more
complaints about pollution from the traffic than residents of non-polluted
areas.

In March 1977, the director-general of the Environment Agency requested the
Central Advisory Council to study the health effects of NO_2 and recommend
standards. The Council organized an expert committee and reported back to the
director-general a year later. The expert committee recommended the following
short- and long-term standards as necessary for the protection of human health:
0.1-0.2 ppm/hr (short-term exposure) and 0.02-0.03 ppm/year (long-term exposure
under conditions of combined air pollution).[75]

The expert committee classified health effects as follows: (i) No effects
are observable with current biological and medical methods. (ii) Medical and
biological effects are observable, but they are reversible and within the
homeostasis range of the living body. (iii) It is unclear whether the observed
effects are reversible or a disruption of the homeostasis or the beginning of
ill health. (iv) The observed effect can be associated with disease. (v) The
observed effect can be diagnosed as disease. (vi) Death.[76]

This can be compared to the classification of health effects for the SO_2
studies in 1968 and 1973 as stated in the Expert Committee Report of the
Environmental Quality Standard for SO_2. There were four classifications: (i)
Exacerbation of patient symptoms cannot be proved by epidemiological studies.
(ii) Increase of mortality rate cannot be proved. (iii) Increase of the prevalence of obstructive pulmonary disease cannot be proved. (iv) Adverse reaction
or hazard of pulmonary function among children cannot be proved by epidemiological studies.

The Central Advisory Council's expert committee interpreted the results of
epidemiological studies differently from the Joint Expert Committee of the
World Health Organization and the UNEP, and the 1977 report of the U.S.
National Academy of Sciences. The National Academy of Sciences report stated
as follows:

Reports of excess chronic respiratory disease associated with low concentrations of ambient nitrogen dioxide (0.053 ppm) do not provide convincing
evidence that other pollutants that were measured at relatively high concentrations were not a probable cause of excess disease. In the presence of low
concentrations of sulfur oxide and particulates, three investigators failed to
detect excess chronic respiratory disease in areas where nitrogen dioxide

exposures were less than 0.053 ppm. Exposure doses calculated only from
ambient air concentrations do not provide realistic estimates of actual human
exposure times, particularly because of extensive movement into and out of
polluted areas by any individual on any given days.[77]

In addition, there were differences between the Prime Minister's inquiry to the
Central Advisory Council in 1970 and the Environment Agency director-general's
inquiry to the Central Advisory Council in 1977. The 1970 inquiry directly
requested proposals for an ambient air quality standard whereas the 1977
inquiry indirectly requested proposals for criteria and guides. Scientific
information constituted the criteria and the expert committee's scientific
judgement constituted the guides. The Environment Agency was responsible for
making the administrative decision regarding the AAQS given the available
scientific information. In 1977, the Environment Agency said, "Criteria and
guides are a matter of science; standards are a matter of administration and
politics. The Environment Agency will choose the AAQS based on the criteria
and guides." The Environment Agency made its role clear at the last session of
the Central Advisory Council when it concluded its report on the criteria and
guides for NO_2, at the press conference, and in the Diet. The weighing of
risks and benefits in the standard setting process was addressed in the World
Health Organization Expert Committee report (TRS-554) issued in 1974.[78]

The debate was set--whether to maintain the high 1972 NO_2 AAQS of 0.02
ppm/24hr (equivalent to 0.01 ppm/year), adopt the mid-level expert committee
proposal of 0.1-0.2 ppm/hr and 0.02-0.03 ppm/year, or concede to the lower
standard of 0.05 ppm/year (equivalent to the U.S. standard) favored by business
interests.[79]

Interested groups attempted to influence the decision-making process for the
NO_2 AAQS. Industrial and economic groups, especially the iron and steel
industry and the automobile industry, waged an extensive propaganda campaign to
revise the AAQS to the U.S. standard of 0.05 ppm/year. On the other side,
environmentalist groups, citizen's organizations, and some local governments,
especially those controlled by the socialist and communist parties, worked to
keep the 1973 standard of 0.02 ppm/24hr. In Chiba and Osaka, patients certified under the Compensation Law filed suits seeking an injunction against
activity by industrial and transport groups opposing the 0.02 ppm/24hr standard. The patient groups also lobbied the Environment Agency to maintain the
current standard. In addition, a group of environment scholars (Kogai Kenkyн),
led by Professor S. Tsuru, announced its opposition to the revision of the NO_2
standard.

The pro-environment groups argued that there was a need to maintain the
safety factor built into the conversion of the 1973 guide to the 1973 standard

TABLE 1.12

The state of compliance with the proposed NO_2 guides of 1978

Proposed-guides	Monitering Site	Saltzmand 0.72	Index 0.84
0.02 ppm/Year	Area Station	53%	68%
(0.04 ppm/24 hr)	Roadside Station	7%	16%
0.03 ppm/Year	Area Station	86%	94%
(0.06 ppm/24 hr)	Roadside Station	39%	53%

Source: Environment Agency; Based on 1977 Monitering Data

of 0.02 ppm/24hr. But the Environment Agency countered that an adequate safety factor had already been built into the guide recommended by the expert committee in 1978, and thus that it did not violate the repeal of the Basic Law's harmony principle to consider economic and technical feasibility factors in the process of converting the guide to the 1978 standard. Feasibility studies indicated that such considerations weighed against a further raising of the proposed 1978 guides. The most difficult problems in adopting a standard higher than 0.02 ppm/year were automobile exhaust emission control and the large numbers of small, urban pollutors.[80]

Moreover, the proposed guides were still the strictest air quality requirements in the world. On the other hand, the Environment Agency did not concede to the demands of business groups for a NO_2 AAQS of 0.05 ppm/year, equivalent to the U.S. standard. The agency reiterated that the Basic Law prohibited the consideration of economic factors to lower the standards beyond those required by the sole consideration of safety factors, as expressed in the proposed 1978 guides.

Table 1.12 shows the state of compliance with the proposed guides in 1977.

In April 1978, the Environment Agency released the third report on NO_x control technology. Because automobile makers had already met the 1978 NO_x emission standard for passenger cars in 1976, the key area in NO_x control planning was stationary sources. The agency implemented the third enforcement schedule for stationary sources in June 1977 based on the progress of the second NO_x control technology report issued in 1977. Scientists had already developed a low NO_x burner and a low NO_x cement kiln (NSP kiln) which both burned fuel more efficiently than the existing burners and kilns. Tables 1.13 and 1.14 show the state of denitrification programs in terms of unit cost and

TABLE 1.13

Installation cost classified by process, per 105 Nm^3/hr gas treatment

	Installation Cost
Direct: Denitrification a Process	0.8 to 2.3 x 10^8 Yen
Direct: Denitrification b Process	1.0 to 2.5 x 10^8 Yen
Heating & Heat Recovery Process	2.0 to 5.3 x 10^8 Yen
Catalyser-Free Reduction Process	2.0 to 0.6 x 10^8 Yen
Wet Process (De-SOx + De-NOx)	8.0 to 9.0 x 10^8 Yen

Source: EA, ACB, April 1978

cost effectiveness.

The Environment Agency developed NO_x control options based on the classification of areas according to NO_2 pollution levels and the classification of NO_x control technology.[81]

For each option, the agency estimated the total cost of pollution control, the annual cost of pollution control, and fuel demand for denitrification plants. The agency also estimated NO_x emissions for each area and space limitations on the installation of denitrification equipment. See Table 1.15.

TABLE 1.14

Annual cost classified by process, equivalent to Yen/Kl of oil

Direct Denitrification a Process	1,000 to 2,100
Direct Process b Process	1,500 to 2,700
Heating & Heat Recovery Process	2,800 to 5,000
Catalyser-Free Reduction Process	700 to 1,300
Wet Process De-SOx + De-NOx	7,700 to 11,800

Source: EA, ACB, April 1978

Table 1.16

Estimated share of types of control investments, classified by NOx control
options. FY 1985

	A Option	B Option	C Option	D Option
Combustion Improvement	68%	22%	19%	15%
Dry Denitrification	18	52	65	75
Catalyser-Free	14	21	16	10
Total	100%	100%	100%	100%

Source: EA, ACB, April 1978

Table 1.15 shows that increases in NO_x investment costs result in a higher
emission cut rate but not in decreases in pollution levels. Based on the data
in Table 1.15, the agency concluded that a reasonable and feasible goal for
roadside stations in A areas was 0.048 ppm/24hr with 64% cut of emission from
stationary sources. With an additional 10% cut in traffic volume, 0.045
ppm/24hr was possible. Option D was feasible only in theory. Table 1.16

TABLE 1.17

NOx control cost rate to production cost, classified by control options &
Industrial Sectors

	A Option	B Option	C Option	D Option
Chemical Industry	0.01%	0.11%	0.18%	0.31%
Petroleum Refinary	0.02	0.06	0.08%	0.18
Cement Industry	0.46	0.51	0.65	1.44
Glass Industry	0	0	0	0.13
Iron & Steel Industry	0.10	0.18	0.21	0.29
Electric Power Industry	0.26	1.43	1.98	2.35

Source: EA, ACB, April 1978

58

Table 1.15

Cost effectiveness of NOx control options, classified by areas graded by pollution level

		A area	B area	C area
98% tile of Annual Data of '75 Daily Av.	Upper 3 Average	0.0093ppm	0.0070ppm	0.0048ppm
	Maximum Minimum	0.112 0.081	0.075 0.061	0.059 0.041
Ground Level Concentration As Target of NOx Control Options Including Emission Cut Rate (%)	A Option 3rd (1977) Enforcement only	0.070	0.054	0.040
	B Option Coal; 0.06 ppm	0.056 −40%	0.049 −24%	keep Present Level
	C Option Coal; 0.04 ppm	0.048 −64%	0.045 −55%	0.035 −21%
	Includes 10% Traffic Cut	0.045	0.043	
	D Option Maximum Feasible by Model	0.044 −76%	0.043 −70%	0.032 −47%
	Includes 10% Traffic Cut	0.041	0.040	
NO available Space for De-NOx Installation	1975FY	50%	40%	40%
	1985FY	30%	25%	25%
Amount of NOx Emission 75 t/year:100% 91.6x10^4		24.7x10^4 27.0%	7.0x10^4 7.7%	19.0x10^4 20.7%

Source: EA, ACB April 1978

D area	Total Investment Cost for NOx Control	Annual Cost for NOx Control	Heating Oil Demand for De-NOx Plant Operation
0.0029ppm			
0.040 0.070			
0.027	194 Billion Yen	88 Billion Yen	8×10^4 Kl/year
keep Present Level	471 Billion Yen	310 Billion Yen	4 to 5 $\times 10^5$ Kl/year
keep Present Level	674 Billion Yen	445 Billion Yen	8 to 9 $\times 10^5$ Kl/year
keep Present Level	859 Billion Yen	572 Billion Yen	1 to 1.2 $\times 10^6$ Kl/year
40%			
25%			
40.9×10^4 44.6%			

presents the estimated share of the types of control investments classified by
NO$_x$ control options. In addition, the Environment Agency calculated the added
value and economic impact on total production costs of each control option.
The impact was different in different economic sectors. See Tables 1.17 and
1.18. Finally, the agency looked at the macroeconomic impact of the control
options. It concluded that an adverse impact on growth, trade,and prices was
detectable but not significant. This conclusion was similar to the conclusion
reached by the OECD in 1975.

In December 1977, MITI published an independently conducted study on the
costs of achieving various ambient NO$_x$ levels at area stations. See Table
1.19. MITI made the assumption that an area station ambient concentration of 46
ppb (0.046 ppm/24hr) was the limit for NO$_x$ control planning. MITI's cost
estimates were higher than the Environment Agency's estimates. This was due in
part to the fact that MITI used control technology data from 1977 while the
Environment Agency used data from early 1978. Both the MITI and Environment
Agency models predicted additional fuel demand for denitrification and fuel
change.

TABLE 1.18

NOx control cost rate to added value classified by control options & industrial
sectors

	NOx Control Cost Rate to Added Value				Surplus Added Value Rate 1975FY
	A Option	B Option	C Option	D Option	
Chemical Industry	0.04%	0.32%	0.55%	0.92%	28.8%
Petroleum Refinary	0.05	0.17	0.22	0.49	12.2
Cement Industry	1.21	4.06	5.03	5.72	24.6
Glass Industry	0	0	0	0.34	24.6
Iron & Steel Industry	0.48	0.90	1.06	1.47	15.2
Electric Power Industry	0.46	2.54	3.52	4.16	26.3

Source: EA, ACB, April 1978

TABLE 1.19

Costs of NOx control for stationary sources. Unit: ¥108 Yen

Ambient Con. of NO$_2$ ppb.	60	55	50	46	30
Control Investment Cost	3,600	5,800	9,500	19,100	57,200
Annualized Control Cost	1,700	2,600	4,000	9,400	24,800

Source: MITI December 1977

The Environment Agency's simulation showed a sharp increase in fuel demand around 0.03 ppm/24hr, and MITI's simulation showed a similar sharp increase around 0.046 ppm/24hr. The Environment Agency study also showed that the stationary sources designated by the Air Pollution Control Law contributed 35% of ground-level concentration in area A. Mobile sources contributed about 1.5 times all stationary sources. The large numbers of small emission sources contributed about 6%. The prediction for the 10% automobile cut was based on the assumption that all trucks and buses would be shifted to the new, standard vehicles of the second target of the long-term goal. This is a rather optimistic assumption. The maximum level of air pollution at a roadside station was 0.124 ppm/24hr at 98th percentile of yearly monitoring data. The Environment Agency estimated that if there is no increase in traffic volume, and all trucks and buses are shifted to the second target of the long-term goal, it is feasible to clear 0.06 ppm/24hr as 98 percentile value. This is another optimistic assumption, in view of the traffic volume and the increasing regional impact of pollution.

The Expert Committee for Criteria and Guides for NO$_2$ reported that the Saltzman Index will change from 0.84 to 0.72. Accordingly, the measured value will be 0.83 times the present measured value.

The ambient air concentration of NO (as opposed to NO$_2$) had declined since the implementation of emission controls for stationary and mobile sources in 1973. Scientists did not understand the mechanisms and kinetics of the conversion of NO to NO$_2$. Thus, this introduced errors in the simulation model of the hour and 24-hour average values.

The Environment Agency estimated that the 0.02 ppm/year standard (equivalent to 0.04 ppm/24hr at 98th percentile) could be achieved in area stations by 1985, if total mass emission regulation of stationary sources could be implemented effectively. However, the agency concluded that it would be impossible to achieve this standard in roadside areas even with all trucks and buses meeting the second stage emission standard. The agency further estimated that the 0.03 ppm/year standard (equivalent to 0.06 ppm/24hr) could be achieved if all trucks and buses meet the second stage emission standard by about 1990 with no increase in traffic volume.

The Environment Agency studied what would happen if a single standard rather than the 0.02-0.03 ppm/year range was adopted. With a single 0.03 ppm/year standard, there would be no further progress in stationary source control. With a single 0.02 ppm/year standard, road expansion in Tokyo, Osaka, and Nagoya would have to be stopped.

For its photochemical oxidant control strategy, the Environment Agency decided to minimize the total amount of photochemical reaction products by limiting NO_x emissions, in addition to hydrocarbon emission control. This strategy differed from U.S. strategy, which was limited to hydrocarbon emission control. Japan stressed the need to minimize photochemical reaction products in order to improve the high peak of oxidant through long-range transport to distant spots. According to the Environment Agency, the U.S. strategy was effective in improving the oxidant peak in the medium-range zone. This was the experience of the Los Angeles Air Pollution Control District, which cut hydrocarbon emissions extensively but NO_x emissions only slightly. The Tokyo Metropolitan Environmental Pollution Control Institute formulated a strategy to keep NO_2 at 0.02 ppm/24hr. But this was not realistic from the point of view of cost-risk-benefit analysis.

All of these issues were exhaustively debated by the Diet, the Central Advisory Council, local governments, economic and industrial organizations, patients' groups, environmentalists' groups, citizens' groups, and journalists. Finally, on July 11th, 1978, the Environment Agency issued a notification setting the NO_2 AAQS as "within the range of 0.06 ppm/24hr to 0.04 ppm/24hr or less." The notification also set 1985, seven years hence, as the target date for achieving the NO_2 AAQS. In addition, the Environment Agency stated that the principle of nondegradation would be applied to areas which currently met the ambient standard.

A small group of environmentalists and citizens filed suit against the Environment Agency and requested a cancellation of the notification. The court ruled for the Environment Agency, and the case is now on appeal in the Tokyo High Court.

In 1979, the agency implemented the fourth stage of the emission control program for stationary sources. In 1982, the government implemented total mass emission regulation to achieve the NO_2 AAQS by 1985. In 1983, the agency implemented the fifth stage of the control program for combustion boilers. The

agency designed the fifth stage to prevent the degradation of NO_2 pollution due
to the energy shift from petroleum to coal after the second energy crisis of
1979. It was also based on the NO_x control technology review for combustion
boilers, especially huge coal-fired electric power stations.

In June 1985, some roadside stations in Tokyo failed to meet the new AAQS.
Accordingly, the Environment Agency began a re-examination of NO_x control
programs.

1.12 AIR POLLUTION CONTROL AND ENERGY

The traditional air pollutants were black smoke and heavy deposited matter
and the Smoke and Soot Regulation Law of 1962 and the Heat Management Law were
designed to control this type of pollution. Coal industrial complexes were a
source of noxious gases as well as black smoke and heavy deposited matter. As
described earlier, the city of Ube developed a successful air pollution control
program to curtail black smoke. Ube's emission standard was incorporated in
the Smoke and Soot Regulation Law.

Beginning in 1955, Japan experienced an energy shift from coal to petroleum.
Whereas coal produced visible, black smoke and soot, petroleum derivatives
produced an invisible gas. The Yokkaichi petroleum refinery, chemical plants,
and high-sulfur crude oil power station generated SO_2 concentrations exceeding
2.5 ppm/hr at the maximum. It was years before the industry began to take
countermeasures, which included the use of low-sulfur fuels, low-sulfur crude
oil, LNG, stack gas desulfurization, low-NO_x combustion, and denitrification.
In December 1969, MITI implemented a low-sulfur fuel supply program to help
achieve the SO_2 AAQS required by the Basic Law. With this, Japan had
integrated its energy, pollution control, and public health policies.

The Air Pollution Control Law of 1968 provided a new emission standard based
on the K-value instead of a volume percent. This led to higher stack construction and desulfurization programs. As the capacity of low-sulfur fuel expanded, the government tightened the K-value.

In 1955, coal comprised 49.2% of the primary energy supply; in 1973, it had
declined to 15.5% During the same period, the share of petroleum increased
from 20.2% to 77.7%. Accordingly, after black smoke and heavy deposits were
under control, the government targeted SO_2 for control. The K-value standard
did not distinguish between petroleum and coal. In Tokyo, Osaka, and Nagoya,
the K-value was tightened almost every two years corresponding to the expansion
in the capacity of low-sulfur fuels. In these cities, coal-fired power stations either installed stack-gas desulfurization equipment or shifted to petroleum. New coal-fired power stations were built far from the Tokyo, Osaka, and
Nagoya bay areas. Also, nuclear power stations were steadily expanded to
supply electricity to the bay areas. These developments were the result of the

pollution control agreements between local governments and electric power stations after 1965. Table 1.20 presents the trends in and structure of primary energy supply.

In 1973, at the time of the first energy crisis, Japan was more than dependent on foreign sources for petroleum. The jump in the price of oil induced a shift in Japan's desulfurization program, from using expensive, low-sulfur residual oil to installing stack-gas desulfurization equipment and using inexpensive, high-sulfur residual oil. At the same time, diesel fuel for automobiles became more popular because of better fuel efficiency and lower fuel price and fuel tax, compared with gasoline. The use of diesel trucks for commodity transport increased as the use of railways decreased. By 1978, the government implemented strict emission control on passenger cars (except diesel cars). The government introduced emission controls for heavy-duty cars, trucks, and trailers gradually, but with longer vehicle life (about 10 years), the shift to the new cars slowed. Thus, there has been little evidence of improvement in air quality in this area. At least, air quality was not getting worse even though the volume of diesel truck and trailer traffic as well as the size of diesel trucks and trailers were increasing. The government did not revise the emission standards because of the oil crisis.

TABLE 1.20

Trends of primary energy supply structure (Share; %)

	1962FY	1965FY	1967FY	1969FY	1970FY	1973FY	1979FY	1983FY
	%	%	%	%	%	%	%	%
Hydropower	13.4	11.3	8.3	7.0	6.3	4.6	5.1	5.7
Nuclear Power	–	0.0	0.1	0.1	0.4	0.6	4.2	7.4
Coal	36.0	27.3	24.6	20.7	20.7	15.6	14.0	18.2
Petroleum	46.1	58.4	64.6	68.3	70.8	77.6	71.1	60.9
Natural Gas	1.3	1.2	1.1	0.0	0.9	0.7	0.6	0.6
LNG	–	–	–	0.1	0.4	0.8	4.9	7.2
Charcol	0.6	0.2	0.1	0.1	0.0	0.0	0.0	0.0
Woodenfire	2.2	1.5	1.0	0.6	0.5	0.2	0.1	
Domestic	47.4%	33.8%	25.5%	19.6%	16.5%	10.1%	13.8%	16.7%
Imported	52.6%	66.2%	74.5%	80.4%	83.5%	89.9%	87.0%	83.3%

Total Amount of Energy Supply; 10^{10} Kcal   113,895 165,614 205,521 270,687 310,468 382,345 408,880 380,741

Source: Comprehensive Energy Statistics; Resource & Energy Agency, MITI,

In 1973, the Diet passed the Pollution-Related Health Damage Compensation Law, and implemented it the next year. The law provided a pollution-load levy, which was calculated based on the total amount of SO_x emission per year. The levy was not a device to control emissions; it was meant merely to provide funds for compensation. Nevertheless, the levy had the unintended effect of encouraging large pollutors to cut their emissions. For example, electric power stations accelerated the shift in fuel in order to minimize the pollution-load levy.

The government began total mass emission regulation for SO_x in 1974 and completed it in 1978. It instituted NO_x control for stationary sources in 1973, and has since instituted the second, third, and fourth enforcement schedules. The government started total mass emission regulation for NO_x in 1982 and ended it in 1985. In 1978, the Environment Agency revised the NO_2 AAQS from the unreasonably stringent standard of 0.02 ppm/24hr to the reasonable and appropriate standard of 0.04-0.06 ppm/24hr.

Beginning in 1973, during the first energy crisis, MITI formulated and implemented an energy-conservation program. Japanese industry commenced research programs to develop energy-conservation technology actively. Specifically, the research centered on improving fuel efficiency and recovering waste heat and waste gases as new energy sources. Also, scientists greatly improved the air pollution control of the coke oven. Nippon Kokan installed equipment for the dry quenching of generator gas in the coke oven at its new iron and steel mill in Oogishima. As a result of these research efforts, the mining and manufacturing sector has experienced a clear reduction in the energy demand per unit of GNP and per unit of production since 1973. See Table 1.21.

TABLE 1.21

Energy demand per unit of GNP and per unit of production in the mining and manufacturing sector

FY	Total Energy Demand 10^{10} Kcal	Population 10^4	GNP 1975 Price 10^8 Yen	Energy Demand per Unit GNP	Mining & Manufacturing Index 1980=100	Energy Demand per Unit of Mining & Manufacturing Index
1973	354,053	10,871	1,449,698	0.244	85.7	1965.9
1975	341,073	11,193	1,498,074	0.228	73.9	2108.1
1978	379,825	11,517	1,741,464	0.218	90.4	1780.3
1980	373,001	11,706	1,916,997	0.195	99.7	1611.6
1983	368,192	11,932	2,128,146	0.173	107.6	1336.4

Source: Comprehensive Energy Satistics; 1984 FY Edition; MITI; December 1984

Between FYs 1973 and 1983, total energy demand hardly grew despite growth in GNP. During that period, energy demand per unit of mining and manufacturing index dropped about 31%. In other words, energy savings, induced by the energy crisis, affected air pollution control favorably.

In 1983, MITI conducted an analysis of the factors which contributed to changes in energy demand during FYs 1981 and 1982. It concluded that 49% was due to energy saving, 29% to production decreases, and 22% to changes in industrial structure. Between FYs 1979 and 1981, production dropped in industries with high inputs of raw materials and energy, and production increased in industries with low inputs of raw materials and energy.[82]

A typical case which illustrates this phenomenon is the electrolytic-process aluminum smelter.

In June 1979, the Tokyo Summit was held to devise strategies to deal with the second energy crisis. Participating countries set upper limits to the amount of petroleum they would consume. This, of course, had a favorable effect on air pollution. MITI's Comprehensive Energy Study Committee started a provisional long-term forecast of energy demand. The forecast took into account the ceiling values on consumption set at the 1979 Tokyo Summit and the introduction of alternative energy sources. The Study Committee recommended that Japan decrease her 99.9% dependence on foreign petroleum for national

TABLE 1.22

Long term prediction of energy demand & supply

Energy Classi- fication	Fiscal Year	1982 Real Data	1990 1983 Prediction	1982 Pre.	1995 1983 Prediction
Petroleum 10^8 Kl Substitute Energy		1.49	ca2.2 ~ ca2.3	3	ca2.7 ~ ca3.0
Coal 10^6 Kl		72	81 ~ 86	115	86 ~ 102
Nuclear Power		27	48 ~ 51	67	74 ~ 79
Natural Gas		27	56 ~ 60	68	65 ~ 63
Hydropower		22	28 ~ 27	30	ca28
Geothermal		0.4	1.5 ~ 2	6	3.5 ~ 4
New Fuel, New Energy, etc.		0.9	7 ~ 12	15	15 ~ 26
Petrolium 10^4 Kl		2.4	ca2.4 ~ ca2.5	2.8	ca2.4 ~ ca2.5
Grand Total Energy Supply 10^8 Kl		3.88	4.5 ~ 4.8	5.8	5.0 ~ 5.5

Ministry of International Trade & Industry, Resource & Energy Agency, 1983.

security purposes.

In August 1979, the Diet passed the Law for the Acceleration of Alternative Energy Sources. Article 3-2 announced the principle of environmental conservation in setting alternative energy policy, and article 5-1 reiterated the principle when introducing alternative energy programs at factories or business enterprises. Under the law, the Cabinet sets the targets in alternative energy supply planning. The Environmental Agency's role in the target setting process

TABLE 1.23

A comparison of the environmental impact and the pollution potential of a petroleum power station and a coal power station

Item	Sub-item	Coal Power Station	Petroleum Power Station
Necessary Space Area. 10^6 kw x 2	Plant Area	90 ha	60 ha
	Depth of Harbour	14m ~ 19m	7.5m
	Length of Bath	750m	Dolphin
Quantity of Fuel 10^6 kw x 2	Annual Quantity (70% operation)	2.3×10^6 t	1.3×10^6 t
	Hourly Maximum	370 t	210 t
Nature of Fuel	Calorific Value	6,200Kcal/kg	10,000Kcal/kg
	Sulfur Content	0.3% ~ 1.6%	Crude Oil 0.14% Residual Oil 0.87%
	Nitrogen Content	1.2% ~ 1.8%	0.05% ~ 0.5%
	Ash Content	15% ~ 20%	0.01%
Effluent Gas etc. 10^6 kw x 2	Quantity of Effluent Gas (Max. Load, Dry)	3.1×10^6 Nm^3/h	2.6×10^6 Nm^3/h
	SO_x Emission Concentration	250ppm 1,300ppm	Crude Oil 80ppm Residual Oil 500ppm
	Emission Quantity of SO_x	780 Nm^3/n	Crude Oil 200 Nm^3/h
	(Max. Load)	4,100 Nm^3/h	Residual Oil 1,300 Nm^3/h
	NO_x Emission Concentration	170ppm ~ 300ppm	130 ppm
	Emission Quantity of NO_x	530 Nm^3/h	340 Nm^3/h
	(Max Load)	930 Nm^3/h	
	Emission Quantity of Smoke & Dust (Max. Load)	6.2t/h ~ 7.8t/h	260 kg/h
	Emission Concentration of Smoke & Dust	20g/Nm^3 ~ 25g/Nm^3	0.1g/Nm^3

Source: Environment Agency; Planning & Co-ordination Bureau; 1980

is one of prior consultation. The Cabinet set the first target in November 1980.

In the spring of 1955, the Environment Agency established the Council for the Examination of Energy and Environmental Problems. The Council noted that the expansion of coal consumption could lead to greater concentration of air pollutants such as suspended particulates, SO_x, and NO_x. It recommended stricter emission control, especially for electric power stations. In addition, it noted that the increased consumption of heavy crude oil could lead to more pollution, and therefore recommended the expansion of refineries to produce light quality residual oil from the crude oil. The Cabinet took these recommendations into account when implementing the alternative energy supply plan. See Table 1.22.

In March 1956, the Council for the Examination of Energy and Environmental Problems published a report which included a comparison of the pollution potentials of petroleum-powered and coal-powered electricity generating stations.[83] See Table 1.23.

The report made the following main points: (i) Coal combustion has a greater emission potential than petroleum combustion. (ii) Industry should control dust pollution occurring during transport, storage, and loading operations. (iii) Scientists should make a study of secondary pollutants, which are pollutants generated by primary pollutants. Examples of secondary pollutants are sulfate, nitrate, and acid rain generated by transformation during the course of long-range transport. (iv) Scientists should study the trace elements in coal and their effect on combustion, emission, and deposits and residues in combustion wastes. In addition, the effect of trace elements and small particles on the efficiency of dust collection should be studied. (v) Scientists should study polycyclic hydrocarbon and fluorine compounds, which are generated during combustion.

The council's report also addressed nuclear power. It classifies nuclear power generation as a clean, alternative energy from the standpoint of air

TABLE 1.24

Electricity generation cost (Yen/Kwhr) classified by energy source; 1984FY

Hydropower	21
Nuclear Power	13
Coal	14
Petroleum	17
LNG	17

Source: Resource, Energy Agency, MITI 1984
Note : Decommission Cost is included for nuclear power case.

pollution control. However, the report also noted the special risks of nuclear power generation. These included the accidental release of radioactive pollutants, the storage of wastes, and the management of nuclear cycle facilities. Finally, the council's report superficially reviewed geothermal power generation. Among other issues, it discussed the release of H_2S and the need for total energy balance.

In response to the recommendations of the council's report, the Environment Agency organized the Study Group of Methods and Criteria in Environmental Impact Assessment of Coal-Fired Power Stations. In addition, the agency established a comprehensive study group with subgroups for coal analysis, combustion, control technology, environmental monitoring, and integration of the various study results. Both study groups completed their deliberations by the end of FY 1984.

In 1982, the Air Pollution Control Law strengthened the emission standard for particulates, which made the revised standards for new, coal-fired power stations more stringent than the emission standards in the U.S. and Europe. In 1983, the Air Pollution Control Law tightened the emission standards for NO_x. At present, the emission standards for pollutants discharged by coal-fired power stations are almost equivalent to the emission standards for petroleum-fired power stations.

The Environment Agency established these strict emission standards for coal combustion boilers primarily to control pollution from small coal boilers in

Table 1.25

International comparison of electricity charge (July 1981)

Name of Country		U.S.A.			U.K.	France	W.Germany	Japan
Name of Electric Power Co.		Consolidated Edison	Common Wealth Edison	Detroit Edison	London Power Bureau	France Electricity Corp.	Rhein West Fahren	Tokyo Electric Co.
Date of Charge Renewal		'81/2	'81/2	'81/7	'81/4	'81/7	'81/6	'80/4
Yen Conversion Based on Currency Exchange Rate July '81	Domestic Use: 190KwH/M.	34.88	18.44	14.74	27.47	18.17	18.73	26.36
	Industrial Use Contract: 2,000Kw: Unit 300KwH	28.66	13.66	14.48	17.19	12.26	12.66	17.89

Source: Japan Iron & Steel Federation, Division of Raw Materials
          Iron & Steel Journal, Vol.31, No.10, October 1981

TABLE 1.26

Structural plan for electric power generation

	1984FY	1989FY	1994FY
Hydropower	19%	18%	17%
LNG	23%	27%	26%
Coal	3%	5%	7%
Petroleum	39%	32%	25%
Nuclear Power	16%	18%	25%
Total Power Generation Kwhr	$12,249 \times 10^8$	$14,634 \times 10^8$	$18,010 \times 10^8$

Source: Japan Electric Power Study Committee
Long Term Demand Forecast; April 1985

air pollution control system for coal-fired power stations to meet the tough, new standards.[84]

Dengen Kaihatsu spent ¥8 billion between 1978 and 1982 for research and development. It has developed several coal centers after conducting careful environmental impact assessments and formulating strict air pollution control plans.

Japanese electric companies charge the highest rates in the world for electricity. This is due to the high price of fuel and the cost of complying with stringent anti-pollution measures. Table 1.24 presents the costs of electricity generation, classified by energy source. Table 1.25 presents an international comparison of electricity charges.[85]

Japan's energy structure for electric power generation has been undergoing a change. It relies less on petroleum and more on LNG, nuclear power, and coal. See Table 1.26. Table 1.26 is based on the assumption that electricity demand will increase by 2.8% annually.

1.13 SPECIFIC AIR POLLUTANTS

Accidental releases. The Smoke and Soot Regulation Law of 1962 set forth measures to be taken in the case of an accident occurring during a company's manufacturing process which results in the release of specified noxious substances. The law permitted the prefectural governor to order an investigation, conduct an on-site inspection, and take enforcement measures, if necessary. These provisions were included as a result of a number of instances of accidental air pollution.

The 1970 amendments. The Air Pollution Control Law of 1968 had the same provisions, but it was extensively amended in 1970. The amendments provided definitions for two new categories of smoke subject to emission control. One category defined specific noxious substances, such as Cd, C_{12}, and Pb and their compounds, NO_x, F, HF, silicon fluoride, and other noxious substances not yet designated. The other category specified substances subject to special measures in the case of accident. These included NH_3, H_2S, HCN, and others. In addition, the law controlled the primary air pollutants which were transformed by photochemical reaction to photochemical oxidant.

During 1972-73, the Environment Agency developed control guides for mercury compounds and PCBs. In 1973, the Chemical Assessment Law designated alkyl-mercury and PCB as chemicals specially toxic to the environment.

Acid rain. Around 1975, the air pollution problem grew worse. In July 1974 and July 1975, officials reported widespread eye irritation and plant damage in the Kanto region. It was assumed that the cause was acid rain. Since then, national and prefectural research institutes and universities have conducted joint regional study projects on acid rain. The incidence of acid rain has declined with the progress of total mass emission control of SO_x and NO_x. According to a study conducted by M. Tamaki in 1985, there were 11 episodes of acid rain with a pH of less than 3 between June 1973 and June 1981. During these 11 episodes, taking place in the summer, Tamaki observed high electroconductivity and a high concentration of nitrate. From 1973-80, scientists observed rain in urban areas with a pH of between 4.3 and 4.8. The pH levels have not been declining.[86]

Spiked tires. Another problem was the use of spiked tires on automobiles during the snow season from October to March. Spiked tires destroyed the road surface, which generated a marked increase in the amount of suspended particulates and heavy deposited matter. In Sendai, scientists recorded 14 tons/km^2/month of deposit matter in October, 92.2 tons/km^2/month in January, and 133 tons/km^2/month in March.[87]

Asbestos. In January 1985, the Environment Agency conducted a survey in which it found the ambient concentration of asbestos to be in the range of 10^{-2} to 10^{-4} times the occupational exposure limit.[88]

Hg. In FY 1975 and FY 1982, the Environment Agency conducted a nationwide survey of the concentration of ambient Hg. The FY 1975 data indicated that the concentration differences between the different areas. The Hg ambient concentration was 10^{-2} to 10^{-3} times the WHO guide of 15 $\mu g/m^3$.[89]

In 1983, the government issued a report on the status of Hg emissions from urban incinerator plants. The report stated that the source of Hg emissions from urban incinerators was Hg contained in dry cells. According to K. Hishida, in April and May 1984, Hg emissions from 12 metropolitan incinerators ranged between 0.12 and 0.34 mg/Nm^3.[90]

MHW and MITI proposed the Hg content in dry cells be cut. Accordingly, the government has conducted research and development programs on emission control for Hg and Hg-free dry cells.

Dioxin. Since FY 1982, the government has been conducting a national comprehensive research project on dioxin. People became alarmed when dioxin was discovered in the residual ash of urban incinerators. This has led to concern about the risk of pollution from 2, 3, 7, 8, TCDD. In May 1984, a MHW Expert Study Group calculated the maximum ground-level concentration of dioxin at 0.25 ng/m^3 and the maximum daily intake at 1.58×10^{-3} ng/kg/day. MHW set the provisional ADI at 0.1 ng/kg/day after reviewing data regarding the non-observable adverse effect level (NOAEL), the non-observable effect level, and ADI reports abroad. The Expert Study Group stressed the need for further research on this and other points.[91]

Carcinogenic and mutagenic pollutants. The public has become increasingly concerned about the problem of carcinogenic and mutagenic pollutants. In 1984, during the 25th Annual Assembly of the Japan Society of Air Pollution, several papers discussed the declining trend of benzo(a)pyrene in Sapporo, Sendai, Tokyo, Kawasaki, Yokohama, and Kita Kyushu.[92]

The papers theorized that the decline was due to the stringent air pollution control of SO_x, NO_x, and particulate emissions from stationary sources and strict automobile emission control. At the same time, the increasing use of large trucks and trailers to transport cargo has caused polycyclic hydrocarbon pollution along heavily travelled roads, particularly 1-nitropyrene and 3-nitrofluoranthene.[93]

The Environment Agency has been studying diesel exhaust continuously.

Fluorocarbon and CO_2. Finally, Japan has become increasingly concerned by some of the global environmental pollution problems, such as fluorocarbon and CO_2. In recent years, the Environment Agency, the Ministry of Transportation, and the Ministry of Education have conducted research projects on CO_2.

1.14 EVOLUTION OF AIR QUALITY MANAGEMENT

Local initiative. In almost every case in Japan, the government undertook to reduce air pollution only after it had become a serious problem. Moreover, it was local government which usually took the initiative to deal with pollution problems. The Ube city government was the first to implement an effective emission control program with the active assistance of local industry and the university. Ube also conducted epidemiological studies and monitored air pollution levels.

National legislation. The Smoke and Soot Regulation Law of 1962 was the beginning of modern air quality management in Japan. It established emission standards, air monitoring programs, and measures to alert the public when pollution reached levels dangerous to health. In FY 1963, MHW subsidized a program to build automatic air monitoring stations which measured the level of suspended particulates and SO$_2$. The issue of alerts to warn the public of dangerous pollution levels served to heighten the awareness of people to the growing pollution problem in Japan.

Pollution measurement and health effect studies. The National Institute of Public Health conducted studies on the impact of air pollution on health. In addition, MHW conducted community health effect studies in Yokkaichi and Osaka from 1964-69. MHW published the results of the Yokkaichi study in 1965.[94] See Table 1.27. After 1965, MHW expanded its research projects to include clinical, pathological, and animal experiments.

The Expert Committee of the Central Advisory Council for Pollution Control Measures consulted the MHW reports and foreign studies as it developed criteria, guides, and standards for SO$_2$. The Cabinet established the first AAQS for SO$_2$ in 1969. Then, MITI formulated a low-sulfur fuel-supply program designed to achieve the SO$_2$ AAQS within ten years. During this time, MHW subsidized the installation of a telemeter system in each designated area. Also, it installed a regional telemeter system in the Osaka Bay and Tokyo Bay areas from 1970. In addition, prefectural governments obtained the voluntary cooperation of industry to build a source telemeter system.

Pre-siting studies and pollution control agreements. In 1961, the Osaka prefectural government and the city of Nishinomiya were the first to conduct air pollution impact assessments. In 1964, in response to the anti-pollution and anti-development movements in Mishima-Numazu, MHW and MITI conducted large-scale environmental impact assessments of the regional industrial development project at Mishima-Numazu. This became the model for later environmental

TABLE 1.27

Prevalence rate of chronic bronchitis symptoms through interview questionaire survey of the British Medical Research Council in Osaka & Yokkaichi

			Osaka	Yokkaichi
Non-smoker	Male	Polluted Area	4.3%	11.1%
		Non-polluted Area	2.1%	3.9%
	Female	Polluted Area	2.6%	12.3%
		Non-polluted Area	0.8%	1.6%
Smoker	Male	Polluted Area	7.8%	16.2%
		Non-polluted Area	5.0%	5.7%
	Female	Polluted Area	4.0%	16.9%
		Non-polluted Area	7.2%	10.3%

Source: Ministry of Health & Welfare; 1965

impact assessments. In 1965, MITI began to conduct factory pre-siting studies in cooperation with local governments. These studies consisted of a detailed source inventory, a wind tunnel experiment, a meteorological study, and a computer simulation. Also, MHW conducted background studies, short-term air pollution studies during the worst meteorological season for air pollution, and field diffusion experiments using tracers. Between FY 1965 and FY 1969, MITI and MHW surveyed 25 and 37 areas, respectively.

MHW and MITI cooperated with local governments in their efforts to develop effective air pollution control programs and to negotiate pollution-control agreements with private companies. In most cases, the pollution-control agreements set terms more stringent and individualized than those required by law. The first such agreement was between Yokohama and Dengen Kaihatsu, an electric power company, in 1964. Yokohama first conducted an environmental impact assessment, and then developed the pollution-control requirements from the results of the assessments. This procedure followed that used in Mishima-Numazu. Yokohama published the data obtained from the environmental impact assessment, but it did not hold a public hearing on the matter.

In 1965, the Electricity Source Development Coordination Council made environmental impact assessments and pollution-control agreements standard parts of the approval process for the siting and expansion of fuel power stations. MITI and the Economic Planning Agency also adopted such procedures.

Criteria, guides, and standards. The government established an AAQS for SO_2 in 1969, for CO in 1970, for suspended particulates in 1977, and for NO_2 and photochemical oxidant in 1973. The government raised the AAQS for SO_2 in 1973, and lowered the AAQS for NO_2 to a more appropriate level in 1978. In addition, it set a provisional air quality guide for hydrocarbon in 1976, in order to control photochemical oxidant. These AAQSs are summarized in Table 1.27.

In 1976, the Environment Agency established an air quality criteria for Pb. However, the agency did not convert the criteria to a guide and then a standard because the lead-free gasoline program had succeeded in reducing the ambient concentration of Pb.

The Expert Committee of the Central Advisory Council developed all of these criteria, guides, and standards based in part on health effect studies conducted by MHW, the environment agencies, and local governments. Also, it relied on expert committee reports issued by WHO. Scientists from the U.S. and Japan cooperated in developing a methodology for the health effect studies.

Area Environmental Pollution Control Plan. The 1967 Basic Law for Environmental Pollution Control Measures authorized the government to institute a pollution-control plan in a designated area if the area already has a high pollution level or if there is a danger of the area developing a high pollution level due to trends in population and industry. The Prime Minister directs the planning and policy-making for this medium-term comprehensive plan for environmental pollution control with the prior consultation of the relevant prefectural governor. The Council of Environmental Pollution Control Measures, chaired by the Prime Minister, must approve the planning and policy. Air pollution control is an integral part of this overall pollution program. In the planning process, the council consults estimates of growth and future pollution levels and data collected by MHW and MITI on emission sources, air pollution monitoring, source inventory, and pre-siting studies. The ambient air quality standards provide the overall goals for the air pollution programs.

The government provides subsidies and other financing measures for several of the pollution control programs, such as the air monitoring network system, the mobile survey unit, and the buffer zone facility development project. In addition, the Environmental Pollution Abatement Corporation provides loans for pollution abatement programs at existing factories. The Law for Cost Bearing

Table 1.28

Progress of aerial environmental pollution control plan

Year	'72	'74	'76	'78	'80	'82	'84	'86	'88	Area
Area 1	-----------------			-------------		xxxxxxxxxxxxx				Yokkaichi, Mizushima
Area 2	------------		------------xxxxxxxxxxxxxxx							Tokyo, Kanagawa, Osaka, Saitama, Kyoto, etc.
Area 3	------------		------------xxxxxxxxxxxxxxxx							Kashima, Nagoya, Hyogo, Ooita, Kitakyushu
Area 4	------------		--------------		xxxxxxxxxxxxx				Fuji, Harima south, Ootake, Iwakuni, Oomuta
Area 5	-----------		----------------			xxxxxxxxxxxxxx			Sendai, Chiba, Toyama, Takaoka, Kobe, etc.
Area 6	--------------xxxxxxxxxxxxxx									Muroran, Niigata, Shizuoka,Okayama, Hiroshima, etc.
Area 7		-------------	xxxxxxxxxxxxx							Sapporo, Hitachi, Akita,Suwa,Gifu, Matsumoto, etc.

Note: ---- old plan,   xxxx present plan
Source: Annual Report of Environmental Quality for 1984 FY. Presented to 102nd Congress; 1985 May

by Polluting Industries requires pollutors to pay for pollution abatement programs undertaken by the government. The prefectural level Local Council for Environmental Pollution Control Measures determines the amount which industry must pay.

The government implemented the first environmental pollution control plan in FY 1971. The Council for Environmental Pollution Control Measures approved the seventh pollution control plan in May 1986. By May 1985, the government had adopted polllution control plans covering 9% of the national area, 55% of the population, and 68% of manufacturing production. Table 1.28 presents a summary of the coverage of the plans.

Total emission regulation and automatic monitoring networks. Total mass emission regulation is a kind of medium term air pollution control plan. It is developed from monitoring data, emission source data, the outlook for energy supply, meteorological background studies, tracer experiments, and computer simulation.

In 1983, there were 1613 automatic SO_2 monitoring stations, and 1284 area

TABLE 1.29

Trends of monitering station expansion & compliance - rate to ambient air quality standard (Osaka Prefecture)

Fiscal Year	On-line Station		Off-line Station		Compliance Rate (%) to AAQS of SO_2
	Total Number	SO_x Autometer	Total Number	SO_x Autometer	
1964FY	–	–	7	7	–
1965FY	–	–	10	10	–
1966FY	–	–	15	15	–
1967FY	–	–	19	19	–
1968FY	15	15	10	10	–
1969FY	22	21	10	4	–
1970FY	28	24	21	10	–
1971FY	29	25	25	18	–
1972FY	34	30	30	21	–
1973FY	38	34	83	65	8.5%
1974FY	40	37	97	70	47.6%
1975FY	42	39	95	67	61.8%
1976FY	42	39	96	68	66.2%
1977FY	42	39	83	56	75.4%
1978FY	42	39	83	57	62.0%
1979FY	42	39	79	57	81.7%
1980FY	42	39	82	56	97.2%
1981FY	42	39	77	51	100.0%
1982FY	42	39	77	46	100.0%
1983FY	42	39	77	46	100.0%

Source: Tatsuya Yamamoto; Thesis Paper, Tsukuba University 1985
        Osaka Prefectural Government

and 274 roadside monitoring stations for NO_2. 99.4% of the SO_2 monitoring stations meet the SO_2 AAQS, and 98.7% of the NO_2 area stations and 75.9% of the NO_2 roadside stations meet the NO_2 AAQS. SO_2 management has advanced to the point where it is concerned with maintaining the AAQS, but NO_2 management is still concerned with abatement.

Air pollution monitoring using telemeters is expensive. The government is considering revising the budgets for this. However, it is recognized in some circles that this is the cost for obtaining the information which forms the basis for air pollution management.

In Osaka prefecture, SO_2 abatement programs cost a total of between 4550 billion to achieve the AAQS. Table 1.29 traces the progress of compliance with the SO_2 AAQS and the expansion of the SO_2 air monitoring system. Total mass emission regulation for SO_x was implemented in 1976.

Table 1.30 presents the cost of the administration of SO_x pollution control. A study of the cost effectiveness of air pollution monitoring systems showed that, in the case of a 10-station monitoring system, one additional air monitoring station can save 0.1 billion in abatement costs. For a 30-station monitoring system, one additional air monitoring station can save 0.1 billion in abatement costs. The study also showed that a 40-station system provides the optimum quantity of information, with a 90% probability of achieving the SO_2 AAQS.

Regional pollution. Photochemical oxidant and acid rain became pollution

Table 1.30

Cost of air pollution control administration (Osaka Prefecture)
1968FY - 1976FY 10^6 Yen

Fiscal Year	Information Cost				Policy & Planning Decision Cost	Control Programme Implementation Cost	Total
	Collection			Analysis			
	Monitering		Surevy Cost	Analysis Cost			
	Facility Cost	Maintenance Cost					
1968FY	84	–	–	–	–	–	84
1969FY	108	–	28	8	–	17	161
1970FY	112	23	132	7	3	34	308
1971FY	68	37	157	8	4	50	281
1972FY	134	38	186	7	14	68	439
1973FY	135	57	132	7	5	67	389
1974FY	95	69	167	8	23	122	471
1975FY	110	84	94	3	5	68	360
1976FY	30	107	64	63	6	36	239

Source: Tatsuya Yamamoto; Thesis Paper; Tsukuba University 1985
         Osaka Prefectural Government

problems in the mid-1970s. Because of this, air monitoring had to be conducted on a regional, rather than a local, scale. The government provided a subsidy to expand the regional telemeter systems in the Tokyo and Osaka Bay areas. In 1974, the National Institute of Environmental Studies initiated a research project conducted by universities and teams from several prefectures. Reports from the U.S. and Europe on acid rain damage have accelerated progress in these research projects. In FY 1986, the government began a nationwide acid rain study project, which also examined pollution from China. The FY 1986 budget allocated funds to the Meteorological Agency to conduct continuous monitoring of CO_2 in order to cooperate with the World Meteorological Organization's global CO_2 monitoring program.

Environmental impact assessments. The government began environmental impact assessments in 1964 as a routine, technical administrative program. Then, the Cabinet issued a regulation requiring such assessments for all public works projects. In 1974, the Industrial Siting Law required environmental impact assessments for designated industrial development projects. Also, total mass emission regulation was applied to such projects. The Industrial Pollution Abatement Manager Law of 1971 established the foundation for the implementation of the Siting Law.

The government broadened the scope of air pollution impact assessments to include road construction projects, airport development projects, and the large bridge project in the Seto Island Sea. In 1980, the Environment Agency submitted a bill to the Diet which would establish a common procedure for environmental impact assessments for public works projects. Although the legislation was not passed, in 1984 the Cabinet issued a resolution based on the bill. The Cabinet resolution made such assessments a standard part of the planning and implementation of public works projects. It also provided for public hearings and disclosure. During 1980-84, when the bill was pending in the Diet, each ministry had developed detailed technical guidelines for environmental impact assessments for electric power stations, highways, and airports. However, the government has not yet established procedures for regional-scale environmental impact assessments for building a coastal highway in the Tokyo Bay area and the cross-bay bridge project.

Econometric Assessment. The government conducted econometric assessments to assist in the evaluation of pollution-control programs. The Environment Agency's econometric assessments of air pollution control programs were an integral part of the formulation of policy options for the Long-Term Environment Conservation Plan. In 1977, the Economic Planning Agency conducted econometric assessments of the Economic and Social Development Plan. In 1978, the Environment Agency conducted an econometric assessment of NO_x control plan options. Between 1975 and 1986, during the agency's reviews of emission-

control technology, it examined fuel efficiency data and cost increases resulting from the plan options.

The Third Comprehensive National Development Plan emphasized regional human
settlements over huge industrial projects. One of the goals of the development
plan was to blend with local culture and community traditions. The Environment
Agency stressed environmental management which anticipated and prevented pollution problems. For example, with the shift from petroleum to alternative
energy sources, in 1979 the Environment Agency developed a plan to deal with
the increase in coal consumption. Today, environmental management in Japan is
the product of 25 years of experience by the central and local governments in
dealing with pollution control.

1.15 INTERNATIONAL PERSPECTIVES IN JAPANESE POLLUTION CONTROL

In many instances, Japan looked to the U.S. and Europe to learn from their
experiences in formulating its own pollution-control policies. In Great
Britain, local governments implemented traditional smoke abatement methods
using the Ringelman chart to control black smoke. Drawing on this experience,
the Tokyo municipal government enacted the Smoke Abatement Ordinance in 1955.
The ordinance contained a provision for black smoke control using the Ringelman
chart. In 1954, Kanichi Nakayasu, president of the steel manufacturing company
Ube Kosan, revisited the United States and was deeply impressed with how the
city of Pittsburgh had managed to control the air pollution caused by its iron
and steel mills. This experience motivated him to propose an air pollution
abatement program in Ube.

Japan has also looked to the west for legal doctrine to be used in the fight
against pollution. For example, local governments in Japan borrowed the concept of nuisance as used in British and U.S. law. In 1949, when the Tokyo
municipal government drafted its Industrial Pollution Control Ordinance, it was
strongly influenced by the German concept of _Imission_. Around 1960, Japan
gained further insight on pollution control by studying reports on smog in
London, Donora, and the Muse Valley; photochemical oxidant in Los Angeles; and
the Poza Rica incident. In addition, the Los Angeles Pollution Control
District's Air Pollution Control Regulation served as the model for the
Japanese program of continuous pollutant monitoring and the issue of alerts
when pollutant concentrations reached levels dangerous to health. In 1961, WHO
arranged fellowships in Great Britain, West Germany, France, and Belgium for
MHW officials who were preparing the Smoke and Soot Regulation Law of 1962.
These fellowships allowed Japan to learn from the accumulated knowledge and
experience of these countries. The MHW officials studies the similarities and
differences in the air pollution control programs of these countries.

At about the same time, the United States Public Health Service began an

environmental health project in Japan. It sent Dr. V. Newill to the medical
laboratory of the U.S. Army in Camp Zama to head the project. MHW sought the
advice of Dr. Newill on the problems it was facing in Yokkaichi concerning air
pollution and health. This exchange in 1959 was the beginning of U.S.-Japan
cooperation in studies on air pollution and health. Dr. T. Suzuki of the
National Institute of Public Health and the executive-secretary of the Japan
Society of Air Pollution led the Japanese team. Japan had a lot to learn from
the United States on scientific and technological issues in the field of air
pollution measurement and health effect studies.

Learning to manage pollution from the new petrochemical complexes, such as
Yokkaichi, presented different problems, however. The West did not have the
knowledge and experience to assist Japan in this field. From the fellowships
to Europe sponsored by WHO, Japan realized that it would have to solve the
problem of SO_x control by itself. Japan came to the conclusion that land use
and factory siting were important considerations in preventing air pollution in
newly developing areas. But this was an area where Japan had made mistakes--
companies had located large industrial complexes with huge emission potentials
near residential areas. Japan devised a three-part approach to air pollution
control for industrial complexes. It consisted of pre-siting surveys, pollution-control agreements between the local government and the pollutor, and
MITI's desulfurization plan. This approach was different from that taken in
the United States, Great Britain, and West Germany.

In the later-1960s, WHO expert committee programs assisted Japan in the
development of air quality criteria, guides, and standards. For example, Japan
received scientific information from WHO and the U.S. Public Health Service
when it formed the AAQSs for SO_2 in 1969 and CO in 1970. In 1968, the OECD
Science Policy Committee's air management program gave Japan an insight into
the problem of acid rain. In return, the OECD sought information from MITI on
its desulfurization plan and from MHW and MTI on their pre-siting surveys.

The United Nation's Report on the Human Environment treated air pollution as
a global problem, and the report was widely circulated in Japan. Also, the
OECD's report on "The Problems of Modern Society" gave Japan insight into the
economic aspects of air pollution control. In response to automobile regulations of the European Economic Commission, the Ministry of Transportation
instituted CO control in 1966. In addition, U.S. federal and California automobile emission control legislation forced Japanese automobile makers to
develop and install hydrocarbon control devices in their export models to the
United States.

Other developments in the United States also helped to shape Japanese pollution-control policy. In 1970, the Japanese press reported and evaluated the
U.S. National Environmental Policy Act with great interest. President Nixon

criticized Japan implicitly for taking an unfair advantage in international trade by not incurring the costs of pollution control. Christian Harter came to Japan as a special envoy of President Nixon to gain the cooperation of Japan in environmental-pollution control.

In March 1970, the International Social Science Council held the International Symposium on Environmental Disruption in Tokyo. The symposium provided an opportunity for other countries to review Japan's pollution problems at their worst stage. Also, in 1970, the OECD established the Environment Committee, which formulated the pollutor-pays-principle. It also started the Air Management Sector Group, which issued the report on "Fuel Combustion and Stationary Sources." The report provided useful information on the prediction of future pollution levels in OECD member countries. In September 1972, the Air Management Sector Group held a special session. During the session, Japan reported to the OECD member countries that it had undertaken drastic environmental policy changes. Also, it advised that Mazda and Honda had met the U.S. automobile exhaust emission standards for 1975 of the Clean Air Act.

When Mr. Ruckelshaus of the U.S. Environmental Protection Agency addressed the U.S. Congress to introduce the Clean Air Act of 1970, he spoke about the worst air pollution in Tokyo, where policemen had to use masks to protect themselves. A number of provisions of the Clean Air Act were studied with interest in Japan. This included the automobile emission standard and the requirements for environmental impact assessments and environmental impact statements. In 1975 and 1976, Japan adopted the U.S. automobile exhaust emission standards of 1975 and 1976, respectively, the so-called Muskie standards. However, when the U.S. changed its pollution policy in mid-course due to the devaluation of the dollar and the energy crisis, Japan maintained a strict pro-environment policy. The stringent U.S. AAQS for NO_2 (0.02 ppm/24hr) in 1973 was the subject of an intense debate in Congress. Consumers demanded an even stricter NO_2 AAQS and the institution of the original NO_2 emission standards for 1975 and 1976.

In 1971, the Environment Agency and other ministries began to participate actively in the international programs of the OECD and the UNEP. In 1972, the director-general of the Environment Agency, Minister Ohishi, addressed the Human Environment Conference in Stockholm, and explained frankly Japan's past negligence in pollution control. At the Nairobi Conference of the UNEP, the director-general of the Environment Agency, Mr. Hara, noted the importance of environmental conservation on a global scale. He proposed that the United Nations establish a special committee to study and make recommendations concerning this topic. Accordingly, in the fall of 1984, the UN General Assembly organized the World Commission on Environment and Development.

In 1976, the WHO-UNEP joint expert committee published its report on air quality guides and criteria for NO_2. The report served as an important scientific contribution to Japan's revision of its NO_x AAQS. In May 1979, the OECD Council issued recommendations on the use of coal as a substitute for petroleum. The recommendations helped Japan to formulate an environmental policy as it shifted its primary energy source from petroleum to coal.

Japanese corporations doing business abroad have been criticized for engaging in environmentally destructive practices. In response to the complaints, the Keidanren issued a "Code of Conduct for Japanese Enterprises in Developing Countries." The Keidanren organized the Japan Overseas Enterprise Association to encourage the implementation of the Code of Conduct. The Association's 1982 annual report stated that pollution-control investments constituted 6.7% of the total investments of Japanese overseas enterprises during the past ten years. Of this, investments for water-pollution control constituted the largest category, and investments for air-pollution control constituted the third largest category.

In 1975, a Japanese consortium and the Indonesian government signed a master agreement for a development project in Asahan. The agreement contained express terms on environmental preservation. The participants spent 20% of their total investment cost for an aluminum smelter on pollution-control equipment. A dry adsorption process with a recycling system has eliminated 98% of HF emissions. Monitoring equipment has recorded ambient HF concentrations of under 1 ppb. In addition, Japan has provided technical assistance for a community health project since 1977. The arrangement is based on an agreement between Japan and Indonesia.

During the 1980s, Japan's experience with environmental pollution control has attracted international interest. Specifically, Canada, the United States, West Germany, and the Scandinavian countries have looked to Japan to find ways to deal with the degradation of their forests due to acid rain. They are interested in Japanese technology and know-how concerning desulfurization, denitrification, and automobile emission control. In addition, Japan has executed bilateral cooperation agreements with West Germany, Turkey, Austria, Greece, China, and other countries, and has cooperated with ASEAN countries.

Since 1974, there have been more and more international seminars and training courses on pollution control. A course on air pollution control was added in 1985. The Environment Agency's Council for Global Environmental Problems has been working to promote international cooperation. It is concerned with the yellow sand in wind from the Chinese continent in the spring, radioactive fallout of nuclear testing on Bikini Island, and large volcanic eruptions. It is also studying the increase of CO_2 leading to the depletion of the ozone layer in the upper atmosphere. These will be the main challenges for humankind in the 21st Century. Japan's role and responsibility in solving these problems are entering a new stage.

1.16 HOW JAPAN CONQUERED AIR POLLUTION: A HISTORICAL SUMMARY

At the end of World War II, Japan had a few statutes dealing with pollution control but it lacked an effective, comprehensive approach. Emissions from plants in the mining and manufacturing industries caused serious damage to farmers and residents in the vicinity. In response to strong demands for pollution control measures, some companies built higher stacks for better diffusion. Also, mining smelters installed sulfuric acid recovery equipment and cement manufacturers installed Cottrell devices.

Between 1945 and 1969, local government initiatives played an important role in the development of modern, industrial pollution programs. For example, in Ube, the municipal government, university, and local industry cooperated to implement an effective pollution-control program. The Ube programs were not mandated by legislation; city ordinances merely created a committee where the parties concerned could meet and exchange views. Committee members included a university professor, an industry manager, a city official, and a city assembly representative. The Ube program was remarkably successful. Pollution levels declined to one-seventh of their previous levels.

In the early 1960s, air pollution from the petrochemical complex at Yokkaichi incensed local residents. The strength of their opposition spawned an anti-development and anti-pollution movement which attacked other planned development projects. In 1964, the movement succeeded in cancelling the planned industrial complex at Mishima-Numazu. The Smoke and Soot Regulation Law of 1962 was effective for controlling black smoke and heavy deposited matter, but not for the SO_2 emissions discharged by the petrochemical complexes. This era of pollution activism started the shift in the weight given to pollution control policy and industrial development policy.

In this period, MHW and MITI began to conduct joint environmental impact assessments of proposed industrial developments. When the Yokohama municipal government demanded that an electric power company consent to a strict pollution-control agreement, MITI urged the power company to sign. MITI feared that, otherwise, the project would be cancelled, as happened in Mishima-Numazu. From this time, municipalities expected electric power companies and other polluting industries to use the best available technology to reduce emissions. This served as an incentive for companies to develop desulfurization and denitrification technology. In 1966, MITI commenced a large project to develop desulfurization technology. Also in 1966, Idemitsu Kosan became the first company to install desulfurization equipment in the refinery process.

The 1967 Basic Law for Environmental Pollution Control Measures required the government to develop AAQSs. The first AAQS, for SO_2, was established in 1969,

Table 1.31

Chronology of national air quality management policy development and relevant issues

			'62	'63	'64	'65	'66	'67	'68	'69
Ambient Air Quality Standard										SO_2

Enforcement for Emission Control	Stationary Source Control	Suspended Particulates	X							
		Concentration; Vol. %	X		X					
		SOx K-Value							X	X
		Total Mass Regulation Concentration ppm								
		NOx Total Mass Regulation								
		Hazardrous Substance; Pb, HF, F, Cd & Their Compounds, NO_2, HCl, Cl_2 (HC)		(X)						
	Automobile Exhaust Control	Passenger Vehicle — CO HC NOx Pb						X	X	
		Truck & Bus Gasoline Diesel — Black Smoke CO HC NOx								
		Diesel Passenger Vehicle — Black Smoke CO HG NOx								

Dust from Mechanical Process (Structure, Management, Operation)

Air Pollution Control Legislation & Important Relevant Legislation	Smoke etc. Control Law '62	Air Pollution Basic Law '67 '70
Energy Policy Issue	Liberarization of Petroleum Boiler '62	Low Sulfur Crisis plan
National Development Issue	Regional Industrial Development; '62 '64 Yokkaichi, Mishima-Numazu, Yokohama '63 '64	Archipelago Reform '69

```
'70 '71 '72 '73 '74 '75 '76 '77 '78 '79 '80 '81 '82 '83 '84 '85
─────────────────────────────────────────────────────────────
CO       SP SO2          (HC)
            Ox           (Pb)
            NO2              NO2
─────────────────────────────────────────────────────────────
    X                                        X
X   X   X   X   X   X   X
                X   X   X
            X       X       X       X                X
                                             X
    X                   X


                         (X)               (X)
─────────────────────────────────────────────────────────────
X   X       X       X
X   X       X       X
            X       X   X       X
    X   X   X       X
- - - - - - - - - - - - - - - - - - - - - - - - - - - - - - - -
        X           X
                X   X
                X   X
                        X   X   X   X   X   X   X   X   X
- - - - - - - - - - - - - - - - - - - - - - - - - - - - - - - -
        X
                X   X
                X   X
                X   X                           X
─────────────────────────────────────────────────────────────
    (X)
```

Control Law   Energy Saving Law
'70 '72 '74   '79
  Compensation Law   Alternative Energy Supply Law
     '73   '80
───
1st Oil Fuel Supply   2nd Oil Alternative Crisis
    '69 '73   Energy '79   Coal, Nuclear

                            Human Settlement   Techno-police
                            Zone Development   '83
                                '77
───
                                        M. Hashimoto   '85
```
```

and MITI developed a desulfurization plan designed to meet the standard in ten years. The Economic Planning Agency conducted an econometric impact assessment of the desulfurization plan. In 1969, the government integrated its energy supply program and air pollution control program. The Air Pollution Control Law of 1968 employed the K-value formula to regulate SO_2 emissions. This encouraged the construction of higher stacks. Each year, the government tightened the K-value, in accordance with the expansion of desulfurization capacity.

In 1970, Prime Minister Sato reacted to the political and social crisis created by past governmental neglect by establishing the pollution control headquarters directly under his leadership. The Diet passed 14 environmental laws and strengthened the Air Pollution Control Law. Events abroad quickened the pace of change in Japan. The OECD described Japan's implementation of anti-pollution measures as non-economic, moral, and emotional.

The courts issued decisions in favor of the victims in the four pollution trials, and this prompted the government to tighten pollution standards and enforcement. In 1972, the Diet passed strict liability legislation, and the Cabinet issued a resolution requiring environmental impact assessments for public works projects. Also in 1972, the government adopted the automobile exhaust emission standards of the U.S. Clean Air Act and incorporated them into the Air Pollution Control Law.

In 1973, Japan began a program of NO_x control with the extremely strict NO_2 AAQS of 0.02 ppm/24hr. In 1974, the Diet amended the Air Pollution Control Law to provide for total mass emission regulation. The regulations were based on similar statutes enacted by Mie prefecture in 1972 and Osaka prefecture in 1973. In 1974, the Environment Agency postponed until 1978 the implementation of the NO_x automobile exhaust emission standards scheduled for 1976. The postponement evoked strong objections from many quarters. Seven large cities organized a team to assess the state of NO_x emission control technology for automobiles. In 1975, the Environment Agency also established a committee to conduct annual assessments of NO_x control technology for automobiles and stationary sources. The agency released a report describing each automobile maker's (non-confidential) pollution control technology. These reports encouraged automobile makers to compete to be the first to develop the most advanced, pollution control technology. In May 1976, all automobile makers had met the stringent NO_x emission standards, and mass production began in October 1976. It turned out that the new, cleaner cars had better fuel efficiency than the old cars which did not meet the emission standards.

The devaluation of the dollar in 1971 and the oil crisis in 1973 did not deter Japan from its anti-pollution campaign. It maintained strict pollution control laws, rationalized industry, and developed energy saving methods to cope with the crises. In 1978, the Environment Agency revised the overly strict 1973 NO_2 AAQS based on scientific information provided by the Central Advisory Council expert committee.

The Energy Saving Law of 1978 and the Alternative Energy Promotion Law of 1980 both took environmental considerations into account. The Diet passed the two laws just after the Tokyo Summit of 1979, which dealt with the second energy crisis. In 1981, the Environment Agency published a report entitled "Environmental Policy During a Stage of Changing Energy Policy." From 1981-84, Japan shifted from petroleum to coal for its energy supply. Accordingly, the government tightened emission standards for particulates and NO_x from coal-fired boilers in 1982 and 1983.

Between 1982 and 1985, the government implemented total mass emission regulation for NO_x. It implemented emission controls for trucks, trailers, and buses between 1978-85. However, due to the extension of the useful life of these vehicles, the changeover to the newer, cleaner vehicles took longer than expected. For this reason, in the summer of 1985, some roadside monitoring stations recorded NO_2 concentrations above the NO_2 AAQSs. Pollution control in transportation presents a challenge in the coming decades.

Table 1.31 presents a chronology of Japan's pollution-control programs beginning in 1962.

1.17 CONCLUSION

Air pollution levels in Japan reached their worst in the mid-1960s, and were very much improved by the late-1970s. A number of factors contributed to the reduction of pollution. Industry invested in expensive pollution control equipment to meet the stringent ambient and emission standards that made pollution abatement possible. Also, nine automobile manufacturers conducted research and development on automobile exhaust emission control technology and succeeded in meeting Japan's strict emission standards. In addition, the government integrated its national energy policy with air pollution control policy in the desulfurization program. Finally, despite the devaluation of the dollar and the oil crisis, Japan maintained its basic environmental policies. It expanded coal consumption after 1979, and put more effort into pollution control after 1980.

The success of Japan's air pollution control efforts can be attributed to the social and political dynamics of change that took place from 1970-74. The process was helped by the government's comprehensive and integrated planning to achieve the SO_2 AAQS. But the key to the entire effort was the public's awareness and persistent demand for change. Farmers and residents first turned to local government for action, and then demanded that the central government take action as well. The public's influence was felt as voters in local and

national elections, and as consumers purchasing clean, fuel-efficient cars.
Also, the mass media's nationwide anti-pollution campaign served as a catalyst
for change.

Local government played an important role in Japan's anti-pollution drive.
The Tokyo Metropolitan Government enacted the first industrial pollution control ordinance in 1949. In the 1950s, Ube instituted a successful air pollution control program with the cooperation of municipal officials, industry
managers, and university scholars. The Yokohama city government pioneered the
idea of pollution control agreements. After making an air pollution assessment, it used the results to gain favorable terms on pollution-control agreements from the Tokyo Electric Power Company. In many local governments, the
public health service and laboratories developed the new scientific and technical methods of analyzing the pollution problem. Finally, the confrontation
between the conservatives and socialists in local government kept the subject
of pollution control on the top of political agendas.

Despite meager budgets during the early days, a small number of scholars and
researchers at universities and research institutes at the local and national
level participated in study projects for air pollution control. Also, the
Japan Society of Air Pollution, established in 1959, made an invaluable contribution.

The cancellation of the Mishima-Numazu petrochemical project in 1964 shocked
economic and industrial organizations. The possibility of a similar cancellation encouraged MITI to lend its support to the pollution-control agreement
which the Yokohama municipal government demanded from the Tokyo Electric Power
Company in 1964. This soon became standard practice all over Japan. Local
governments conducted pre-siting environmental impact assessments and negotiated pollution-control agreements based on the findings of the assessment. The
terms of many of the agreements required companies to use the best available
pollution-control technology. Companies found it in their interests to negotiate the pollution-control agreements in good faith for two reasons. First,
they wanted good relations with the communities in which their factories were
located, and, second, they wanted to increase market share.

MHW expanded the scope of its pollution monitoring and health-effect
studies. As a result, the government established criteria, guides, and an AAQS
for SO_2 in 1969. In the same year, MITI developed a desulfurization program.
This was the most successful example of MITI-MHW cooperation. In addition,
MITI adjusted the charges for electricity to cover the costs of pollution
control incurred by electric power companies.

In 1970, Prime Minister Sato responded quickly to a serious social and
political crisis by establishing the pollution control headquarters directly
under his supervision. The pollution headquarters succeeded in guiding the

preparation and passage of 14 pieces of anti-pollution legislation. All political parties supported the efforts to adopt the new environmental laws.

The court's decision in the Yokkaichi case served as an important catalyst in the government's receptivity to the need for change in environmental policy. The Yokkaichi court made new doctrine in its treatment of negligence, causation, and damages in a pollution context. Also, it faulted the administration for its handling of pollution control at the Yokkaichi industrial complex. Prompted by the Yokkaichi case, the government quickly prepared the Pollution-Related Health Damage Compensation Law, total mass emission regulation, and the Industrial Siting Law. The Diet passed these bills during 1973 and 1974.

The fact that automobile makers met the stringent emission standards of 1975, 1976, and 1978 is attributable to the intense competition among the nine automobile manufacturers. Consumers disliked air pollution in their cities and demanded clean and fuel-efficient cars, which forced automobile makers to work quickly to meet the standards. At first, automobile makers rushed to install pollution-control devices without regard to cost effectiveness. But after the devaluation of the dollar, the automobile makers rationalized production costs to lower prices and gain a greater market share. After the oil crisis in 1973, government and industry worked to conserve energy. It took an accelerated program of research and development to achieve pollution-control, cost rationalization, and energy conservation.

In 1971, the Diet passed the Industrial Pollution Abatement Factory Manager Law. This law required each factory to designate an individual to be responsible for pollution control. Also, the Yokkaichi decision in 1972 gave notice to companies that the courts would apply the concepts of negligence and joint tort very strictly in pollution cases. These factors created an awareness among companies of their responsibilities for pollution control.

Scientific uncertainty is an ever-present problem in the management of pollution control issues. Consequently, even experts disagreed on related scientific and technological issues. Even where there is a degree of certainty on these factual matters, administrators differed in what policies to pursue, in what judgments to make. The OECD characterized Japan's environmental policies as non-economic, moral, and emotional. But Japan faced a dire need for a quick, dramatic reverse of the environmental degradation of its air and water. In any event, the government implemented pollution-control laws in a gradual manner, with annual reviews of the state of pollution-control technology and studies of their econometric impact. Moreover, the government publicly disclosed much of the information gained from the technology reviews and econometric assessments despite the controversy over the wisdom of such a disclosure. This provided the foundation for the most important determinant of Japanese environmental policy--the public's awareness, criticism, and active participation. But this has been the story of the past. Japan will face new challenges in air pollution control in the 21st Century.

REFERENCES

1. Hayashi, S., et al. (Eds.): Compilation of Papers by M.P. Shozo Tanaka (Supplementary Edition), 1980, 397-398.
2. Gresser, J., K. Fujikura and A. Morishima: Environmental Law in Japan, The MIT Press, Cambridge and London, 1981, 5.
3. Kamioka, N.: Kogai, Saigai (Environmental Pollution and Disaster, Urban Problem Series No.6) 1965, 45.
4. Iijima, N.: Chronological Table of Environmental Pollution, Labor Accidents & Occupational Diseases, 1977, 38-39.
5. Iijima, N.: Chronological Table of Environmental Pollution, Labor Accidents & Occupational Diseases, 1977, 64-65.
6. Iijima, N.: Chronological Table of Environmental Pollution, Labor Accidents & Occupational Diseases, 1977, 38, 42, 47-48, 51.
7. Iijima, N.: Chronological Table of Environmental Pollution, Labor Accidents & Occupational Diseases, 1977, 56.
8. Arisawa, H. (Ed.): 100 Years' History of Japanese Industry, 1966, 13, 62; N. Iijima: Chronological Table of Environmental Pollution, Labor Accidents and Occupational Diseases, 1977, 54.
9. Kato, I.: Kogai, Saigai (Environmental Pollution and Disaster, Urban Problems Series No.6), 1965, 170-171; S. Shimomura: Jurist (Supplement) No.65, 1980, 10-13; J. Gresser, K. Fujikura, A. Morishima: Environmental Law in Japan, The MIT Press, Cambridge and London, 1981, 12-13.
10. Kamioka, N.: Kogai, Saigai (Environmental Pollution and Disaster, Urban Problem Series No.6), 1965, 47-49.
11. Ookasumikai (Ed.): The History of the Interior, 1980, 480-481; M. Hoshimoto: Thinking on Environmental Pollution (Nikkeishinsho No.121), 1970, 14,38.
12. M. Nakano, The Proceedings of the 25th Assembly of the Japan Society of Air Pollution, 1984, 103-104.
13. Kamioka, N.: Kogai, Saigai (Environmental Pollution and Disaster, Urban Problem Series No.6), 1965, 49.
14. Japan Public Health Association: Development of Public Health (Continued), 1983, 67-68.
15. Miyamoto, K.: Kogai, Saigai (Environmental Pollution and Disaster; Urban Problems Series No.6), 1965, 32-34; I. Kato: Kogai, Saigai (Environmental Pollution and Disaster; Urban Problems Series No.6), 1965, 178-179; M. Hashimoto, Development of Environmental Policy and Its Institutional Mechanisms of Administration and Finance (UNCRD, UNEP, International Workshop on Environmental Management for Local and Regional Development, Nagoya, Japan, 1985), 1985, 7.
16. Nose, Y.: The Proceedings of the 25th Assembly of the Japan Society of Air Pollution, 1984, 67-92.
17. Yoshida, K.: The Proceedings of the 25th Assembly of the Japan Society of Air Pollution, 1984, 67-92.
18. Yoshida, K.: The Proceedings of the 25th Assembly of the Japan Society of Air Pollution, 1984, 69-73.
19. Hashimoto, M.: Thinking on Environmental Pollution (Nikkeishinsho 121), 1970, 20-24; M. Hashimoto: Quarterly Social Security Studies (Special Edition on Social Development), 1967, 68-70.
20. Hashimoto, M.: Kankyo (Environment), 4(6), 1979, 42; M. Hashimoto: Thinking on Environmental Pollution (Nikkeishinsho 121), 1970, 23-24; J. Gresser, K. Fujikura and A. Morishima: Environmental Law in Japan, The MIT Press, Cambridge and London, 1981, 19.
21. Gresser, J., K. Fujikura and A. Morishima: Environmental Law in Japan, The

MIT Press, Cambridge and London, 1981, 248.

22. Hashimoto, M.: Kankyo (Environment), 4(6), 1979, 43; M. Hashimoto: Thinking on Environmental Pollution (Nikkeishinsho 121), 1970, 24.

23. Gresser, J., K. Fujikura and A. Morishima: Environmental Law in Japan, The MIT Press, Cambridge and London, 1981, 47.

24. Hashimoto, M.: Kankyo (Environment), 5(1), 1980, 54; M. Hashimoto: Jichi Kenkyu (Local Autonomy Studies), 46(2), 1970, 65-78.

25. Japanese Government: Annual Report on the State of the Environemnt for FY 1983, 1984, 191.

26. Bureau of Environmental Sanitation, Ministry of Health and Welfare: The Report of the National Survey on Environmental Pollution (Based on Complaints Filed with 43 Prefectural Governments), 1954.

27. Hashimoto, M.: Kankyo (Environment), 4(6), 1979, 40.

28. Gresser, J., K. Fujikura and A. Morishima: Environmental Law in Japan, The MIT Press, Cambridge and London, 1981. 264.

29. Kato, I: Kogai, Saigai (Environmental Pollution and Disaster; Urban Problems Series No.6), 1965, 179-189; M. Hashimoto: Rodo no Kagaku (Science of Labor), 19(12), 1964, 7-9.

30. Hashimoto, M: Quarterly Social Securities (Supplementary Edition, Special Edition of Social Development), 1967, 68-71.

31. Hashimoto, M.: Thinking on Environmental Pollution (Nikkeishinsho 121), 1970, 22-24.

32. Gresser, J., K. Fujikura and A. Morishima: Environmental Law in Japan, The MIT Press, Cambridge and London, 1981, 264.

33. Gresser, J., K. Fujikura and A. Morishima: Environmental Law in Japan, The MIT Press, Cambridge and London, 1981, 263.

34. Hashimoto, M.: Nihonyosui (Japan Water Utilization), 5(11), 1965, 6-10.

35. Gresser, J., K. Fujikura and A. Morishima: Environmental Law in Japan, The MIT Press, Cambridge and London, 1981, 242.

36. Gresser, J., K. Fujikura and A. Morishima: Environmental Law in Japan, The MIT Press, Cambridge and London, 1981, 21.

37. Hashimoto, M.: Nihonyosui (Japan Water Utilization), 5(11), 1965, 6-10.

38. Hashimoto, M.: Jijitsushin (Jiji Press, Health and Welfare Edition), No.1448, 1967, 2-5.

39. OECD: Environmental Policies in Japan, 1977, 28.

40. Mie Prefecture Environmental Pollution Analysis Project Team: Analysis of SO_2 Pollution in Yokkaichi, 1972.

41. The Expert Committee for Environmental Quality Standards for SO_2: The Report of the Environmental Quality Standard for SO_2, January 1968.

42. Hashimoto, M.: Compensation Research, 6(6), 1968, 15-20.

43. Gresser, J., K. Fujikura and A. Morishima: Environmental Law in Japan, The MIT Press, Cambridge and London, 1981, 257-258.

44. Environmental Quality Standard of SO_2, Cabinet Decision, Feburuary 12th 1969.

45. The Report of the Comprehensive Energy Council of the Ministry of International Trade and Industry, December 17th 1969.

46. Hashimoto, M.: Jiji Press (Health and Welfare Edition), No.1362, 1966, 2-5.

47. Hashimoto, M.: Jiji Kenkyu (Local Autonomy Studies), 46(2), 1965, 65-78.

48. Hashimoto, M.: Community Survey on the Health Effects of Air Pollution in Osaka and Yokkaichi (Ministry of Health and Welfare, Division of Environmental Pollution Control, 1964), 1966.

49. Tokyo Metropolitan Government, Department of Public Health: Biological Response to Ambient Lead among Residents in the Tokyo Capital Area, 1972.

50. Institute of Environmental Pollution of the Tokyo Metropolitan Government: Confirmation of the Occurence of Photo-chemical Smog, July 18, 1970.

51. Hashimoto, M.: Kankyo (Environment), 5(3), 1980, 31-38; general reference: Teikoku Chiho Gyoseigakkai (Ed.), Compilation of and Commentary on Pollution Legislation, 1977.

52. Kato, Y.: Jurist (Supplement), No.65, 1980, 17-23; J. Gresser, K. Fujikura and A. Morishima: Environmental Law in Japan, The MIT Press, Cambridge and

London, 1981, 105-124.

53. OECD: Environmental Policies in Japan, 1977, 89-94.
54. The Economic Council, The Committee of Econometrics: Multi-Sector Econometric Models for Economic Planning (Fifth Report of the Committee of Econometrics), 1977, 356-363.
55. Environemnt Agency: The Long-Term Environmental Conservation Plan, 1977.
56. OECD: Environmental Policies in Japan, 1977, 76-82, 86-87.
57. Gresser, J., K. Fujikura and A. Morishima: Environmental Law in Japan, The MIT Press, Cambridge and London, 1981, 256.
58. Hashimoto, M.: Internal Combustion Engine, 6(10), 1967, 17-25.
59. Hashimoto, M.: Internal Combustion Engine, 6(10), 1967, 17-25.
60. Hashimoto, M. and W. Fujiwara: Journal of the Automotive Engine Society of Japan, 23(11), 1969, 1151-1163.
61. Motor Vehicle Nirogen Oxide Emission Control Technology: Environment Agency, December 1975.
62. The Office of Science and Technology, The Executive Office of the President: Cumulative Regulatory Effects on the Cost of Automotive Transport, February 1972.
63. Hongo, S.: Document, 0.25, 1978, 25-32.
64. Hongo, S.: Document, 0.25, 1978, 43-49.
65. The Group for the Study of Motor Vehicle Nitrogen Oxide Emission Control Technology, Environment Agency, December 1975 (first edition), May 1976 (second edition), October 1976 (third edition).
66. OECD: Environmental Policies in Japan, 1977, 30-31.
67. Environment Agency, Bureau of Air Conservation: Medium-Term Perspective on NO_x Control Measures in Large Metropolitan Areas, 1985.
68. Nakajima, Y., et al.: The Study Report of the Osaka Public Health Institute, 1968 (No.6) and 1969 (No.7); G. Freeman, et al.: Arch. Environmental Health, (1966) 13, 145 and (1968) 17, 181-92.
69. Environment Agency, Division of Pollution-Related Health: The Interim Report of the Study on the Health Effects of Air Pollution in FY 1970, 1970.
70. Heuss, J.M., et al.: National Air Quality Stnadard for Automotive Pollutants, September 1971; Council of Environmental Quality: Environmental Quality 1972, 1973, 110-112.
71. Expert Committee for an Environmental Quality Standard of SO_2, Central Advisory Council for Environmental Pollution Control Measures: The Report on the Environmental Quality Standard for SO_2, March 1973.
72. Shishido, S. and A. Oshizaka: Econometric Analysis of the Impact of Pollution Control Costs in Japan, 1976; OECD: Environmental Policies in Japan, 1977, 77-78.
73. Kiyoura, R.: The Information Material of the Scientific Research Institute for Industrial Pollution, No.39, April 1975.
74. OECD: Environmental Policies in Japan, 1977, 26.
75. The Expert Committee for Criteria and Guides for NO_2, The Central Advisory Council of Environmental Pollution Control Measures: The Report of the Expert Committee Related to the Criteria and Guides for NO_2, 1978.
76. Takeo, T.: Additional Note to the Expert Committee Report Related to Criteria and Guides for NO_2, Annex to the Expert Committee Report 1978, 1978.
77. The National Research Council: Nitrogen Oxides, 1977, 272, 286.
78. WHO: Expert Committee Report, TRS-554 (Japanese Edition), 1974, 26-35.
79. Hashimoto, M.: Kikan Kankyo Kenkyu (Environmental Research Quarterly), No.21, 1978, 1-17.
80. Environment Agency, Bureau of Air Conservation: The Review Process of the Environmental Quality Standard for NO_2 and the Main Issues of Controversy, June 1978.
81. Environment Agency: Study Group on Comparison of Cost Effectiveness of NO_x Control Options, April 1978.
82. Resource and Energy Agency, MITI (Ed.), Energy Strategy of the Third Generation, 1983, 73-78.

83. Environment Agency, Council for the Examination of Energy and Environmental Problems: Study Group on the Environmental Impact of the Energy Shift from Petroleum to Coal, Environmental Policy during a Period of Energy Shift, 1981, 42-49.
84. Kinoshita, A.: OCED, Costs of Coal-Pollution Abatement, 1983, 120-127.
85. The Department of Raw Materials, Japan Federation of Iron and Steel Industry: Tekkokai (The Iron and Steel Industry), 1981, 62-70.
86. Tamaki, M.: Environmental Engineering, 14(2), 1985.
87. Environment Agency, Air Conservation Bureau: Report on Dust Pollution Caused by Spiked Tires, FY 1983, 1984.
88. Environment Agency, Air Conservation Bureau: Report on Asbestos Pollution, 1985.
89. Environment Agency, Air Conservation Bureau: Report on the Distribution of Air Pollutants in the Environment, FY 1975, 1976.
90. Hishida, K.: The Proceedings of the 25th Annual Assembly of the Japan Society of Air Pollution, 1984, 132-140.
91. Ministry of Health and Welfare, Expert Committee for Dioxin Study Related to Waste Incineration, The Problem of Dioxin Related to Waste Incineration, 1984.
92. The Panel for Carcinogens: The Proceedings of the 25th Annual Assembly of the Japan Society of Air Pollution, 1984, 173-186.
93. The Panel for Carcinogens: The Proceedings of the 25th Annual Assembly of the Japan Society of Air Pollution, 1985, 163-168.
94. Ministry of Health and Welfare, Division of Environmental Pollution Control: Results of the Study on the Health Effects of Air Pollution, 1965.

Chapter 2

HEALTH EFFECTS OF AIR POLLUTION

HITOSHI   KASUGA

2.1 BASIS OF EPIDEMIOLOGICAL STUDY

It is only natural that any air pollution control program may not have any
practical results until the mechanisms of air pollution and its health effects
are revealed by epidemiological studies.

2.1.1 Measurement of exposure

The first step of an epidemiological study of air pollution is to establish
an association between pollutant exposures and health effects.

Estimates of personal exposure to a pollutant which are compared with health
effects in the community are usually derived from ambient air quality
measurements made at one or more authorized monitoring stations within a
community. The Japanese air monitoring network[1] organized by the Environment
Agency consists of: 1,648 stations for SO_2; 1,319 stations for NO_2; 506
stations for suspended particulate matter; and 1,021 stations for photochemical
air pollutants. In most studies, it is assumed that values measured by such
monitoring stations are representative of exposures throughout the community
where corresponding health effects are observed.

However, in the case of NO_2, indoor NO_2 pollution should be considered
because, in contrast to SO_2, there are commonly several indoor combustion appliances in each home serving as domestic sources e.g., gas ranges and unvented
space heaters using gas or kerosene. Since most housewives and older persons
spend over 80% of their time indoors most of their NO_2 exposure may be ascribed
to indoor NO_2. Roadside NO_2 pollution from automobile exhaust is another
characteristic of urban life and it may be worth considering in epidemiological
studies.

2.1.2 Air pollution indices

During the first decade after World War II, dustfall measurements of coal
combustion particle emissions were the main index of air pollution. SO_2 then
attracted public attention over the two decades between 1950 and 1970. During

the 1970s, air pollution priorities shifted to NO_2 with photochemical air pollutants accompanying the rapid decrease in SO_2 and the sudden increase in the number of automobiles.

Since community air pollution is generally not caused by a single pollutant but consists of complex and variable mixtures of pollutants, epidemiological analysis must be performed carefully. Since pollutant mixtures cannot be measured directly, a single index pollutant may often be chosen to indicate the severity of a given pollution episode.

2.1.3 Health effects markers related to air pollution

Just as air pollution is a complex phenomenon, so too are human responses to pollutant insults. Necessary conditions for markers are: a) a capacity to demonstrate a significant dose-response relationship for all health effects regardless of the presence of apparent symptoms, and b) a capacity to explain the mechanisms of possible health effects caused by an index pollutant.

Clinical markers. The prevalence rate of symptoms selected by a standardized questionnaire such as that of the BMRC (British Medical Research Council) or ATS-DLD (American Thoracic Association, Department of Lung Diseases) has been used as representative of health effects (response) related to air pollution. In the 1960s, symptoms caused by chronic bronchitis with phlegm were applied as a marker and thereafter the persistence of coughs and phlegm has been used. However, it has become difficult to obtain a sufficient number of cases with the BMRC questionnaire. Originally the BMRC questionnaire was used by interviewers for a small sample. Even if the sampling size is only enlarged from 500 to 2,000 persons, it might be difficult to interview all the people. The ATS-DLD questionnaire, developed in 1978, was designed to be completed by the subject without the presence of an interviewer, and it has been widely employed in place of the BMRC questionnaire for such purposes in Japan.

The prevalence of asthma was used as a marker during the postwar period of severe air pollution. The early Tokyo-Yokohama asthma and Yokkaichi asthma episodes were remarkable events because of this asthma-air pollution relationship. However, no significant relationship between asthma and air pollution has been observed in any study conducted in the 1980s.

The incidence of influenza and excess deaths was also used in the early period after the war, but it seems that both have lost their significance as markers under the present conditions of air pollution.

Functional markers. In place of clinical markers, a reduction in resipiratory function as measured with spirometry was formerly used. Currently, respiratory functions such as flow volume, closing volume, etc. are used as functional markers. Functional markers are very useful in adults but, for children,

clinical markers are still useful for detecting health effects related to air
pollution. However, we should not expect too much from either functional or
clinical markers, judging from the results of recent epidemiological studies.

Biochemical markers. For the above mentioned reasons, more sensitive
biochemical markers have been in demand. Urinary hydroxyproline[27-29] is a
typical biochemical marker for respiratory disorders caused by air pollution
which was developed by Kasuga and Matsuki, although it has also been used for
smoking and passive smoking effects.

2.1.4 Study populations

The subjects used for epidemiological studies may be categorized into two
types. The first group is selected at random from a population in the study
area with an appropriate sampling method. The main purpose of such a study is
to assess the actual health effects in a community affected by air pollution.
Therefore, this type of study accounts for the majority of the studies carried
out by central or local health authorities. The other type of study uses
individuals from a population who are currently experiencing health effects.
Such a subject is usually used for an asthma panel study by the diary method.

2.1.5 Designs of studies and their application

In general, epidemiological designs are classified as case control studies,
cross-sectional and repeated studies, and cohort studies. Cross-sectional
studies have been used widely but it is necessary to solve the following
problems: 1) obtaining an adequate sample size ; 2) obtaining accurate
exposure estimates for air pollutants ; and 3) controlling the effects of a
wide range of confusing factors. It is difficult to perform cohort studies on
the relationship between air pollution and its health effects, but repeated
cross-sectional studies over many years on the populations in the same
geographical area are sometimes substituted for cohort studies. Using such
repeated cross-sectional studies, a statistical analysis of secular changes in
the prevalence of coughs and phlegm in the Osaka area was completed by the
Osaka municipal authority[2] in 1976. Similar studies of compound air pollution
have also been attempted by Tsunetoshi[3], Adachi[4], Shimizu[5] etc. The
Environment Agency conducted a survey of compound air pollution using the same
repeated sample method for five years in six communities. Kasuga et al.[6] are
using children in a primary school located beside a highway in Tokyo. They are
investigating possible health effects related to NO_2 in automobile exhaust from
the highway over a 10 year period using repeated cross sectional surveys.
Case-control studies are used for asthma panel studies to determine the
relationship between the occurrence of asthma attacks or aggravation of
symptoms and changes in environmental conditions.

2.2 AIR POLLUTION AND ITS HEALTH EFFECTS IN JAPAN FOR THE TWO POSTWAR DECADES

The main industries and urban communities in Japan were almost all reduced to rubble in World War II. During the 1950s Japanese industry rose from the ashes and returned to the prewar level. Air pollution accompanied this process of economic rehabilitation and urban rebuilding together with a shift of population to the cities. Health effects related to air pollution began to appear in the form of "Tokyo-Yokohama asthma". Toyama reviewed the status of air pollution studies for the two postwar decades and the corresponding epidemiological studies.[7] He summarized the difficulties related to epidemiological studies conducted at the time as follows: "In general, Japan is lagging behind in the development and manufacture of sampling devices and analytical instruments. There are few specialists in this field, but interest is growing as indicated by the increasing number of reports concerning air pollution that have been presented in various recent scientific meetings. Studies on health effects are making very slow progress in Japan. Morbidity surveys are actually just beginning in only a few cities. Bronchitis, asthmatic diseases and pulmonary emphysema, important diseases in relation to air pollution, because of inaccuracies in diagnosis, may have been masquerading under the diagnosis of tuberculosis or other diseases. Therefore, past medical statistics are inadequate for use in the present interpretation of the effects of air pollution. The government plans to establish a National Sampling Network, but at present the technological development for such a system is insufficient. General air pollution has been estimated by measurement of monthly dustfall using deposit gauges and of sulfur dioxide using lead peroxide candles which gather data from rather wide areas. These techniques have been standardized for use in the routine evaluation of city air. Suspended matter, determined by darkened spots on paper tape, is being studied on an experimental basis in a few cities. Measurement of nitrogen oxides, hydrocarbons and other chemical substances is being studied in a few laboratories on an experimental basis only, and SO_2 automatic recording devices are being developed."

During the 1950s, the major districts where air pollution presented a problem for community health were the Sapporo, Kamaishi, Tokyo-Kawasaki-Yokohama, Yokkaichi, Osaka-Amagasaki-Kobe, Ube and Northern Kyushu districts.

Of these cities, Osaka has the longest history of air pollution, especially with problems caused by smoke. Here the annual mean values of monthly dustfall after the war were at much higher levels than before the war. Air pollution sources, except for those in the Sapporo district in Hokkaido, were mainly the result of industrial activities. Outstanding among these were the iron and steel industry in Kamaishi, the petroleum industry in Yokkaichi, the steel industry in Kobe, and the petroleum and cement industries in Ube. The

Tokyo-Kawasaki-Yokohama district consisted of these three cities and formed the largest area affected by air pollution from industrial activity. The air of Tokyo was polluted by somewhat smaller industries along the Sumida River and by exhaust gas from motor vehicles. Yokohama and Kawasaki, especially the downtown factory area of Kawasaki, were darkened by smoke from heavy industries. These were the major contributors to the air pollution covering the Kanto Plain, containing Tokyo, Kawasaki and Yokohama.

In the postwar period there was an enormous increase in the population of Tokyo. In addition, a vast amount of coal and gasoline was being consumed due to the increasing number of motor vehicles and, as a result, the number of days with dense smog had begun to increase. The local concentrations correlated roughly with the surrounding factory density. In the Kawasaki factory area the peak of the dustfall was in the spring when it often reached 70-80 tons/sq km/mo. The authorities in these three municipalities routinely measured air pollution and meteorological conditions.

Air pollution in Sapporo, Hokkaido was caused by coal smoke from domestic and industrial sources. In his survey, Abe[8] found both more respiratory diseases in city residents than in suburbanites, and a higher standardized mortality rate for lung cancer in Sapporo than in the other districts. Suzuki[9] observed in Amagasaki, near Osaka, that out-patient visits to hospitals, especially visits involving upper respiratory diseases, increased in number on days of heavy air pollution. Over the last ten years, Nose[10] reported from Ube, near Hiroshima, that a high correlation coefficient existed between dustfall and mortality from pulmonary diseases, especially pneumonia and bronchitis. In several industrial cities in northern Kyushu, Saruta[11] showed a higher proportional morbidity ratio of respiratory disease than in other districts in Kyushu. Segi[12] and Hirayama[13] also found that lung cancer mortality had suddenly increased during these same ten years and the lung cancer death rate in 1960 had reached the same level as that in the United States in 1940.

2.3 TOKYO-YOKOHAMA ASTHMA

According to Toyama[7], Japan has seen no severe air pollution episodes similar to those seen in London in 1952 and in Donora in 1948. However, an exception to this might be Tokyo-Yokohama asthma. Outbreaks of asthmatic disease were noted among American military personnel and their families living in Yokohama during 1946 and 1949. This disease was first reported by Huber[14] in 1954 as a new environmental respiratory disease (Yokohama-asthma) because it appeared to be different from classic bronchial asthma. However, Phelps[15] concluded in 1962 that this condition corresponded clinically to chronic asthmatic bronchitis. Toyama assumed that there was an autumn phase of

Yokohama-asthma associated with meteorological factors and a winter-spring
phase associated with air pollution. In addition, he noted in 1964 that causes
of Tokyo-Yokohama asthma had been reported from the Japanese population, not as
chronic asthmatic bronchitis associated with air pollution, but rather as
tuberculosis, classic asthma or some other respiratory disease. As a result,
the term Yokohama-asthma was changed to Tokyo-Yokohama asthma. Miyamoto (1962)
suspected that Tokyo-Yokohama asthma also included many patients with chronic
asthmatic bronchitis, at least in cases where the onset of the asthmatic attack
and symptoms were induced or aggravated by air pollution and meterological
factors. In addition, he concluded that air pollution alone could not cause
classic bronchial asthma. With this episode as a turning-point, Japanese
interest in the air pollution problem became increasingly active.

2.4 YOKKAICHI ASTHMA

Air pollution in the city of Yokkaichi was a major environmental problem,
ranking with the Minamata disease and Itai-itai disease. This episode brought
about an epidemic of chronic obstructive lung disease including bronchial
asthma (the so-called Yokkaichi asthma). A great deal of damage was done to
the community. Various efforts that went into the epidemiological research
resulted in the earliest enforcement of area-wide air pollution emission
regulations in Japan and a colossal investment by industries forced to conform
to the regulations.

By the 1980s, Yokkaichi again had blue skies and its affected inhabitants
had regained their health. Experience acquired during the Yokkaichi episode
has been of inestimable value for Japanese pollution control systems and for
maintaining a healthly environment in Japan.

Yoshida conducted an epidemiological study of this episode while he was a
professor at a medical school in the Mie prefecture where Yokkaichi is
situated[16,17]. He was also in charge of the administrative work on counter
measures as Chairman of the Mie Environmental Council.

The following is a summary of Yoshida's monograph:

The city of Yokkaichi is situated in the middle of Japan, near Nagoya. A
petroleum and petrochemical complex was established in 1955 in the southern
district of the city, and it was rapidly enlarged to become the largest of its
kind at that time in Japan.

The major factories in Yokkaichi in 1965 were steam power installations, oil
refineries and petrochemical plants.

These factories were closely surrounded by many residential districts
including Isozu, Shiohama, Mihama, Akebono and Umaokoshi. These areas were
occupied before the industrial complex was established.

Trends in local sulfur oxides distribution closely corresponded to the direction of wind. Prevalent southeasterly winds in summer carried sulfur oxides to Mihama, Akebono or Shiohama, and northwesterly winds in winter carried them to Isozu. As a result, the Isozu district had the highest sulfur oxide pollution from December to March.

Remarkably high peak concentrations, up to the level of 1 ppm, were observed frequently. The cause of these high concentrations was imported crude oil with a sulfur content of over 3%. Annual SO_2 emissions in this area totaled over 100,000 tons. In 1964 in Isozu, the annual average concentration was 0.1 ppm and in winter 0.16 ppm. These concentrations were over ten times higher than the current standard values for SO_2.

A decrease in the pH of rain water was caused by the atmospheric oxidation of SO_2 to H_2SO_4, sulfuric acid mist.

Since about 1960, increasing attention has been paid to the abnormally high incidence of asthmatic disorders in the polluted districts, especially in Isozu.

To study the health effects of air pollution, they investigated the incidence of respiratory diseases using National Health Insurance records in the 13 districts of Yokkaichi. These districts differed in the level of pollution. The incidence of some respiratory diseases in the more polluted districts was compared with that in non-polluted districts. Remarkable differences were found for asthmatic diseases. With increasing age, the differences became even greater, especially in those over 50 years old. There was a very clear correlation between the accumulated prevalence of asthma in those over 50 years old and sulfur oxides levels.

To investigate the relationship between asthmatic attacks and SO_2, the medical records of 13 asthmatic patients in Isozu were studied with the cooperation of Dr. Nakayama, a general practitioner in Isozu. The correlation coefficent between the weekly average SO_2 concentration and the number of asthmatic attacks was as high as +0.88.

The epidemiology of chronic bronchitis and pulmonary obstructive disorders in polluted and non-polluted districts was studied. Inhabitants over 40 years old in six districts, (three polluted and three non-polluted), were investigated by the BMRC method. An increased prevalence of chronic bronchitis was found in the polluted districts.

A relationship between the prevalence of chronic bronchitis and the sulfur oxide level was confirmed. In May 1965, the mayor of Yokkaichi decided to subsidize all the medical expenses of the patients approved by the official city medical committee on air pollution. By the end of 1969, medical expenses of over 600 approved patients were subsidized by the city. At the end of 1970, the Relief Act for the Sufferers from Environmental Pollution was enacted by the Government. In 1967, some asthmatic patients in Isozu charged the complex with legal responsibility and demanded compensation according to the Japanese Civil Code. They won their suit.

The first attempt to solve the problem was made in 1964 by the Joint National Investigation Committee of the Ministry of Health and Welfare and the Ministry of International Trade and Industry. The committee, known as the Kurokawa Group, recommended the raising of stack heights to avoid downwash of SO_2 from the stacks. In those days, the heights of stacks, even with high SO_2 emissions, were not over 60 meters.

Based on the experience in Yokkaichi, the Air Pollution Prevention Act was established and the emission of SO_2 was limited according to effective stack height. This system is called K-value regulation in Japan. (See Chapter 5) This regulation was effective in preventing high peak surface concentrations in neighboring districts, but the increased number of high stacks with high emissions concentrated in small geographical areas caused yet another problem. In Yokkaichi, from about 1967, increased dispersion from high stacks spread the SO_2 pollution over a larger area. In 1971, over 50% of the entire city area was polluted above the SO_2 standard concentration.

For a complete solution of the problem, a new control system, the prefectural ordinance for total emission control of sulfur oxides was promulgated in 1971. In this new prefectural ordinance, limits on allowable total emission from each factory were set by means of atmospheric dispersion estimation techniques using computer simulation. A special project team was formed in April 1972 for this purpose. Yoshida was the head of this team.

By this prefectural ordinance, pre-1971 emissions of over 100,000 tons of SO_2 were drastically reduced to 17,000 tons in 1975. About 30% of this reduction was achieved by desulfurization of stack gas, and other decreases resulted from a reduction in the sulfur content of fuel oil or a change from heavy oil to gas. As a result of the new regulations, the annual average concentration of SO_2 in the city dropped and reached the target value in 1975.

Prior to these controls, the mortality rates from chronic obstructive diseases such as chronic bronchitis, bronchial asthma and emphysema were higher in the polluted Yokkaichi districts than in the non-polluted districts. For example, the mortality rate for chronic bronchitis and emphysema was gradually increasing until 1975, then the mortality rates began to decrease. As of 1985, Yokkaichi actually shows slightly lower morbidity and mortality than in other unpolluted areas.

2.5 RELATIONSHIP BETWEEN ASTHMA AND AIR POLLUTION

As already noted in the case of Yokkaichi asthma, an abnormally high incidence of asthmatic disorders was observed in the polluted districts, especially in Isozu, after and around 1960. It appears that the asthmatic cases in Isozu occurring after 1960 were caused by air pollution, in contrast to most of the classic asthma cases which appeared before 1960. Clinical features of Yokkaichi asthma were similar to those of classic asthma but corresponding family histories of classic asthma were rare, positive rates for allergens such as house-dust and pollen were significantly low, and treatment by changing the air was much more effective than with classic asthma. As Miyamoto[18] stressed in his study on Tokyo-Yokohama asthma, it is very difficult to explain the hypothesis that chemical pollutants such as SO_2 and NO_2 may be causes of classic asthma on the basis of present medical knowledge. However, SO_2 air pollution in Yokkaichi during the 1960s was over ten times higher than the national air quality standards. Furthermore the circumstances in Yokohama might have been the same. We therefore assume that, at least in the case of some persons with a predisposition to asthma, such a high level of air pollution by SO_2 could induce asthmatic symptoms.

As of 1985, SO_2 concentrations are much lower than the national standard, not only in the rural areas but in all industrial areas. Since NO_2 concentrations are still increasing or are stable in contrast to SO_2, the relationship between NO_2 and asthma has attracted the attention of epidemiologists. Although a weak, significant correlation between them has been reported by a project (the CHESS study by the American EPA) using the asthma panel study, its conclusions are now criticized. In Japan, four studies using the same method as the CHESS study -- the self-written diary method -- were reported. Yoshida[19] reported a positive relationship between NO_2 and asthma in 1977, Mizoguchi[20] showed a correlation between NO_2 and orthopnea at night in 1977, and Oka[21] noted a significant association of temperature drops with asthma attacks in 1980.

The latest study is by Inaoka in 1983[22]. She conducted an asthma panel study to examine the health effects of air pollution in Tokyo from October 1980 to August 1981. An analysis was performed based on a multiple effects model including terms influencing the individual's probability of suffering from an attack. This probability was associated with daily levels of air pollution, climatological measurements and the occurrence of an attack on the preceding day. (1) Applying the factor analysis to the variables related to asthma attacks, three factors (SO_2, NO_2, and TSP) could be extracted. However, there were no significant associations with asthma attacks. (2) The presence of attacks on the previous day showed a marked and significant association. (3) A significant relationship between some characteristics of the patients was observed.

No consistent association has been demonstrated except for a comparatory study using the flow volume curve test by Tsunetoshi and his coworkers[23]. In addition, according to a study of the relationship between respiratory disease mortality and air pollution in Tokyo by Makino[24] (1984), asthma mortality was not correlated with NO_2 levels. The relationship between roadside NO_2 air pollution from automobile exhaust and respiratory symptoms was studied by the Environment Agency[25] (1977), Kitabatake[26] (1977), Nitta[27] (1983) and Kasuga and his coworkers[28-30] (1983). Although some chronic respiratory symptoms such as chronic coughing, phlegm and wheezing, and moderate breathlessness were reported more frequently among residents nearer to roads, asthma was unchanged except for the report of Kitabatake.

2.6 COMPOUND AIR POLLUTION

Air pollution does not consist of a single pollutant but many different kinds of pollutants. Dustfall in combination with SO_2 was regarded as the most important pollutant in the early postwar days. Thereafter, as ambient SO_2 levels rapidly decreased a combination of NO_2 and SPM attracted epidemiologists' attention. Therefore epidemiological studies of NO_2 air pollution must consider that other pollutants always coexist. Yoshida[31] (1976) showed that the prevalence rate of persistent coughing and phlegm was significantly correlated with indices of air pollution including NO_2 and SO_2. Tsunetoshi[32] (1977) demonstrated a significant relation between the prevalence rate and NO_2 coexisting with SO_2, SPM and NO_2. Tsubota[33] (1977) found a significant relation between the prevalence rate and levels of NO_2, NO_x and SPM in excess of the national standards for NO_2 and SO_2. Naturally, various types of statistical analysis were used in these studies. Shimizu[34] (1974) reported a statistical study on the relation between the symptom prevalence of chronic bronchitis and compound air pollution with SO_2 and NO_2 in people over 40 years of age living in communities in the Osaka region. The relation between the symptoms and SO_2 and NO_2 ,which were used as air pollution indices, led to the following :

(1) $y = 1.94 \ SO_2 + 2.87$,　(2) $y = 0.88 \ NO_x + 2.81$
(3) $y = 1.0 \ (SO_2 - 1.0 \ ) + 0.6 \ NO_x + 2.7$

where y is the symptom prevalence,

(1)　SO_2 values by the PbO_2 method,
(2)　NO_x value estimated from the smoke diffusion equation,
(3)　combined effect of SO_2 and NO_x.

A very important and influential report was published by Suzuki[35] (Chairman of the Air Pollution Department, Central Council for Environmental Pollution Control) and his coworkers based on research conducted by the Environmental Agency. A cross-sectional survey was repeated each year beginning in 1970 and running through 1974 to obtain data on air pollution and health effects. The major survey results were reported by the Environment Agency in 1977. Suzuki and his coworkers analyzed these data.

The survey subjects consisted of about 400 women, each 30 years of age at the start of the study selected randomly in each of the six communities. An average of 78.6% of the survey subjects were interviewed by means of the BMRC questionnaire. A respiratory function test (spirometry) was also performed on 38.3% to 84.4% of the survey subjects. A health examination was conducted in the fall each year.

Air pollution levels were measured for eight pollutants : SO_2 (conductometric), SO_x (sulfation rate by the lead peroxide method), NO (Saltzman method), NO_2 (Saltzman method), NO_x ($NO+NO_2$), CO (nondispersive infrared absorption method), suspended particulate matter (SPM, gravimetric high volume method) and dustfall (dust air or deposit gauge method). The 6 air quality monitoring stations were located within the study area or within a distance of 5 kilometers from the center of the study area.

The six survey areas ranged from an agricultural area to new and old industrial areas. The degree of air pollution in each of these areas was, in general, relatively low.

The degree of air pollution differed between the survey areas. The five-year overall average for the 6 areas for 1970-1974 ranged from 0.012 to 0.033 ppm for SO_2, from 0.013 to 0.043 ppm for NO_2 and from 0.6 to 4.2 ppm for CO. During that five-year period SO_2 and CO declined while NO_x did not change or increased slightly. However, the relationship between the pollutants and the relative level of air pollution in the six areas remained unchanged during the five-year period.

Analysis of air pollution data revealed that sulfur oxides, SPM and dustfall formed one group of pollutants and nitrogen oxides formed another. The former group was dominant in the period before 1972 and the latter group was dominant in the period after 1972. Thus, the major air pollutant or "index pollutant" seemed to have changed in 1972.

Based on this cross-sectional study, no particular relationship was observed between death rate, population density, degree of air pollution and socioeconomic factors. However, industrialization and urbanization were notable in each survey area during the survey period.

No clear relationship was observed between the degree of air pollution and results of the respiratory function test.

The prevalence rate of respiratory symptoms; coughing, phlegm and persistent coughing and phlegm differed from one area to another ranging from 0.9 to 6.0% for persistent coughing and phlegm. The prevalence rate of the same symptoms declined during the study period. The declining trend could be attributed to decreasing air pollution, the repeated interview effect and other reasons.

No clear relationship was observed between age and respiratory symptoms.

Simple correlation coefficients between the prevalence rate of persistent coughing and phlegm and SO_2, SO_x, CO and SPM were high in 1970, while the coefficients between the same prevalence rate and NO, NO_2 and NO_x were high in 1974, also suggesting that the major pollutants changed from sulfur oxides and SPM to nitrogen oxides.

A chi-square test based on a linear model between the prevalence rate of persistent coughing and phlegm and the degree of air pollution revealed that the relationship between the prevalence of these symptoms and SO_2, NO_2, NO_x, SPM and dustfall in 1972, and NO, NO_2 and NO_x in 1973 and 1974 were statistically significant. The possible relationship between persistent coughing and phlegm and nitrogen oxides in 1972-1974 was noted, but it should be kept in mind that the relationship existed in the presence of other pollutants.

When the annual average concentrations of NO_2, SO_2 and SPM were below 0.02 ppm, 0.03 ppm and 100 micrograms/m^3 respectively, the prevalence rate of persistent coughing and phlegm was below 2%, but when the degree of air pollution exceeded these levels, the prevalence rate was 4-6%.

The above is a summary of this influential study. The Public Works Committee in the US Senate submitted this Japanese study for consideration in December 1973. The reason the Senate took an interest in this unfinished study was not clear. However, since Japanese air quality standards for NO_2 had been established only six months before with more stringent values than those of the U.S.A., it might be that the Senate wanted to know the relationship between Japanese standards and the results of this study as soon as possible, especially since the Japanese EPA was scheduled to promulgate a strict reduction program for automobile exhaust.

This study depended on ambient air quality measurements at a single site within a community for correlation with observed health effects. In addition since the subjects selected in each study area were housewives, it is assumed that they were subjected to the impacts of indoor air pollution. Although the authors were certainly aware of indoor air pollution, its impact on the outcome of these studies was unclear, since a personal sampler for NO_2 had not been developed. At present, the national ambient air quality standards for NO_2 in various countries ignore indoor air pollution, as noted by the WHO Expert Committee[36] (1958). However, the impact of indoor air pollution on ambient standards must be considered in spite of legislative difficulties. Therefore, it is essential to determine whether the higher indoor concentrations of NO_2 often experienced in daily life have adverse health effects.

2.7 HEALTH EFFECT OF NO_2

2.7.1 $\underline{NO_2}$ air pollution[36,37]

By the 1970s, SO_2 air pollution was already under control and the annual average concentrations were generally below the national air quality standards. Sudden outbreaks of a characteristic acute disease which was suspected as being associated with photochemical air pollution were reported among school children in Tokyo, Osaka and other cities, These episodes created a sensation, since many of the cases exhibited several questionable symptoms, perhaps resulting from a mass psychogenic illness[38], in addition to acute general symptoms usually caused by photochemical air pollution. Although the controversy over whether or not these symptoms were caused by mass psychogenic systemic illness has still not been settled, the anti-air pollution movement in Japan used this opportunity to create a scenario ascribing obstructive respiratory diseases, including asthma, to ambient NO_2 air pollution. As a result, the Environment Agency promulgated the world's strictest automobile exhaust regulations. The automobile industry responded with a series of brilliant technical advances conforming to these regulations. However, the health effects associated with ambient NO_2 pollution have not been demonstrated by epidemiological studies in spite of the relaxation of the national air quality standards for NO_2 from a 24-hour average value of 0.02 ppm to 0.06 ppm in 1978.

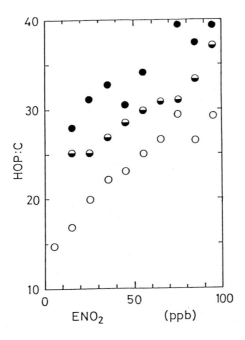

Fig. 2.1. Effect of personal NO_2 exposure to urinary hydroxyproline to creatinine ratio, with smoking habits as parameters: ● active smoker of 11-20 cig/day, ◕ passive smoker of 11-20 cig/day, ○ nonsmoker.[50]

It is necessary to consider that health effects caused by accidental
exposure to high NO_2 levels (many ppm) might be different from those due to NO_2
at or below 0.1 ppm.

According to a series of long term exposure experiments on rats using 4.0,
0.4 and 0.04 ppm of NO_2 by Sagai, Ichinose et al.[39] (National Institute for
Environment Studies), it seems that indices of the effects with NO_2 change from
respiratory symptoms to morphogenic changes in the alveolar wall, and finally
to changes in various decomposition products of collagen and elastin such as
urinary hydroxyproline, demosine and hydroxylysine as NO_2 levels decrease.

Matsuki, Kasuga et al.[30] reported in 1983 that personal NO_2 exposures were
correlated significantly with urinary hydroxyproline (HOP)[#] but not with
cigarette smoking.

The health effect of NO_2 was most clearly demonstrated by the work of
Yanagisawa et al.[50] They investigated the effect by examining the personal NO_2
exposure, smoking habit and urinary hydroxyproline of about 800 adult women in
winter. The personal exposure was measured with the personal monitor developed
by Yanagisawa et al.[40] Instead of hydroxyproline ocncentration, the
hydroxyproline to creatinine ratio (HOP:C) was used in order to compensate for
contingent dilution of urine samples. The personal NO_2 exposure was found to
range from 10 to 100 ppb, which means the personal NO_2 exposure is
predominantly determined by the indoor NO_2 level. When the subjects were
devided into active smokers, passive smokers and nonsmokers, the HOP:C for each
group was found to increase linearly with the personal NO_2 exposure level as
shown in Fig. 2.1. This means that an NO_2 exposure level as low as 20 or
30 ppm clearly affects the level of urinary HOP as does smoking.

2.7.2 Indoor NO_2 air pollution

When studying indoor air pollution, it is essential to measure personal
exposures. Yanagisawa[40] developed a diffusion type personal sampler for NO_2
(filter badge) in 1981. Maeda was the first to use this sampler in
epidemiological studies.

The main sources of indoor NO_2 are combustion appliances such as stoves for
cooking and space heating. Epidemiological studies usually categorize
households according to the fuel used for stoves. In Japan, households are
divided into two categories, according to whether or not unvented stoves for
space heating are used. In contrast, categories in the U.S.A. and the U.K. are
generally based on whether the cooking fuel is electricity or gas and
secondarily on the presence of unvented combustion space heaters. The reason
for the Japanese classification is that electric kitchen ranges and central
heating systems are not in general use in Japan.

A year round survey of 10 housewives living in a residential area of Tokyo was performed by Yanagisawa, Matsuki et al.[41] Daily average exposures were measured with a filter badge for 7 consecutive days in every month. The ratio of subjects who used unvented space heaters depended on the minimum temperature during the day and changed from 1.5 to 1.0 at 10°C. Annual geometrical averages of exposure could be estimated from personal exposures in February and in July, and the ratio of days with the minimum temperature below 10°C per year. Annual averages thus estimated agreed well with the observed data.

Matsuki, Yanagisawa et al.[30] reported in 1985 a typical comparative study by season and by area. The subjects were 531 school children and 310 of their mothers in three areas with different ambient NO_2 concentrations. Average personal NO_2 exposures of subjects living in households with unvented space heaters were 2-3 times higher in winter than in summer. However, subjects with vented stoves also had moderate exposures in winter due to NO_2 originating from the kitchen and trapped by poor ventilation. Possible health effects caused by indoor NO_2 were demonstrated by urinary hydroxyproline (HOP) levels. Since the indoor NO_2 level of each study area in the summer was almost the same as the ambient NO_2 level, regional differences of indoor NO_2 were observed. In contrast, in winter, indoor levels were the same in each area as long as unvented stoves were used. These data suggest that indoor air pollution in winter is independent of ambient air pollution and is driven by indoor sources.

The roadside NO_2 air pollution was associated with urinary HOP only during summer because it was overshadowed by the higher indoor NO_2 in winter.

The urinary HOP levels were also higher in winter than in summer but the range of variation was smaller than that of personal NO_2 exposures. Judging from the urinary HOP levels, health effects of active and passive smoking increased with the numbers of cigarettes smoked in all seasons.

2.7.3 Roadside NO_2 air pollution

Health effects caused by the dispersion of automobile exhaust from the roads should be examined, because NO_2 concentrations near roadside areas (within 50m) are sometimes twice as high as background areas. Nitta and Maeda (1983) found a high prevalence of chronic respiratory symptoms among 2,217 female residents, 40 to 59 year of age, in two areas along traffic arteries in Tokyo. Each resident was placed in one of two groups according to the distances from the major arteries to the house. Chronic coughing, phlegm, wheezing and moderate shortness of breath were reported more frequently among residents nearer to roads, although this was not true for asthma.

In an earlier study, Kasuga, Matsuki et al.[28] (1977) demonstrated that the elevated prevalence of asthmatic symptoms among metropolitan Tokyo school children was related to compound air pollution from automobile exhaust and passive smoking. Their study used the same method as Nitta, but this relationship disappeared with a decrease in automobile exhaust.

Kitabatake[26] (1977) also found higher visit rates to physicians due to respiratory disorders in residents living in areas within 20m of the highway. Almost the same study conducted by the Environment Agency (1977) failed to indicate such a relation.

Kasuga, Matsuki et al.[6] reported results of a repeated cross-sectional study from 1977 to 1983. School children were divided into three categories based on distances from the road to the house, i.e.) within 50m, 51-100m and over 101m. Urinary hydroxyproline (HOP) was used as a marker for health effects.

Since urinary HOP increases with smoking and passive smoking, subjects were limited to non-passive smokers who were not affected by family smoking. Urinary HOP in children living within 50m of roads has been the highest every year and its trends with time agree with annual changes in NO_2 concentrations measured by a monitoring station located beside a road. This relation was observed in a study of indoor air pollution in 1985, as already noted. Urinary HOP decreased with distance from the road.

2.8 OTHER TYPES OF AIR POLLUTION

2.8.1 Roadside air pollution produced by studded tires

Since 1980, citizens living in districts with snow have been troubled by dust originating from friction between the road surface and studded tires on automobiles during the period from late winter to early spring. Health effects caused by this roadside dust were found not only in the fields of opthalmology and otolaryngology, but also in the respiratory system. Takishima[42] estimated amounts of such inhaled dust in Sendai using a method of measuring extremely weak magnetic fields emanating from the lungs. He found that more than 70% of commuters riding motorbikes, street sweepers and shoes polishers at the roadside had abnormally high values. An asthma panel study found significant differences between school children living in the center and suburbs of Sendai. Other researchers performed cross sectional studies in other cities using standardized questionnaires and had similar findings.

2.8.2 Air pollution and lung cancer

Tominaga[43] (1981) reported that the mortality due to lung cancer in males was correlated with the ambient concentrations of SO_2 and NO_2, and those in females were correlated with NO_2, population sizes, population densities, and smoking rates. This study used a multiple regression analysis on data from 40 towns and cities.

Shimizu[44] (1977) found in Nagoya that the mortality rate from lung cancer in both sexes increased among residents living along roads with increasing numbers of automobiles but these rates were not related to distances from the road to the house. Shimizu[45] (1979) reported that the mortality rate from lung cancer was correlated with SO_2 and SPM in Nagoya.

Imai[46] (1980) noted an association between the rates of visits to physicians due to lung cancer and air pollution in Yokkaichi but the association was not significant.

2.8.3 Air pollution and excess deaths

Watanabe[47] (1979) reported a relationship between the ambient concentration of pollutants and the number of deaths per day for a 10 year period (1962-1972) in Osaka. Significant relations between the number of deaths and (temperature + SO_2), (temp. + NO_2) or (temp. + SPM) were demonstrated.

2.8.4 Air pollution and volcanic ash

Health effects associated with volcanic ash originating from the eruptions of Mt. Sakurajima (1980s) were noted by Wakisaka[48]; there were negative correlations between both the prevalence rates of bronchial asthma and nasopharyngitis, and the distance from Mt. Sakurajima but in the case of the prevalence of conjunctivities, a positive correlation was reported.

The effect of the 1977 eruption of the Usu volcano was reported by Saito[49]. The most commonly reported symptoms were headache and shoulder or neck stiffness. Approximately 30% of symptoms were considered to relate to the ash falls. Physical examinations indicated that most of the people suffered from eye diseases, coughing and the sense of a "foreign body" in the eye.

REFERENCES

1. Environment Agency : Quality of the environment in Japan, Environment Agency, Japan, 1984
2. Division of environment control, Municipality of Osaka : Indices of air pollution and prevalence rates, J. Japan Soc Air Pollut, 13(1), 1-9, 1976
3. Tsunetoshi, Y. et al : Correlation of air pollution and chronic respiratory symptoms, J. J. PH., 24(4), 293-300, 1977
4. Adachi, S. and Toyama, T. : 10 years variation of respiratory symptoms in rapidly industrialized region, J. Japan Soc Air Pollut, 11(2), 1-9, 1978
5. Shimizu, T. : A statistical study on relationship between symptom prevalence of chronic bronchitis and air pollution, J. Japan Res Dis, 12(4), 199-206, 1974
6. Kasuga, H. et al : Annual Reports on the health effects to school children by the Chuo High Way in Suginami Ward, Tokyo Vol. I - VIII, Suginami Board of Education, Tokyo, 1976-1983
7. Toyama, T. : Air pollution and its health effect in Japan, Arch Environ Health, 8, 153-173, 1964
8. Abe, S. Air Pollution in Sapporo, Science of Labor, 13, 98-108, 1964
9. Suzuki, T. : Air Pollution and its effects in Amagasaki City, The report of air pollution commitee of Amagasaki, 1962

112

10. Nose, Y. : Effects of exposure to air pollution on community health,
     Proceedings of the Clean Air Conference, London, pp209-221, 1955
11. Saruta, N. : Effects of air pollution on the health of people of Northern
     Kyushu, Japan, First report, Kyushu J. Kyushu Med Sci, 12, 167-176, 1961
12. Segi, M. : Geographic epidemiology of lung cancer, Advances Res Pulmon Dis
     (Tokyo), 31, 4-20, 1962
13. Hirayama, T. : Cigarette smoking and lung cancer, Advances Res Pulmon Dis
     (Tokyo), 31, 72-92, 1962
14. Huber, T. F. et al : New environmental respiratory disease (Yokohama
     Asthma), AMA Arch Industry Hyg, 10, 399-408, 1954
15. Phelps, H. W. et al : "Tokyo-Yokohama Asthma", Amer Rev Res Dis, 86,
     55-63, 1962
16. Yoshida, K. : Air pollution and asthma in Yokkaichi, Arch Environ Health,
     13, 763-768, 1966
17. Yoshida, K. et al : Air pollution and its health effects in Yokkaichi
     area, review on Yokkaichi as Asthma, Mie Med J. XVIII, 3, 195-209, 1969
18. Miyamoto, T. and Kabe, J., Air Pollution and Respiratory Disease, pp15-21,
     1968, Nankodo Press., Tokyo
19. Yoshida, T. : A study on the relationship between asthma bronchitis and
     meteorological factors and air pollutional factors in Hachioji district,
     J. Japan Med Assoc, 77(5), 507-517, 1977
20. Mizoguchi, K. : Relationship between asthmatic symptoms and air pollutants
     among school children in Tokyo, Proceeding the 18th Japan Soc Air Pollut,
     p241, 1977
21. Oka, M. et al : Asthma attack and air pollution - with special reference
     to Nitrogen Dioxide - , Seikatsu Eisei, 24(3), 72-81, 1980
22. Inaoka, N. et al : Study on the association asthma attack and status of
     air pollution, J.J.P.H., 31(12), 625-636, 1984
23. Tsunetoshi, Y. et al : Follow-up study of respiratory function in school
     children, J.J.P.H., 26(6), 278-288, 1979
24. Makino, K. : Relationship between respiratory disease mortality and air
     pollution or social indices in the Ku-area of Tokyo(1), J.J.P.H., 21(7),
     297-303, 1984
25. Division of Environmental Health, Environment Agency : Report on the
     health effects with automobile exhaust to inhabitants living in the
     roadside, Environment Agency, 1977
26. Kitabatake, M. et al : Health effects with automobile exhaust, J. Mie Univ
     Environ Sci, 2, 9-14, 1977
27. Nitta, H., Maeda, K. et al : Respiratory symptoms among residents living
     closely along major traffic arterials in Tokyo, J.J.P.H., 30(9), 381-389,
     1983
28. Kasuga, H. et al : Respiratory symptoms in school children and the role of
     passive smoking, Tokai J. Exp Clin Med, 4(2), 101-114, 1979
29. Matsuki, H. et al : Epidemiological study on the effects of smoking and
     air pollution using urinary hydroxyproline on the healthy school children
     and adults, J.J.P.H., 28, 505-515, 1981
30. Matsuki, H. et al : A comparative study on the health effects of indoor
     air pollution with special reference to nitrogen dioxide and smoking in
     winter and summer, J.J.P.H., 32(9), 549-559, 1985
31. Yoshida, R. : Epidemiological study on chronic bronchitis in Chiba
     prefecture, J.J.P.H., 23(7), 435-441, 1976
32. Tsunetoshi, Y. et al : Effects of with pollution to chronic bronchitis,
     J.J.P.H., 24, 293-300, 1977
33. Tsubota, N. : Epidemiological study on chronic bronchial symptoms in
     Okayama prefecture, Proceeding, the 18th Japan Soc Air Pollut, p247, 1977
34. Shimizu, T. : A statistical study on relation between the symptom
     prevalence of chronic bronchitis and air pollution, J.J. Res Dis, 12(4),
     199-206, 1974
35. Suzuki, et al: An interpretation of the results of the "Survey of compound
     air pollution and health effects in six communities of Chiba, Osaka and
     Fukuoka prefectures" conducted by the Enviroment Agency, J. Japan Soci Air

Pollut, 13(8), 310-355, 1978

36. Bureau of Air Quality, Environment Agency : Criteria on the health effects caused by nitrogen dioxide, Society of Air Quality, Tokyo, 1978

37. Yoshida, K. et al : Study on the literature of the health effects caused by nitrogen dioxide, Division of Environmental Health, Environment Agency, 1983

38. Araki, S. and Aono, H. : Photochemical air pollution and mass psychogenic systemic illness, Japan J. Hyg., 40(1), pp276, 1985

39. Ichinose, T. and Sagai, M. : Changes of lipid peroxidative protective systems in lung of rats. Exposed acutely, subacutely and chronically to nitrogen dioxide, J. Japan Soc Air Pollut, 18, 132-146, 1983

40. Yanagisawa, Y. and Nishimura, H. : A sampler for measurement of nitrogen oxide in ambient air, J. Japan Soci Air Pollut, 15, 316-323, 1980

41. Yanagisawa, Y. and Matsuki, H. et al : Estimation 41. Yaannual average of personal NO_2 exposure from short period measurements, J. Japan Soci Air Pollut, 19(4), 292-299, 1984

42. Takishima, J. et al : Seasonal change of dustfall in lung originated from roadside air pollution by studded tires, Japan Med Journal, No.3186, 31-34, May, 1985

43. Tominaga, S. : Air pollution and mortality rates of lung cancer, Lung Cancer, 21(3), 376, 1981

44. Shimizu, H. et al : Epidemiological study on lung cancer, Lung Cancer, 17(2), 103-112, 1977

45. Shimizu, H. et al : Epidemiological study on lung cancer, J. Japan Soci Air Pollut, 14(8), 14-23, 1979

46. Imai, M. et al : Air pollution and lung cancer, Japan. J. Hyg., 35(2), 493-498, 1980

47. Watanabe, H. et al : Air pollution and excess deaths, J. Japan Soci Air Pollut, 15, 234-247, 1979

48. Wakisaka, I. et al : Health effects of volcanic activities of Mt. Sakurajima on school children, J.J.P.H., 30(3), 101-108, 1983

49. Saito, K. et al : Effect of the 1977 eruption of Usu volcano on human living environment and health, Usu Eruption and its Impact on Environment, Hokkaido University, December 1978, p.169-206

50. Yanagisawa, Y. et al : Urinary hydroxyproline to creatinine ratio as a biological effect marker for exposure to NO_2 and tobacco smoke, Atmospheric Environment, 22, 2195-2203, 1988

Chapter 3

EMISSION CONTROL TECHNOLOGY

HAJIME NISHIMURA and MASAYOSHI SADAKATA

3.1 AUTOMOBILE EMISSION CONTROL

3.1.1 How it became possible —— socio-technological analysis ——

If stated simply, Japan's goal for the automobile emission control
requirement for passenger cars is an exact copy of the US goal, which was
demanded in the Clean Air Act of 1970, called the Muskie Act. However, Japan
achieved the goal in 1978, five years earlier than in California, while it has
not yet been achieved at federal level in the United States. Japan was the
first to succeed in the development and mass production of low emission
motorcars necessary for the restoration of clean air in urban areas. Perhaps,
Japan's success and its implementation of a very stringent emission control
regulation may have had no small influence on the attitudes of other countries,
especially of the U.S., towards the same problem.

What drove Japan to become the leader in this hard race and what was the
cause of its success? It was not because Japan was more advanced in automobile
technology but rather it was a result of the people's serious concern over air
pollution, and a result of political strife between the central and local
governments. It was also a result of severe competition among automobile
makers seeking a larger share of the market. The stringent regulation was
possible to plan and implement not because the technology meeting the
requirement was already available but the technology was advanced and became
available because the stringent regulation was planned and enforced.

Before reviewing the present status of automobile emission control
technology, it would be worthwhile looking at the history of its development as
an example of the interplay between social needs and technology.

In order to relate the history of automobile emission control
systematically, one must start from the Clean Air Act of 1970 of the United
States known as the Muskie Act. The Clean Air Act called for the reduction of
each of three kinds of major emissions from automobiles to one tenth of the
current level in 1970. Carbon monoxide, hydrocarbon and nitrogen oxide were
three major pollutants, and their emissions were to be reduced to 3.4 g/mile,

0.41 g/mile and 0.4 g/mile, respectively.

The reduction requirement, to one tenth, was determined from a rough estimate of the measures necessary to restore and maintain good air quality with the foreseeable increase in the amount of traffic.

A remarkable, and even revolutionary, aspect of the Clean Air Act was that the requirement for reduction was solely determined from the demand for restoring good air quality and no special heed was paid to the availability of the technology to meet the requirement. It was only considered at the time of implementation.

In 1970, no developed technology was available which could reduce the emissions of carbon monoxide and hydrocarbon to the required levels and no technical possibility was foreseen which could reduce the emission of nitrogen oxide to one tenth of the current level. The reduction of nitrogen oxide was considered much more difficult than the treatment of carbon monoxide and hydrocarbon because carbon monoxide and hydrocarbon are byproducts of fuel combustion and, therefore, can be removed by introducing them into an afterburner or oxidizing catalytic bed. On the other hand, nitrogen oxide is formed by a reaction between nitrogen and oxygen in the air at a high temperature. Therefore, either the suppression of formation of nitrogen oxide within the engine or the reduction of nitrogen oxide by some reducing agent is necessary for lowering the nitrogen oxide emission, both of which were not technically feasibile at that time.

However, in the Clean Air Act of the U.S., the date of the implementation of

Table 3.1

The progression of auto-emission control standards for carbon monoxide (CO), hydrocarbon (H.C.) and nitrogen oxide (NO_x) in Federal, California and Japanese regulations expressed in g/mile

	CO			H.C.			NO_x		
	Fed.	Cal.	Japan	Fed.	Cal.	Japan	Fed.	Cal.	Japan
1973			29.4			4.7			3.5
1975	15	9.0	3.4	1.5	0.9	0.4	3.1	2.0	1.9
1976	15	9.0		1.5	0.9		3.1	2.0	1.0
1978	15	9.0		1.5	0.41		2.0	1.5	0.4
1980	7.0	9.0		0.41	0.39		2.0	1.0	
1981	3.4	7.0		0.41	0.39		1.0	0.7	
1983	3.4	7.0		0.41	0.39		1.0	0.4	
Clean Air Act	3.4	effective 1975		0.41	effective 1975		0.4	effective 1976	

the regulation was set as 1975 for carbon monoxide and hydrocarbon and 1976 for nitrogen oxide. The waiving of the implementation was possible only when it was sufficiently proved that in spite of all the efforts of the automobile makers, the technology meeting the requirements was non-existent. Constant examination and assessment of the emission control technology became necessary. The task was assigned to the Academy of Science. It was also proposed that the regulation would be implemented when at least a single technical possibility was proved to be available.

Thus the US Clean Air Act of 1970 was revolutionary in that it aimed to promote the development of the necessary technology by legal enforcement and by competition among automobile makers.

Japanese automobile emisison control regulation basically followed the outline of the US Clean Air Act of 1970. The kinds of pollutants to be controlled, the target level of the emission control requirement for each pollutant and the planned date of implementation were exactly same. The legal procedure for the waiver was similar. In place of the Academy of Science in the United States, a committee called the Investigation Committee for Motor Vehicle Pollution Control Technology was set up and assigned the task of investigating and assessing the availability of the demanded emission control technology.

Thus Japan had started automobile emission control regulation following in the footsteps of the United States. However, later developments caused a change in their positions and the United States was forced to follow in the footsteps of Japan. This is clearly shown in Table 3.1. It compares the progress of the emission control requirements in the United States and in Japan. In the United States, the federal and Californian requirements are also compared. The target for hydrocarbon was attained in Japan as scheduled in 1975 but it was only attained in 1978 in California and in 1980 at the federal level. The target for carbon monoxide was also reached in Japan in 1975 as scheduled, but in California it was delayed six years to 1981 and at the federal level it has not been reached yet. The situation for nitrogen oxide was similar. Although Japan could implement the planned regulation in 1978 with two years delay, California postponed the implementation seven years, and at the federal level it has not been implemented yet. Although the emission reduction requirements for CO and hydrocarbon were very severe, they were rather easy problems technically when compared with the requirement for nitrogen oxide. CO emission can be reduced drastically by bringing the air fuel ratio close to the stoichiometric ratio. The emission of hydrocarbon can be reduced by preventing evaporation from the fuel tank and the blow-by from the crank case. In either case, the remaining constituents in the exhaust gas can be removed by passing them through a thermal reactor or an oxidizing catalyst.

Though it seemed simple, the United States delayed five years more than
Japan before its implementation. What caused such a difference? The key to
the problem is Japan's early shift to lead-free gasoline. Japan started to
decrease the lead content in regular gasoline gradually from 1971 and the shift
to lead-free gasoline was completed in 1975. The shift to lead-free gasoline
was not an easy task because the octane number must be kept at the same level
regardless of the decrease in lead content by increasing the content of
aromatic hydrocarbon in the gasoline. Another problem associated with the use
of lead free gasoline for existing vehicles was the valve seat recession
problem which causes engine stalling, hard-start and reduced output.
Therefore, the complete transition to lead-free gasoline was a gradual process
taking five years. However, just at the time of enforcement of emission
control of CO and hydrocarbon, lead-free gasoline was available. The
availability of lead-free gasoline made the stringent emission control
requirement possible. On the contrary, the United States was rather slow in
shifting to lead-free gasoline.

It is worthy to note that in Japan regulation for carbon monoxide and
hydrocarbons was implemented as scheduled but the implementation of regulation
for nitrogen oxide was two years behind schedule. This was caused partly by
the difficulty of controlling the emission of nitrogen oxide. But the major
reason was something else.

The oil crisis shocked the world in 1973. The pendulum of public concern
once swung fully towards environment began to swing towards energy. In the
United States, the implementation of the regulations on carbon monoxide and
hydrocarbon was postponed without sufficient reason. In Japan, although the
regulation of these two pollutants was implemented as initially scheduled
because it was planned before the oil crisis, the implementation of the
regulation of nitrogen oxide became quite uncertain.

Japanese automobile makers had agreed to the enforcement of the regulation
demanded in the Clean Air Act of the U.S. and were preparing for its complete
implementation by developing the necessary technology. However, it was evident
that they agreed to the regulation because they thought the technology meeting
the requirement was indispensable for their export of cars to the United States
once the regulation was implemented there. Therefore it was natural that most
of them lost any motivation for developing technology meeting the nitrogen
oxide emission control regulation once they found the United States was
postponing every emission control requirement. Probably, they exerted
influence on the government so as to postpone the implementation of the
regulation of nitrogen oxide emission control. The government was said to be
inclined to postpone the scheduled implementation.

Such an attitude of the central government aroused serious concerns in municipal governments. At that time, the municipal governments of major cities like Tokyo, Yokohama, Osaka and Kobe were all supported by the progressive parties, including the socialist and the communist parties, and were very eager to control pollution in urban areas. They were in constant conflict with the central government by trying to enforce more stringent pollution control regulation than that required by the central government.

They had already made plans for air pollution control presuming that the automobile emission control regulation would be implemented according to the schedule. Indefinite postponement would totally scrap the plans.

When the mayors of the major cities assembled to discuss the problem in 1974, Tokyo mayor Ryokichi Minobe proposed the setting up of a committee, completely independent from the government one, to investigate the state of technology of nitrogen emission control and to examine the feasibility of the implementation of the planned regulation. The proposal was soon accepted but the problem was to find experts who would work for the committee which would have to unveil the facts which all the automobile makers wanted to conceal.

The committee summoned six automobile makers, Toyota, Nissan, Honda, Mazda, Fuji and Isuzu, and interviewed them individually. Although they unanimously denied totally the technical feasibility of implementing the regulation according to the schedule, evaluation of the current state of the technology was different between large makers and small makers. Toyota and Nissan strongly denied any remarkable achievement in the emission control technology and insisted that any requirement below 1.9 g per mile was impossible to meet. Honda and Mazda, on the other hand, admitted that the emission control of 1 g nitrogen oxide per mile could be met readily. Honda, especially, boasted 0.4 g per mile had already been reached by their experimental vehicle fitted with the newly invented CVCC engine, although it was still plagued with the problem of drivability.

The committee drafted a report on the technical feasibility based on the results of the interviews and the analysis of published materials and acquired data. As there was no direct evidence showing the feasibility of the proposed regulation, the committee had to depend on a more elaborate method of technology assessment. They analyzed the available technical data and estimated the effects of various factors influencing the emission of nitrogen oxide, such as air fuel ratio and the amount of recycling gas, and then synthesized these effects to simulate the performance of an improved engine of which the performance data was not available. In spite of such efforts, the performance of the reduction catalyst was impossible to estimate because scientific data showing the results of experiment under the actual conditions of the exhaust gas or close to them were not available. Concerted intentional concealment of data was suspected.

The report was not a simple survey of the published data of the emission performance of the tested vehicle, but rather it was a report of a system design showing the feasibility of a new engine using various methods of emission control technology.

The report had no small impact on public opinion. It aroused strong reactions from both sides. It especially provoked the Environmental Agency. A director general publicly attacked the report as unscientific speculation. The attack again triggered reaction against the apparent attitude of the central government to loosen the control over emission and pollution. Therefore it was not so strange that the technical feasibility of nitrogen oxide emission control became one of the most important social concerns in 1974.

In the midst of such social concern, the Investigation Committee for Motor Vehicle Pollution Control Technology of the central government advised the postponement of the planned 1976 regulation on nitrogen oxide emission control on the ground that the technology meeting the requirement was not yet available.

The decision did not calm the situation. Doubt and protest against the decision were continuously expressed by people annoyed by automobile emission and finally a scandalous fact which ultimately reversed the decision was brought to the Diet by the secretary general of the Japanese Communist Party. The Investigation Committee for Motor Vehicle Pollution Control Technology was commissioned as a neutral committee consisting of scholars and experts and meetings were held behind closed doors. The public was completely excluded from the proceedings. However, it was learned that the secretary of the automobile makers' association was allowed to attend every meeting, to take note of the proceedings and report them to the automobile makers.

This meant that the committee was completely open to and constantly watched by the automobile makers. One wonders if the necessary neutrality could be possible in such a situation. The disclosed notes revealed that the discussion leading to the final decision was far from technical but was a kind of political deal. The disclosure again ignited the social concern over the problem. In the midst of the concern, a fact was revealed. A vehicle completely meeting the Muskie goal had already been developed by Mitsubishi. A technical feasibility existed. It was fitted with an engine invented by Professor Kumagai of Tokyo University. The committee, being well aware of the fact, had completely neglected it when they made the final decision.

Amidst public protest and anger, all the members of the committee were forced to resign and the decision they made was virtually scrapped.

The dissolution of the committee and the organization of a new one showed the automobile makers that the assessment from now on would be made on a genuinely technological basis and if at least one company had developed feasible technology, the regulation would be implemented. Seeing this, every automobile maker rushed to develop nitrogen oxide control technology meeting the original 1976 requirement, or the Muskie requirement. The technological development in the year after this event was amazing. All the automobile makers, except Toyota, announced that they had succeeded in developing technology satisfying the Muskie requirement. Honda, Mitsubishi and Toyo Kogyo announced that they were ready to market cars meeting the Muskie requirement if some tax benefits were allowed.

It was evident that these companies had already succeeded in the development of cars meeting the requirement when the Investigation Committee concluded that it was not technically feasibile. They had concealed or were compelled to conceal the facts. It should be mentioned that they were rather supportive to the activity of the technology assessment committee formed by the seven cities. Their attitudes contrasted remarkably with the reluctant and offensive attitudes of Toyota and Nissan. Probably, they wanted more stringent control to be implemented at that time so that they could enjoy the advantage in expanding their share in the market which had been monopolized by Toyota and Nissan.

Now it had become clear that the goal, once thought unattainable, could be reached in various ways such as engine modification, lean combustion, stratified combustion, rich-lean combustion, exhaust gas recycling, dual bed catalysts, three way catalysts, etc. The main concern of automobile makers had shifted and fierce competition was now focused on fuel economy. The result was marvelous. It turned out that the introduction of nitrogen oxide emission control did not decrease the average fuel economy at all but on the contrary the average fuel economy was improved about 30% in four years from 1976 to 1980.

A major reason for the opposition to exhaust emission control was the decrease in fuel economy. It was based on the ideas of automobile engineers. They believed there was a definite trade-off between the emission control and the fuel economy. There is some truth in this but they neglected the fact that the automobile engine is far from ideal and there remains abundant room for its improvement. The improvement required scientific research on the combustion process in the engine. This was also the research necessary for the reduction of nitrogen oxide emission. Therefore, the same research that enabled the satisfactory control of nitrogen oxide emission undoubtedly contributed to the improvement in fuel economy. An interesting question to pose would be whether the fuel economy would be improved further if the stringent emission control were removed now. Experts agree that there is no factor which would further improve the fuel economy even if the emission control is now abolished. The lesson we learn from history is that the emission control was not detrimental

122

to the fuel economy. Rather it facilitated the improvement of fuel economy by forcing the automobile makers to investigate the combustion process in the engine, which did not concern them until then.

The present example tells us that once the target is fixed, free competition is the best means of ensuring the development of technology. However, free competition is not enough to fix the target by itself, especially when the goal is a non-economical one. Social enforcement backed by people's will is necessary.

3.1.2 Present state of technology

(i) Lean combustion system. The generation of all three pollutants can be reduced by lean combustion or making the air-to-fuel ratio (A/F) higher than the stoichiometric ratio. The concentrations of these pollutants in the exhaust varies with the air-to-fuel ratio, as shown in Fig. 3.1. Carbon monoxide and hydrocarbons are high for rich mixtures. They diminish to very low levels when the air-fuel exceeds the stoichiometric ratio 14.6. The amount of nitrogen oxide is at the maximum for the stoichiometric ratio and diminishes for both rich and lean mixtures.

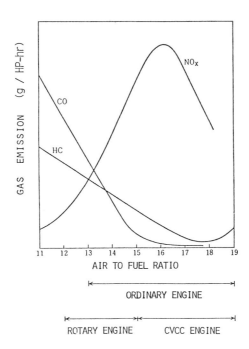

Fig. 3.1. The emissions of carbon monooxide (CO), hydrocarbons (HC) and nirogen oxides (NO_x) from automobile engines vary with air-to-fuel ratio.

Therefore, if we employ a sufficiently lean mixture having an air-to-fuel ratio as high as 20, the levels of pollutants in the exhaust can be kept sufficiently low. This is the principle of lean combustion. Although the principle is simple, its embodiment as technology is not a simple task. It requires considerable modification of the engine. First, the distribution of the air-fuel mixture among cylinders must be improved so that the difference among air-to-fuel ratios in the cylinders is virtually eliminated. This is because, when the average A/F is high, a slight deviation from the average will produce too lean a mixture which is difficult to ignite.

In order to eliminate variation of the A/F among cylinders and to provide exactly the same mixture to all of them, the carburetor must be improved so as to produce a completely homogeneous mixture. Second, the lean mixture, though flammable, is difficult to ignite and tends to cause a misfire or a failure of ignition which causes an increase in hydrocarbon emission. The ignition can be facilitated by making a rich mixture around each ignition plug. This is called stratified combustion. It usually required separate fuel injection pumps. Honda solved the problem by merely providing an auxiliary carburetor. This provided an ignitable mixture around the ignition plug. This is the principle of the CVCC engine which made Honda famous world-wide.

The outstanding merit of the lean combustion engine is that it can be used in a leaded environment where lead-free gasoline is not available.

(ii) Catalytic removal system. The catalytic removal system removes the three pollutants in the exhaust by letting the gas pass through a catalytic converter. A catalyst has been used to remove carbon monoxide and hydrocarbon. This is an oxidizing catalyst. In order to remove nitrogen oxides from the exhaust, another type of catalyst which can reduce nitrogen oxides to nitrogen is necessary. This is called a reducing catalyst. For the reducing agent, carbon monoxide and hydrocarbons present in the exhaust gas are used, thereby enabling simultaneous removal of all three pollutants. However, as the complete simultaneous removal of all three pollutants is difficult, a combination of the reducing and oxidizing catalysts is usually used. The reducing catalyst, which is placed first, reduces nitrogen oxide using the carbon monoxide and hydrocarbons present and the oxidizing catalyst then oxidizes the remaining carbon monoxide and hydrocarbons when more air is introduced.

The reducing catalyst can now be called a three-way catalyst. It can reduce or remove all three pollutants simultaneously if the composition of the exhaust is in the right range, which depends on the air/fuel ratio. A three-way catalyst is used alone or in conjunction with an oxidizing catalyst. The critical factor ensuring good performance of the three-way catalyst is the maintenance of the air/fuel ratio at an appropriate value very close to the

stoichiometric ratio i.e. 14.6. For that purpose, automatic control of the
air/fuel ratio is essential. The system for this essentially consists of an
oxygen sensor, an electronic control device, which is usually a microprocessor,
and a fuel injection system or an electromechanical carburetor. If the
air/fuel ratio is kept strictly around 14.6, the three-way catalyst alone can
lower the levels of the three pollutants to the levels satisfying the control
requirements. It often happens that a lower A/F is preferred as strict
adherence to the stoichiometric ratio cannot be ensured. In such a case an
oxidizing catalyst is placed after the three-way catalyst and the remaining
carbon monoxide and hydrocarbons are oxidized over the catalyst when more air
is introduced.

(iii) Other methods of reducing emission. The generation of nitrogen oxide
during combustion can be reduced considerably by lowering the temperature of
combustion. An effective way of lowering the temperature is to dilute the
inflammable mixture by introducing inert gas. The exhaust gas recycling system
is a system which utilizes the exhaust gas from the engine as the inert gas for
dilution. The exhaust gas recycling method is the surest way of reducing the
emission of nitrogen oxide without modifying any other process or the
structure. It can be applied to any system, whether it be the prototype or an
improved system, and it can reduce the emission considerably. In a prototype
engine, recycling of 10% of the exhaust gas can reduce the emission to one
third of the original level. In the improved system, though the percentage of
reduction becomes smaller, recycling of around 10 or 20% of the exhaust gas can
effectively reduce the emission to a considerable extent.

Lowering the combustion temperature by increasing the heat loss by making
the engine out of a good heat-conducting metal such as aluminium can also
contribute to reduction of the emission, although it also reduces the fuel
economy.

(iv) Emission control of the diesel engine. The emission control of the
diesel engine poses another difficult problem. The three-way catalyst cannot
be used because the diesel engine must be operated with an oxidizing
air-to-fuel ratio in order to prevent smoke generation. Lean combustion can
reduce the emission of nitrogen oxide but as the combustion in the diesel engine
is not combustion of the premixed mixture, lean combustion is not so effective
as in the gasoline engine.

The remaining effective measures are exhaust gas recycling, injection retard
and engine modification. The injection retard is effective both for reduction
of smoke and nitrogen oxide but fuel economy deteriorates. Although exhaust
gas recycling is considerably effective in reducing nitrogen oxide emission, it
increases smoke emission. Modification of the combustion chamber is sometimes
effective.

By joint application of these techniques, the exhaust quality has been improved considerably. In 1981, the regulation specifying the emission control requirement for the diesel powered passenger car, which is to be obligatory from 1986, was announced. The new requirement is 3.4 g/mile for CO, 0.64 g/mile for hydrocarbon and 1.1 g/mile for nitrogen oxides.

Emission control from diesel engine powered trucks is still a difficult problem. According to the regulation in 1983, the NO_x concentration in the exhaust from a direct injection type diesel engine must be lower than 610 ppm and an average of 470 ppm. The requirement for 1974 was an average of 770 ppm, which means only 40% reduction in ten years.

3.2 NO_x EMISSION CONTROL FROM STATIONARY SOURCES

It is well known that nitrogen oxides (NO_x) are among the major species causing photochemical smog. In Japan, the ill effects of photochemical smog were first seen in early 1970 when many junior high school students in Tokyo were affected. Since 1973, progressively tighter NO_x emission standards have been established for all stationary pollution sources, consequently, the Japanese emission standard has become the most stringent standard in the world. In order to comply with emission standards, NO_x abatement technology for stationary sources has improved significantly. As a result, NO_x control technology for coal combustion boilers, for example, is now exported to European countries. However, atmospheric NO_x levels have not yet dropped enough in spite of innovative emission controls. Control technology, particularly for dirty fuel combustion facilities, is still inadequate. The development of economical NO_x control technology for developing countries also requires attention.

Anthropomorphic sources of NO_x are classified into mobile sources such as cars and stationary sources such as boilers. Although the contribution from each source category varies from area to area, the contribution of stationary sources is significant especially in areas with heavy industry. NO_x emitted by stationary sources comes almost entirely from combustion processes. Although NO_x is defined as the total of NO and NO_2, more than 90% of NO_x at the end of combustion is in the form of NO. The NO from the combustion process has two different origins. One is from nitrogen gas in the air and the other is from nitrogen compounds in the fuel. The NO from nitrogen in the air is called thermal NO_x while NO_x from fuel nitrogen is called fuel NO_x.

There are two general approaches to NO_x reduction. The first involves combustion modificiation methods and the second is the NO_x removal methods. The former methods aim at controlling the NO_x concentration at the combustor exit or the furnace outlet by modifying the combustion process through changing fuel type, improving the burner design or changing the furnace configuration. Since NO formation is strongly influenced by the combustion process, the details of the NO_x formation process during combustion provide many useful ideas for NO_x control by combustion modification. The latter NO_x removal methods reduce or remove NO_x after combustion is complete and the exhaust gas leaves the combustor or the furnace. NO_x removal processes usually require the construction of a large scale decontamination facility before the exhaust gas reaches the stack, so this method is expensive compared to combustion modification methods. Hence, combustion modification methods are the economically favored methods for NO_x emission reduction.

Next, we will discuss in greater detail combustion modification methods and NO_x removal methods respectively.

3.2.1 Combustion modification methods for NO_x reduction

An engineer's first task in applying any combustion modification method to a particular combustion process, is to clarify whether the NO formed in a process is thermal NO or fuel NO. If the NO from the process is predominantly thermal NO, an effective control method will achieve at least one of following:

decrease of flame temperatures;

decrease of furnace oxygen levels;

decrease of residence time in the high temperature
    region.

On the other hand, if the process NO is predominantly fuel NO, a control method based on any of the following is effective:

1) decrease of fuel nitrogen content;

2) decrease of furnace oxygen level;

3) control of fuel and air mixing conditions at the
    burner.

The type of NO can be roughly predicted from the fuel nitrogen content and the

Table 3.2

Nitrogen content in fuels [15]

Fuel	Nitrogen content (wt%)
Crude oil (Middle East)	0.09-0.22
No.6 heavy oil	0.1-0.4
No.4 heavy oil	0.05-0.1
light oil	0.002-0.03
kerosene	0.0001-0.0005
coal	0.2-3.4
LPG, City gas	0

maximum temperature in the furnace. If the nitrogen content in the fuel is under 0.01% and the maximum temperature is over 1500°C, the observed NO is mainly thermal NO. On the other hand, if the fuel nitrogen content is over 0.5

Table 3.3
Summary of combustion modification method for control of NO_x

Name of Technology	Principle	Type of NO reduced	Type of fuel liquid	Average reduction rate
Fuel Modification				
1) Low nitrogen fuel	Decrease of Nitrogen	fuel NO	liquid fuel and coal	*
2) Emulsified oil fuel	Decrease of Temperature and Oxygen	thermal NO	liquid fuel	30-50%
Operation Modification				
3) Low excess air ratio combustion	Decrease of Oxygen	fuel NO and thermal NO	all fuel	10-20%
4) Low load combustion	Decrease of Temperature	thermal NO	all fuel	10-30%
5) Low temperature air preheating	Decrease of Temperature	thermal NO	all fuel	10-30%
Low NOx Burner				
6) Self recirculation burner	Decrease of Oxygen and Temperature	thermal NO	liquid	20-40%
7) Rapid mixing burner	Decrease of Tempeature	thermal NO	gas and liquid fuel	20-40%
8) Off-stoichiometric combustion burner	Decrease of Oxygen and Temperature	fuel NO and thermal NO	all fuel	30-40%
Furnace Modification				
9) Two staged combustion	Decrease of Temperature and Oxygen	fuel NO and thermal NO	all fuel	30-50%
10) Fuel gas recirculation	Decrease of Temperature	thermal NO	all fuel	30-50%
11) Water or steam injection	Decrease of Temperature	thermal NO	gas and liquid fuel	30-50%
12) Staged fuel injection	Removal by Reducing Species	fuel NO and thermal NO	all fuel	30-50%

* depends on fuel employed

wt.% and the maximum temperature is under 1400°C, the observed NO is mainly fuel NO. In general, the NO from the combustion of light oil, gasoline and gaseous fuel without ammonia is thermal NO while the NO from the combustion of the residual oil and coal is mainly fuel NO (Table 3.2).

The various combustion modification methods developed so far are listed in Table 3.3.

We will now discuss the most practical combustion modification methods listed in the table.

(i) <u>Low NO$_x$ burner</u>. Use of a low NO$_x$ burner (LNB) is an attractive control technique since it requires only replacement of burners without modification of the furnace. Hence, this method is relatively inexpensive. The principle of a LNB is either:

(1) control of NO formation by forming a local reducing region in the flame through changing the burner structure; or

(2) formation of a thin flame having a large surface area to increase radiative heat transfer to the boiler wall and consequently reduce the flame temperature.

Examples of systems based on the former principle are the self-recirculation burner and the off-stoichiometric burner. An example of the latter principle is the rapid mixing flame.

a) Self-recirculating burner

This burner was developed for the furnace of petroleum chemical plants. A diagram of the burner is shown in Fig. 3.2. In this burner, the initial part

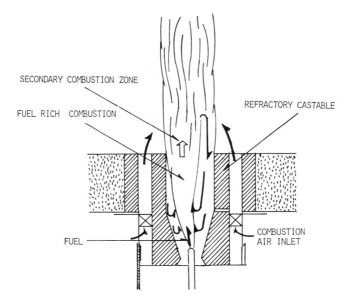

Fig. 3.2. Self-recirculating-type burner

of the flame is surrounded by the cylindrical burner wall in order to reduce
the entrainment of ambient air to the fuel. Hence, only a limited amount of
air is recirculated from the proximal section of the burner and entrained into
the flame. Because of lack of oxygen, a very fuel-rich combustion takes place
in this burner section and consequently NO formation is suppressed. The
afterburning of unburnt species such as CO, H_2 and HC takes place at the burner
opening where secondary air is supplied.

This type of burner can be used to control thermal NO and can be used to
improve the fuel economy. This burner can reduce NO_x levels by 30 to 40%.
The cost of this burner (capacity : 100 l oil/hr) is around 2000 to 5000 US
dollars.

b) Off-stoichiometric combustion burner

This burner can be applied to the control of both thermal and fuel NO from
boilers using gaseous, liquid or coal fuels.

In Fig. 3.3 we show the relationship between emissions of thermal NO and
fuel NO from a premixed flame as a function of air ratio. The emission level
of thermal NO peaks near the stoichiometric point. Hence, if combustion
conditions can be reduced below the stoichiometric point, NO emissions can be
reduced. In practice, off-stoichiometric combustion means that half of the
burners are operated at an air ratio lower than 1.0 (point A in Fig. 3.3) and
the other half of the burners are operated at an air ratio higher than 1.0

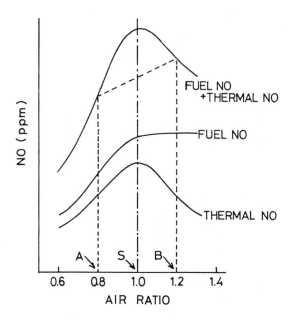

Fig. 3.3. Emissions of thermal NO and fuel NO from a premixed flame as a
function of air-to-fuel ratio.

(point B in Fig. 3.3). An example of this type of burner is called the PM (Pollution Minimum) burner developed by Mitsubishi Heavy Industry. In this burner system, all the burners are operated under premixed fuel-air conditions. The upper and lower burners on both sides of the furnace are operated at an air ratio of 1.2 and the center burner is operated at an air ratio of 0.8. The system reduces NO emissions by 30 to 40%.

c) Rapid mixing type burner

This burner reduces thermal NO by forming a thin, flat flame. When the thin flat flame is formed, the flame temperature drops due to the increased radiant heat transfer to the furnace walls and consequently the emission of thermal NO is reduced. Because of this principle, this burner is suitable for water-cooled wall furnaces.

This burner has the advantage of improved combustion efficiency, and reduced CO and soot emissions, as well as reduced thermal NO emissions. An example of the rapid mixing type burner designed for liquid fuel combustion is shown in Fig. 3.4. In liquid fuel combustion, the fuel is atomized radially and rapidly mixed with air consequently forming a large surface thin flat flame (Fig. 3.4). Accordingly, the flame area is large compared to a conventional burner. This burner was developed by the Nippon furnace industry under the name of the NFK-TRW burner.

This type of burner is used in boilers burning gaseous or liquid fuel with little or no nitrogen. This burner reduces NO emissions by about 40%.

(ii) Emulsified oil combustion. This method has the advantage of not requiring the reconstruction of the furnace. In addition it increases combustion efficiency and suppresses soot emissions. The method is applicable to small scale boilers.

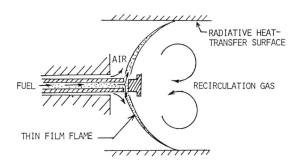

Fig. 3.4. Rapid mixing burner.

Emulsified fuel is made by dispersing water in oil with the aid of small amounts of emulsfier. Emulsions are classified into i) water droplets in oil which is called the W/O type and ii) oil droplets in water which is called the O/W type. Usually, the W/O type emulsion is used because of low viscosity and easy handling. When emulsified fuel is atomized in a high temperature atmosphere, the water in the oil is instantly evaporated and induces secondary atomization. This initiates very rapid and efficient combustion. As combustion heat is partly lost by the vaporization of water, the flame temperature is reduced and thermal NO emission is reduced. In the case of emulsified oil combustion, the efficient combustion allows the air ratio to be held near the stoichiometric point without the formation of CO or soot. The emission of fuel NO can thereby be reduced while keeping high combustion efficiency. This method can be mainly applied to combustion facilities which use liquid fuel of low nitrogen content.

The disadvantage of this method is the reduction of energy efficiency. However, this can be compensated for by the increased combustion efficiency and the decrease in the air ratio. The NO reduction of this method is between 30 and 40%. The cost of emulsification is only 5% of the fuel cost. The emulsification unit for a boiler of 40,000 m^3/h requires an area of only 4 m^2.

(iii) Two-stage combustion. The two-stage combustion method (TSC) is effective for both thermal NO and fuel NO not only for gas or liquid combustion but also coal combustion. Furthermore, the TSC method may be more effective in reducing NO compared to the low NO_x burners.

The principle of TSC is illustrated in Fig. 3.5. The primary combustion is

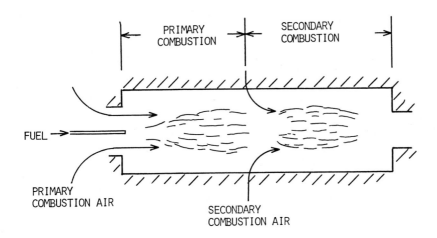

Fig. 3.5. The principle of two-stage combustion.

kept fuel-rich by controlling combustion air. Then, fuel lean combustion follows at the secondary stage where the combustion air is introduced. Thermal NO can be reduced by this method because the temperature distribution becomes flat and the peak temperature, which is the main cause for the formation of thermal NO, is reduced. The fuel NO can also be reduced because the fuel nitrogen is mostly converted to N_2 at the primary stage under the fuel-rich combustion. Sadakata examined the optimum TSC conditions for NO_x reduction experimentally and found that the location of the air injection point during the second stage was important.[24] The effect on the final NO levels of the air injection point in the second stage is shown in Fig. 3.6. The final NO_x is sharply decreased as the injection point is moved downstream. This shows that the air injection point should be located at least 1200 mm downstream from the burner port. Wendt et al. found the same for coal combustion[25]. Sadakata also found that there is an optimum air ratio for the efficient reduction of NO.[15] Fig. 3.7 shows the effect of the primary air ratio on the final emission of NO from methane-air turbulent combustion. In this figure, the dotted line shows the NO emissions at the primary stage while the solid line shows the final NO emissions. Although the primary stage NO decreases with a decrease in the primary air ratio, the final NO level reaches a minimum when the air ratio equals 0.8 and then increases again as the primary air ratio is reduced. This

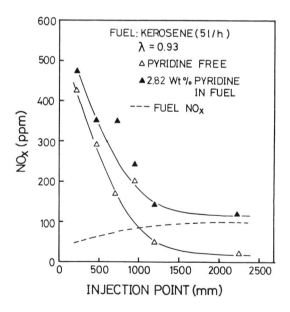

Fig. 3.6. Effect of the injection point of secondary stage air on the final NO_x emission.

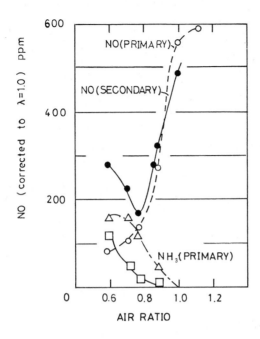

Fig. 3.7. Emissions of nitric oxide and ammonia from the combustion of a fuel doped with 0.23 vol.% ammonia as a function of primary air ratio.[3]

is because a high concentration of intermediate reduced species such as NH_3 or HCN is formed instead of NO at very low air ratios and these intermediate species are converted to NO during the secondary stage combustion. On the other hand, the level of intermediate species formed at a primary air ratio of 0.8 is nearly the same level as that of NO. Under such conditions, NO and the intermediate species react and form N_2 by the following chemical reaction.

$$NO + I = N_2$$

TSC can be applied to gas and oil combustion boilers and high temperature furnaces using residual oil such as glass fusion furnaces and rotary cement kilns. It can also be used in utility plant coal combustion boilers and small scale coal combustion furnaces. An example of applying the TSC method to a boiler is shown in Fig. 3.8. In this case, the burner port at the upper boiler section is used as the secondary air injection port. The NO_x reduction was around 30%. The TSC method can be applied also to fluidized coal combustion. In this case, secondary air is injected into the freeboard above the bed. The reduction in this case is around 20%.

The disadvantage of TSC is that the heat energy efficiency is lowered because of the reduced flame temperature. However, this disadvantage can be

134

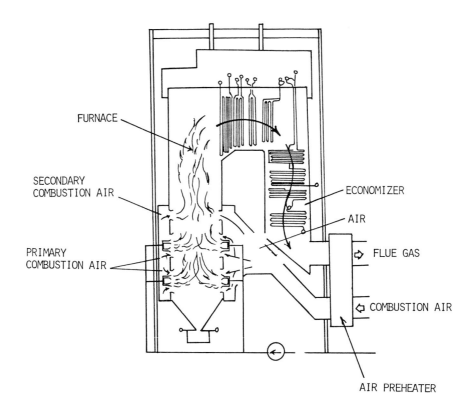

FURNACE

SECONDARY
COMBUSTION AIR

PRIMARY
COMBUSTION AIR

ECONOMIZER

AIR

FLUE GAS

COMBUSTION AIR

AIR PREHEATER

Fig. 3.8. Two-stage combustion applied to a power plant boiler.[4)]

offset by preheating the combustion air with high temperature flue gas since
the flame temperature can thereby be raised. It was shown by Sadakata that air
preheating has only a slight effect on the final emission level of fuel NO.
Another disadvantage of TSC is that it produces elevated levels of unburnt
species such as CO, HC and soot. However, this problem can probably be solved
by improving the secondary stage mixing of unburnt species and injected air.

(iv) Staged-fuel injection method. The staged-fuel injection method (SFIM)
has three advantages: i) it is useful for both thermal NO_x and fuel NO_x, ii)
it can be applied to the combustion of gaseous, liquid and solid fuels and iii)
it can be applied to many different types of furnaces such as boilers, rotary
cement kilns or glass furnaces.

The idea of NO reduction by hydrocarbon injection was first proposed by
Myerson.[27)] He tried injecting various kinds of hydrocarbons such as isobutane
or gasoline into a simulated flue gas containing NO in an attempt to reduce NO
levels by oxidizing hydrocarbon with NO. He obtained a rapid reduction of NO

in the presence of oxygen. He presented the following global reaction mechanism:

$$6NO + 4CH = 4CO + 2H_2O + 3N_2$$

The SFIM is mainly based upon Myerson's study. The outline of this method is illustrated in Fig. 3.9. In this method, secondary fuel is injected at the position where the primary fuel lean combustion is complete. NO is rapidly reduced by hydrocarbon radicals through the above reaction leaving behind the unburnt hydrocarbon species, CO and HCN. These species are removed by tertiary air injected into the downstream region.

As previously mentioned, this method can be applied to a broad range of combustion facilities including boilers or rotary cement kilns and as well as to the combustion of various fuels including coal. A pulverized coal combustion facility is shown in Fig. 3.10 as an example. This NO_x control technology was developed by Mitsubishi Heavy Industry and named "MACT" (Mitsubishi Advanced Combustion Technology). The process is unique in that pulverized coal is used as the injected hydrocarbon. HC, CO and HCN are almost entirely removed by introducing tertiary low oxygen level air for afterburning. A final NO level of 50 ppm can be realized by this method if low NO_x burners are employed at the same time.

The disadvantage of this method is that it can only be used in large scale boilers since it requires additional furnace volume for both NO reduction by hydrocarbon and for the secondary combustion to remove unburnt species. As a result, the cost of this method is significantly higher than other low NO_x methods or the two-stage combustion method.

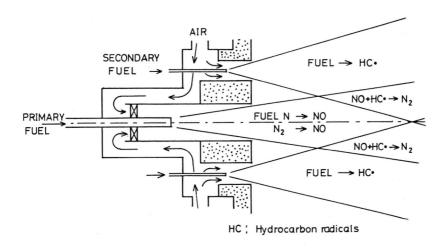

HC : Hydrocarbon radicals

Fig. 3.9. Principle of staged fuel injection.[6]

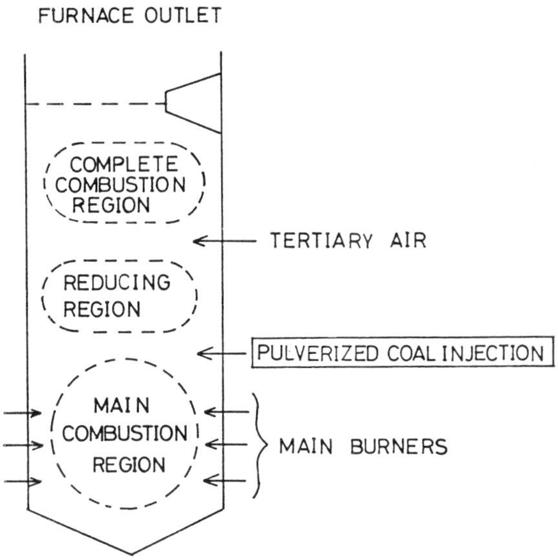

136

FURNACE OUTLET

Fig. 3.10. Staged fuel injection applied to pulverized coal combustion.[7]

(v) <u>Other methods</u>. We will briefly explain other forms of NO_x control technology.

Low nitrogen fuels can be substituted for high nitrogen fuels in certain cases. However, this method is only useful for fuel NO. The disadvantage of this method is, of course, an increase in fuel cost.

Low excess air ratio combustion is the method used for controlling the air ratio near 1.0 in order to reduce both thermal NO and fuel NO by lowering the combustion oxygen level. Although this method can easily be employed in various conventional facilities, the reduction of NO obtained by this method is relatively low compared to other methods. Furthermore, emissions of unburnt species such as CO and soot tend to increase unless some improvements in fuel-air mixing and fuel atomization are carried out. Hence, an improvement of the burners is sometimes required in order to utilize low excess air ratio combustion.

Low heat release rate combustion is a method of reducing the combustion heat release rate in order to reduce thermal NO by a decrease in flame temperature. Here, the combustion heat release rate is defined as the quantity of heat released by combustion per unit volume per unit time in the combustion chamber. The disadvantage of this method is that a high heat release rate is sacrificed in exchange for the reduction of NO_x.

Low temperature air preheating is a method of decreasing the preheat temperature of combustion air in order to reduce thermal NO_x by a reduction of the flame temperature. A disadvantage of this method is a lowered thermal efficiency due to a lowering of the flame temperature.

In the flue gas recirculation method the flue gas is recycled from the furnace outlet, cooled and mixed with combustion air in order to reduce thermal NO by reducing the flame temperature. However, this method has the following disadvantages. It will not reduce fuel NO since fuel NO is insensitive to temperature change. Furthermore, the flame tends to be unstable when this method is used. The repair costs for a flue gas recirculation system are relatively high compared to that of low NO_x burners. This method is applicable only to large scale furnaces with flue gas volumes larger than 10^5 m^3/h since the repair cost for this method in medium or small scale furnaces is too high.

In the water or steam injection method, water or steam is injected into a furnace in order to decrease thermal NO by reducing the flame temperature. The disadvantage of this method is the lowered energy efficiency since the combustion heat is partly consumed by water vaporization.

3.2.2 NO_x removal methods

NO_x removal processes can be classified into dry processes and wet processes, referring to the reagent used for NO_x removal.

Dry processes reduce NO levels without using a liquid absorbent. One type of these processes is where a reducing gas such as NH_3 and CO is sometimes introduced into the flue gas to reduce NO with the help of a catalyst. In another type of dry process the NO_x is removed by a solid absorbent such as activated carbon or molecular sieve.

Wet processes use liquid absorbents. This requires the following two steps:

i) Oxidation of NO to NO_2 or N_2O_5 by O_3.

ii) Absorption of N_2O_5 by water to HNO_3 or absorption of NO_2 or SO_2 by NaOH with final reduction to N_2. The wet process was initially more highly developed than the dry process. However, the wet process has the following disadvantages. First, it requires large amounts of electrical energy to form O_3 which is necessary to oxidize NO during the primary oxidation process. Second, an absorption tower is usually needed for the secondary absorption process where large volumes of flue gas must contact the liquid phase reagent and, third, the wet process usually needs water treatment to remove alkali or acid.

On the other hand, the catalytic dry process requires only a small surface contact area with a catalyst since the reduction reaction on the catalyst is very rapid. This allows the dry process to be used on a small scale. Furthermore, the dry process does not, of course, require water treatment. Hence, this process is potentially more economical. Unlike SO_x, NO_x can be converted in the gas phase to a non-pollutant, stable species, N_2, so the dry process holds greater promise for future development than the wet process.

Next, we will review several workable dry processes.

(i) Non-catalytic reducing method. As the combustion flue gas usually contains over 1% O_2, an injected reducing species such as CO or H_2 is oxidized by O_2 before reducing NO. Many researchers have sought a reducing species which can reduce NO selectively in the presence of O_2. Of them, Lyon at Exxon research found that NH_3 can selectively reduce NO in the presence of O_2 at temperatures between 800 and 900°C.[30] Although the exact reaction mechanism is not yet known, the overall reaction is as follows:

$$4NO + 4NH_3 + O_2 = 4N_2 + 6H_2O$$

The above equation indicates that some O_2 is necessary for the reaction to proceed.

The non-catalytic NO_x removal method is an application of this reaction. NH_3 is introduced into the furnace or the flue in the 800 to 1000°C temperature zone in the presence of oxygen. The above reaction proceeds and NO is reduced within 0.5 sec. More than 90% of the NO is reduced when the temperature is between 900 and 1000°C. However, only a 40% NO reduction has been obtained when this method is applied to a real furnace. This may be because of the increasingly poor mixing between NH_3 and NO with the increase in furnace size since the turbulent mixing time is directly proportional to the furnace size. Hence, the reduction rate must be improved by improving the NH_3 injection method. This may be a chemical engineering task.

The advantage of this method is its low cost because it does not require a catalytic reactor in the flue system. Furthermore, this method can be applied to both clean flue gas and to dirty flue gas such as residual oil or coal flue gas. On the other hand, it has the disadvantage of leaving some unreacted NH_3 in the flue gas after the injection since excess NH_3 is sometimes required to attain a high reduction rate. The unreacted NH_3 may corrode the heat exchanger. Furthermore, NH_3 reacts with SO_3 to form NH_4HSO_4 (acid ammonium sulfate) which can corrode the air preheater of the boiler. In order to correct these problems, the excess of NH_3 compared to NO must be reduced.

This method is very cheap compared to the selective catalytic method which will be discussed next.

(ii) Selective catalytic method. As previously mentioned, a residence time of 0.5 sec in the high temperature zone of the furnace is required for the non-catalytic method to work well. Hence, the application of the non-catalytic method has been limited. In the selective catalytic method, NO_x is selectively reduced by NH_3 at low temperatures with the help of a solid catalyst. This method has been widely accepted compared to the non-catalytic reducing method. The method is illustrated in Fig. 3.11. NH_3 is introduced into the flue

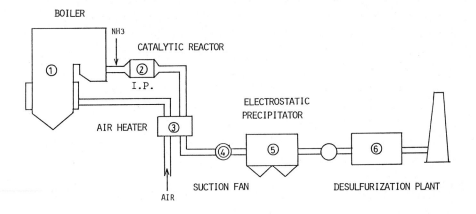

Fig. 3.11. Process flow sheet of selective catalytic method.

upstream of the reactor which is labeled I.P. in the figure. The flue gas
mixed with NH_3 flows into the catalytic reactor where the selective reduction
of NO by NH_3 occurs on the catalyst surface. The reactor temperature ranges
from 200°C to 400°C. The catalysts employed here include, V_2O_5 on TiO and CuO
on TiO_2. Usually, TiO_2 is selected as a carrier because of its sulfur
resistance. The NO reduction by this method sometimes exceeds 90% when the SV
value is 10 hr^{-1}. The SV value is defined as the special velocity with units
of flue gas volume treated per cubic metre catalytic volume per hour. Special
provisions are necessary for using this method in particle-laden gas streams.
One must use a catalyst which will not become blocked by particles. A
dustproof catalyst which can be used in coal combustion flue gas with particle
burdens of 20 to 30 g/m^3 has been developed recently. More than 200 combustion
facilities currently use this denitrification process in Japan .

This method is most commonly used in boilers. However, it is also used in
metal heating furnaces, oil heating furnaces, cokes ovens and sludge and
garbage incinerators. Just as with the non-catalytic method, this method has
the disadvantage of causing corrosion from acid ammonium sulfate formed after
the NO reduction from excess NH_3 reagent. So, excess NH_3 injection should be
minimized. Another serious disadvantage of this method is the cost.

(iii) The cost of the selective catalytic method. The construction and
operational costs for the selective catalytic process in Japanese 700 MW
boilers constructed from 1978 to 1981 are shown in Table 3.4 with the
contribution of the catalyst to the total cost. The catalyst contributes
around 20% of the total construction cost for the gaseous fuel boilers while it
is over 60% for the coal boilers. Note that the total cost per KW for coal

Table 3.4

Cost of the selective catalytic method for various fuels[10]

Boiler Name	A	B	C	D	E	F
Fuel	Natural gas	Natural gas	Low sulfur oil	High sulfur oil	Low sulfur coal	High sulfur coal
Design specifications						
Inlet NOx (ppm)	50	100	200	200	400	400
Outlet NOx (ppm)	10	20	40	40	80	80
Reduction rate (%)	80	80	80	80	80	80
SV (h^{-1})	20,000	16,000	4,000	3,000	2,400	2,000
NH_3/NOx mole ratio	0.92	0.86	0.83	0.83	0.82	0.82
Construction cost						
Total (10^6\$)	8.5	9.0	16.8	21.0	27.8	31.7
\$/kw	12.1	13.1	24.0	30.0	39.7	45.2
Contribution of catalyst (%)	17.6	21.1	49.2	52.3	60.4	63.7
Operating cost						
Total (10^6\$)	3.53	3.78	7.40	9.07	15.7	18.0
mill/kwh	0.80	0.90	1.70	2.10	3.65	4.2
Contribution of catalyst (%)	10	12.5	37	40	53	56

combustion boilers is three times higher than gaseous fuel boilers and twice as high as liquid fueled boilers. This is because a very expensive catalyst such as titanium must be used for a coal combustion boiler because cheaper catalysts such as alumina are easily attacked by the sodium or halogen in the coal flue gas. Furthermore, one cannot increase the SV value (flue gas flow volume/catalyst volume) for a coal boiler since the increased flue gas velocity causes abrasion of the catalyst by fly ash. This means a large volume of catalyst is required for coal systems. The catalyst contribution to the operational cost of a coal boiler is also 2 to 3 times higher than that of oil or gaseous combustion boilers since the catalyst life in coal combustion boilers is less than two years while for natural gas or oil combustion boilers lifetimes are over four years. The operational cost of the selective catalytic method depends significantly on the catalyst life. Hence, the development of long lived catalysts is very important.

3.2.3 <u>Choosing the NO_x control technology and the cost for individual</u>
<u>facilities</u>

The appropriate NO_x control technology and its cost is dependent on the type
and the scale of the pollution generating facility. Hence, it is necessary to
analyze the potential control technology and the repair and operational costs
for each facility. The repair costs include the total cost for repairing and
exchanging burners, storage, transport facilities and a duct. It is expressed
in units such as dollars per 10^3 m^3 flue gas treated per hour. The operational
cost is expressed as the ratio of the cost with NO_x control technology to the
cost without NO_x control technology. The cost calculations were carried out
primarily by Mitsubishi Research Institute[33] under the supervision of the
author. Basic data for the calculations were obtained from several burner and
boiler makers and from the literature. The cost, of course, depends on local
conditions such as site price, labor and material costs, price of electricity
or price of water. Hence, the reader must note that the costs calculated here
cannot be strictly compared to costs in other countries.

(i) <u>Large-scale industrial boilers</u>. The average NO_x emission levels
corrected to 3% oxygen in the flue for the large scale industrial boilers (flue
gas volume over 40,000 m^3/hr) without NO_x control are 290 ppm for No.6 heavy
oil (0.2%N) and 600 ppm for coal (1%N).

Applicable types of NO_x control technology for the large scale industrial
boiler are "Flue gas recirculation (FGR)", "Two stage combustion (TSC)" and
"Low NO_x burners (LNB). The NO_x level can be reduced to 50 ppm for gaseous
fuel, 60-100 ppm for light fuel and 290 ppm for coal by using a combination of
the above methods.

The cost for controlling the above techniques for large scale industrial
boilers using No.6 oil is shown in Table 3.5. A multiplicative correction
factor must be applied to the above costs when one uses fuels other than No.6
oil. The cost of employing LNB is relatively low. The repair cost for coal
combustion boilers is 15 times higher than for No.6 oil fueled boilers. This
is because of high maintenance and repair costs for the delivery system. On
the other hand, the operating cost is 30% less than for No.6 oil, because the
cost of coal is lower than heavy oil.

(ii) <u>Medium scale industrial boiler</u>. The average NO_x emission level
corrected to 4% oxygen in the flue for a medium scale industrial boiler (flue
gas volume from 5,000 to 40,000 m^3/h) without NO_x control is 220 ppm for No.6
oil (0.2%N) and 350 ppm for coal (1%N).

The appropriate types of NO_x control technology for medium scale industrial
boilers are nearly the same as for large scale boilers. However, water or
steam injection and emulsified oil fuel methods are also applicable. The NO_x
level can be reduced to 35 ppm for gaseous fuel, 100 ppm for liquid fuel and

Table 3.5

Reconstruction and operating cost for several NO_x control technologies applied to large scale industrial boilers

Applicable Technology	Reconstruction cost ($/10^3 m^3$/h)	Increase rate in operating cost (%)
FGR	325	50
TSC	125	30
LNB	100	0
FGR+TSC	450	80
TSC+LNB	200	30
FGR+LNB	425	50
FGR+TSC+LNB	525	80

FGR: Flue Gas Recirculation
TSC: Two Stage Combustion
LNB: Low NO_x Burner

230 ppm for coal.

The control costs are shown in Table 3.6. The cost of water or steam injection (WSI) is the lowest of the available methods. The cost per $10^3 m^3$ per hour of flue gas for medium scale boilers is 3 to 10 times higher than that for large scale boilers.

(iii) <u>Small-scale industrial boilers</u>. The average NO_x emission level corrected to 4% oxygen in the flue for small scale industrial boilers (flue gas volume under 5,000 m^3/h) is 240 ppm for No.6 heavy oil (0.2%N) and 350 ppm for coal (1%N).

Table 3.6

Reconstruction and operating cost for applying each NO_x control technology to medium scale industrial boiler

Applicable Technology	Reconstruction cost ($/10^3 m^3$/h)	Increase rate of operational cost (%)
FGR	850	50
TSC	350	30
LNB	1000	0
WSI	250	10
FGR+TSC	1250	80
TSC+LNB	1350	30
LNB+WSI	1250	10

WSI: Water or Steam Injection

Suitable types of NO_x control technology for small scale industrial boilers are "Two-stage combustion (TSC)", "Low NO_x burners (LNB)" and "Water or steam injection (WSI)". The flue gas recirculation method is not applicable to this scale of boiler. The NO_x level can be reduced to 25-40 ppm for gaseous fuel, 30 to 100 ppm for liquid fuel and 230 ppm for coal.

The costs are shown in Table 3.7.

Table 3.7

Reconstruction and operating cost for applying each NO_x control technologies applied to small scale industrial boiler

Applicable Technology	Reconstruction cost ($/10^3 m^3$/h)	Increase in operating cost (%)
TSC	850	30
LNB	1350	0
WSI	850	10
TSC+LNB	2150	30
LNB+WSI	2150	10
TSC+WSI	1650	40
TSC+LNB+WSI	3000	40

(iv) <u>Rotary cement kiln</u>. The temperatures in the rotary cement kiln are about 1450°C for the kiln body and 1800°C for the flame temperature. The NO_x emission level is as high as 800 to 1200 ppm without NO_x control technology. The conversion from No.6 oil to coal has progressed quickly in Japan and now more than 90% of all Japanese cement kilns use coal. However, the flame temperature cannot be changed easily since the product quality is closely related to the calcination temperature. Thermal NO_x cannot be controlled by decreasing flame temperature. Selective NO_x removal using a catalyst is also difficult since alkaline metals such as Na, K and Ca from the cement materials poison the catalyst. NO_x reduction in a conventional rotary cement kiln is difficult. The possibility exists for NO_x control in the new suspension preheater (NSP) rotary cement kiln. The NSP method is an improvement over the conventional suspension preheater (SP) method. In the NSP process, the calcination furnace is moved to a position between the suspension preheater and the rotary cement kiln as is shown in Fig. 3.12. About 40 to 60% of the total process fuel is consumed in the NSP calcination furnace for the decarbonization process which had previously been carried out in the rotary kiln for the conventional S.P. method. The advantages of the NSP process are that the kiln length can be shortened by 50% because the calcination section is separated from the kiln and thermal NO formation is reduced since the gas temperature

144

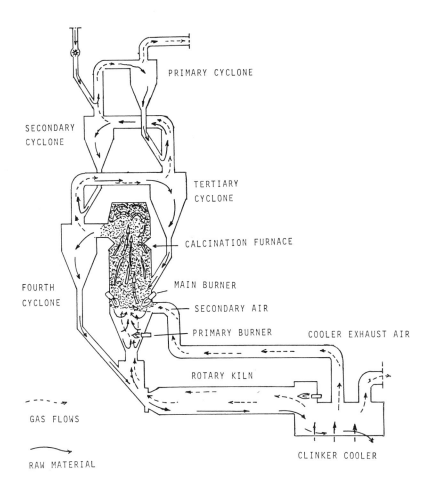

PRIMARY CYCLONE

SECONDARY
CYCLONE

TERTIARY
CYCLONE

CALCINATION FURNACE

FOURTH
CYCLONE

MAIN BURNER

SECONDARY AIR

PRIMARY BURNER

COOLER EXHAUST AIR

ROTARY KILN

GAS FLOWS

RAW MATERIAL

CLINKER COOLER

Fig. 3.12. New suspension preheater type cement kiln with denitration calciner.

during calcination is in the range 750-900°C. The appropriate method for reducing NO in the NSP kiln is by using the two-stage combustion method in the calcination furnace. Fuel-rich combustion or low excess air ratio combustion is used in the upstream part of the calcination furnace. Pulverized coal is injected through the primary burner and then secondary air from the clinker cooler is injected for downstream afterburning of unburnt species such as CO, hydrocarbon and soot. It has been reported that calcium particles act as a NO_x removal catalyst in the calcination furnace.[35] Reduction rates of 20-30% can be achieved by this method. The reduction rate is likely to be further improved since this technology is still being developed.

The annual repair and maintenance costs for the TSW method are $15,000 to $95,000 10^3 m^3/h. Accordingly, the total maintenance cost for a NSP plant of 110×10^3 m^3/h flue gas capacity is from $1.6 million to $10 million which is 3 to 13.0% of the total construction cost of the NSP plant.

(v) <u>Glass fusion furnaces</u>. Glass fusion furnaces are classified into continuous tank furnaces and batch-type crucible furnaces. In a continuous tank furnace, the combustion air is usually preheated to 1000-1300°C. As a result, the flame temperature is increased to 1700-1800°C and the furnace temperature is 1400-1550°C. The emission level of NO_x may reach 800-2000 ppm without NO_x control technology. NO_x emission levels from a batch-type crucible furnace are 100-150 ppm because the flame temperature ranges from 1300 to 1400°C. Therefore, NO from the continuous tank furnace is mainly thermal NO based on the Zeldovich mechanism. However, a fuel NO contribution of 100-150 ppm is also expected since No.6 oil containing 0.1-0.2 wt.% N is the usual fuel.

The stringent combustion conditions of the glass furnace greatly restrict the application of ordinary NO_x control technology. For example, NO_x control based on a lower flame temperature is ruled out because of the high flame temperature required for glass fusion. Methods based on the formation of a local reducing region in the furnace cannot be used because of the soot contamination produced in the reducing region which lowers the glass quality. Catalytic NO_x removal is not suitable since the flue gas has high dust and SO_x levels. The NH_3 removal method is unsuitable since excess NH_3 from the process corrodes the furnace lining. The low excess air ratio method is the only suitable method for thermal NO suppression under the high temperature, oxidizing conditions of a glass furnace. In order to reduce the air ratio to near 1.0 without soot formation a burner capable of thorough atomization is required. For this purpose, the ultrasonic burner was developed by the Nippon-Gaishi Kogyo company. This burner achieves good atomization using ultrasonic waves generated by a resonator located at the exit of the atomizing air. The pressurized oil burner has also been developed for the same purpose. The pressurized oil burner can form the thin fan type flame required for high heat efficiency. The NO reduction rate of this burner is 20 to 30%.

The maintenance costs of the pressurized oil burner are $15,000-$20,000 10^3 m^3/h flue gas. This relatively high cost is due to the high pressure pipe system needed, although the fuel cost is decreased by 20-30% due to the high heat efficiency.

(vi) <u>Waste incinerators</u>. The NO emission level from incinerators of city garbage is 150 to 200 ppm without NO_x control technology. City incinerators produce mainly fuel NO since city garbage includes high nitrogen content compounds such as proteins and the combustion chamber temperature is controlled

between 700 and 900°C. There are two types of waste incinerator. The
multi-stage type and the fluidized bed type. The two stage combustion method
is the most suitable NO_x control technology for waste incinerators. NO
emissions can be reduced by 40% when this method is incorporated in the
original design of the incinerator and by 20-30% when the method is applied to
an existing incinerator.

The non-catalytic reducing method using NH_3 is also suitable for
incinerators. This method reduces NO by around 50%.

The maintenance costs for the non-catalytic method are around $20,000/10^3$
m^3/h flue gas while the operational cost is 25-100 mill per 1t waste.

(vii) <u>Heating furnaces for metal rolling</u>. The NO_x emission level from a
metal rolling heating furnace is 70-120 ppm for gaseous fuel, 70-140 ppm for
liquid fuel and 400 ppm for coal without NO_x control technology.

Types of NO_x control technology for a medium scale industrial heating
furnace include "Two-stage combustion" and the "Low NO_x burner". The NO_x level
can be reduced to 30-50 ppm for gaseous fuel, 30-80 ppm for liquid fuel, and
230 ppm for coal by using TSC and LNB in combination.

(viii) <u>Lime kilns</u>. The average NO_x emission level from a lime baking
furnace without NO_x control technology is 100 ppm for No.6 oil (0.2%N)
combustion and 300 ppm for coal (1%N) combustion.

Types of Technology suitable for NO_x reduction from a lime burning furnace
are "Flue gas recirculation", "Two stage combustion" and the "Low NO_x burner".
The NO_x level can be reduced to 40-60 ppm for liquid fuel and 250 ppm for coal
by using them in combination.

(ix) <u>Metal fusion furnace for aluminum degumming</u>. The average NO_x emission
level from a metal fusion furnace for aluminum degumming is 300 ppm at 10%
oxygen in the flue for No.6 oil combustion (0.2%N) without NO_x control
technology.

The types of technology suitable for NO_x reduction from a metal fusion
furnace are "Two-stage combustion" and the "The low NO_x burner". The NO_x level
can be reduced to 180 ppm for No.4 oil and 230 ppm for No.6 heavy oil by using
the above methods in combination.

3.3 SO_x EMISSION CONTROL FROM STATIONARY SOURCES

In Japan, the problem of oxides of sulfur (SO_x) from industry was first
publicly recognized in the early 1960s when citizens in Yokkaichi suffered from
an asthma caused by sulfur oxides emitted from a chemical complex located near
the city. This asthma was called "Yokkaich Zensoku". SO_x emission standards
for stationary sources were established in 1962 and have been revised downward
more than 15 times so far. In order to comply with the emission regulations,
facilities have progressively converted from high sulfur oil to low sulfur oil.

Flue gas desulfurization processes have been developed and installed in more than 1100 stationary SO_x sources. As a result, SO_x levels in the atmosphere have decreased to one third of the original peak level in the ensuing twenty years. For SO_x, both emission regulation and the development of sulfur control technology have worked effectively. However, the global SO_x problem has not yet been solved, as is evidenced by acid rain. Conventional desulfurization technology which was developed mainly for power plants in Japan cannot be straightforwardly applied to stationary sources in other parts of the world such as Europe and China since the scale of facilities is different, SO_x emission levels are different and the costs are different. Conventional technology is usually too expensive to use for a small stationary source. From this point of view, desulfurization technology is not yet fully mature and must be further developed to fill these various needs. The need for economical technology is especially pressing.

In this section, representative established technology will first be introduced and then developing technology will be discussed.

3.3.1 Sources of SO_x

SO_x sources may be classified into natural sources such as volcanoes and artificial sources such as power plant boilers. Artificial sources contribute about 50% to the total atmospheric sulfur burden. The influence of artificial sources on human health is more severe than the above figure indicates since artificial sources are usually located near human residential areas. The contribution of artificial sources varies from one country to another. However, the contribution of combustion facilities is significant compared to other sources in the U.S.A. and Japan.

Table 3.8 shows the typical sulfur content of gaseous, liquid and solid fuels. Note that the sulfur content in residual oil and coal is considerably

Table 3.8

Sulfur content in fuels

Fuel	Sulfur content (wt%)
Crude oil (Middle East)	1.3-4.2
No.6 heavy oil	0.16-3.4
No.4 heavy oil	0.10-1.79
light oil	0.06-0.90
kerosene	0.0-0.32
coal	0.5-2.0
LPG, City gas	0.02

higher than other fuels. Unlike NO_x, all of the SO_x from a combustion facility comes from the sulfur originally contained in the fuel. According to our study[36], the conversion rate of fuel sulfur to SO_x ranges from 70 to 90% for pulverized coal combustion. Another 10 to 30% of fuel sulfur is retained by the fly ash. Hence, the emission level of SO_x can be predicted from the sulfur content in the fuel.

The form of sulfur compound in the fuel varies from fuel to fuel. The sulfur in heavy oil is in the form of polycyclic sulfide, as shown in Fig. 3.13. Sulfur compounds in coal are classified into inorganic and organic sulfur compounds. The inorganic sulfur consists of sulfate ($CaSO_4$, $FeSO_4$, $BaSO_4$, etc.), sulfide (PbS, ZnS, FeS, CaS etc.) and free sulfur[8] of the inorganic sulfur compounds, iron pyrites (FeS_2) predominates. The organic sulfur is bonded chemically to the carbonaceous coal substrate.

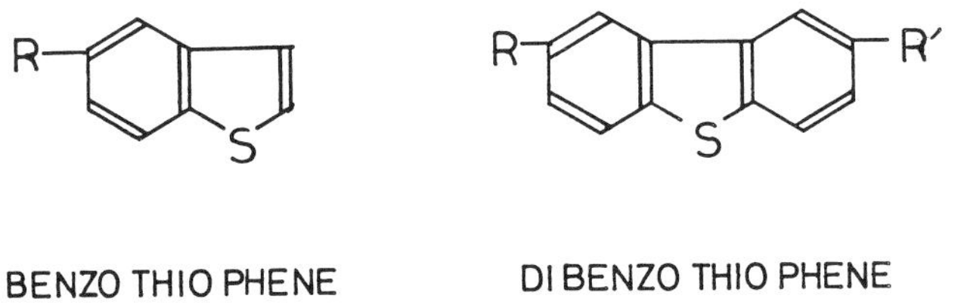

BENZO THIO PHENE   **DI BENZO THIO PHENE**

Fig. 3.13. Typical polycyclic sulfide in heavy oil.

3.3.2 Formation and behavior of SO_x in the combustion furnace

The conversion from fuel sulfur to SO_x is largely carried out during combustion in the furnace. The fuel sulfur is initially converted to SO_2 during combustion. However, for fuel-rich combustion, the fuel sulfur is partly converted to H_2S (hydrogen sulfide) which is easily oxidized to SO_2 in the excess oxygen conditions found downstream. The fuel sulfur is, however, partly converted to SO_3. The SO_3 is, then, converted to sulfuric acid in the downstream low temperature region and causes the corrosion of the metal surfaces of the heat exchanger. The SO_3 also tends to form fine particles of sulfuric acid under humid, low temperature conditions. These particles easily bypass the desulfurization process and cause respiratory troubles after they are released into the atmosphere.[32] The emission of SO_3 may influence the behavior and level of other pollutants, for example, submicron fly ash or mercury in coal combustion. An increase of the SO_3 level also improves the collection efficiency of fly ash by an electrostatic precipitator.[37] This is because the condensation of sulfuric acid decreases the electrical resistivity of fly ash to the optimum level for high collection efficiency. It has also been shown that both sulfur and mercury are condensed on the soot carbon rather than the mineral fly ash.[38] The mechanism of mercury condensation may be as follows. Sulfur is condensed on the soot carbon particle in the form of hydrogen sulfide or sulfuric acid and, then, mercury vapor is absorbed by hydrogen sulfide or sulfuric acid. The selective condensation of sulfur on the soot particles was shown by Okazaki.[39]

The emission level of SO_3 from the combustion of natural fuel containing 5.5 wt.% of sulfur is around 40 ppm.[40] On the other hand, the emission of SO_3 from pulverized coal combustion is lower than that of heavy oil. This is because the SO_3 condenses to form sulfuric acid on the surface of soot carbon and submicron fly ash particles.

The SO_3 is formed mainly in the flame zone by the oxidation of SO_2 by super-equilibrium oxygen radicals. Hence, the most important variable influencing SO_3 emission is the air ratio since the oxygen level in the flame zone is determined by the air ratio. Fig. 3.14 shows the effect of air ratio on SO_3 emission for gas combustion. It clearly shows that low air ratio combustion is effective for the control of SO_3 as well as NO. Hence, the air ratio can be used to control SO_3 emission levels.

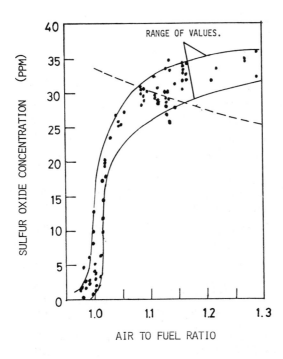

Fig. 3.14. Effect of excess air on sulfur oxide emission from gas combustion.[19]

3.3.3 SO_x control technology

Desulfurization technology is classified into wet and dry processes similar to NO_x removal processes. However, the desulfurization process most commonly used in power plant boilers is the wet process. The advantage of the wet process is that it can be used on dirty flue gas with high particle burdens while still realizing a high reduction rate. On the other hand, the wet process requires a large scale absorbing tower to provide the large surface contact area between flue gas and absorbing liquid. Because of this, the construction cost for the wet process approaches half the cost of the main combustion furnace. Furthermore, the wet process requires extensive water treatment to remove or recover the final product and consequently it needs large amounts of fresh water. Utility costs are therefore high. Another disadvantage of the wet process is that the collection efficiency of the sulfuric acid mist which is formed from SO_3 is low. The SO_3 is sometimes more toxic than SO_2.

The development of a dry process to replace the wet process continues. Unlike NO, it is impossible to convert SO_x to a nontoxic, stable, gaseous species. The final product must be a solid such as $CaSO_4$, Na_2SO_4, $MgSO_4$. Therefore, the dry process needs the solid-gas reaction. This type of reaction is generally very slow in the low temperature region of flue compared to a catalytic reaction such as $NO-NH_3$ in the NO_x removal process. A large scale reactor is needed compared to the catalytic reactor of the NO_x removal process. Furthermore, the handling of solid particles or powder is necessary in this process since the reaction product has to be continuously purged from the reactor and recycled solid particles have to be fed into the reactor. For all of these reasons, development of the dry process has not been completed yet.

Next, we will introduce examples of established desulfurization processes and then we will discuss the newly developing dry process.

(i) The lime and gypsum method. This is the representative wet process. The operating principle is the removal of SO_x by contacting the flue gas with a lime slurry. Initially, SO_2 in the flue gas is absorbed by reaction with the lime slurry and converted to $CaSO_4$.

$$CaCO_3 + SO_2 + 1/2 \ O_2 = CaSO_4 + CO_2$$
$$CaCO_3 + 2SO_2 + H_2O = Ca(HSO_3)_2 + CO_2$$

The acid calcium sulfite ($Ca(HSO_3)_2$) is finally oxidized by air in the oxidizing tower to form gypsum ($CaSO_4$) which can sometimes be utilized commercially in cement or gypsum board. This method has the advantage of not requiring expensive chemicals such as caustic soda. This process is especially attractive in Japan where the cost of lime is relatively low. Another advantage is that soot and fly ash which are not collected by the electrostatic precipitator can be caught at the absorbant tower. The disadvantage of this process is that special care has to be taken to avoid problems with the scale caused by the lime slurry.

This process has been frequently used in large scale boiler desulfurization processes such as power plant boilers.

The SO_x removal rates approach 70% for this process.

(ii) <u>The soda method</u>. The principle of this method is to remove SO_2 by contacting flue gas with an aqueous NaOH solution using a conventional gas-liquid contact unit such as a packed column, a spray tower, or a venturi type scrubber.

Initially, the SO_x is absorbed by reaction with the aqueous NaOH solution and converted to Na_2SO_3 as follows.

$$NaOH + SO_2 = NaHSO_3$$
$$NaHSO_3 + NaOH = Na_2SO_3 + H_2O$$

Na_2SO_3 is oxidized by air to Glauber's salt (Na_2SO_4) in the oxidizing tower. The Glauber's salt is sometimes recovered and sold. The advantage of this process is the lack of scale problems found in the lime-gypsum method. The disadvantage of this process is that it requires expensive chemicals such as NaOH.

This method is suitable for small scale facilities. There are many units in operation since the system is relatively simple.

(iii) <u>Active carbon absorption method</u>. Active carbon absorption is currently the typical dry process. In this process SO_x is absorbed in the flue using the activated carbon. SO_2 in the flue gas is initially absorbed onto the active carbon. The oxidation of SO_2 to SO_3 takes place in the active carbon and finally the SO_3 is reacted with H_2O in the flue gas and changed to H_2SO_4. The absorbed sulfur is purged from the carbon by heating it up to 400°C or by contacting with water and recovering the sulfuric acid.

This method is still very costly. The cost is primarily determined by the cost of the active carbon. The success of this process depends on the development of a cheap and efficient active carbon source.

(iv) <u>Direct desulfurization method</u>. The ideal method of controlling SO_x is to directly remove SO_x in the furnace without a flue gas desulfurization process. To this end, numerous studies of desulfurization in fluidized bed coal combustion (FBC) have been undertaken. This method is very different from other desulfurization technology and the early development of direct desulfurization in FBC has been carried out mainly in Europe rather than in Japan. Direct desulfurization in FBC is expected to solve the difficulties of dry process SO_x removal.

In this method $CaCO_3$ is put directly into the bed so that simultaneous combustion and desulfurization occurs. The reaction scheme is as follows. $CaCO_3$ is thermally cracked to CaO and CO_2 at temperatures between 750°C and

152

1000°C.

$$CaCO_3 = CaO + CO_2$$

Then, CaO absorbes SO_2 to form $CaSO_4$ in the presence of oxygen

$$CaO + SO_2 + 1/2\ O_2 = CaSO_4$$

In some experiments, the optimum temperature region for the above reaction was found to be 800°C to 900°C. If the above desulfurization reaction can be completed in the bed, then flue gas desulfurization is unnecessary. However, a serious problem was found in the research and development process. Fig. 3.15 shows the effect of the mole ratio of calcium to sulfur on the desulfurization rate . The reduction rate at a Ca/S ratio of 1 is only 30 to 50% which is insufficient for practical use. A Ca/S ratio of at least 4 to 5 is necessary in order to attain a reduction rate of 95% which is equivalent to that of a wet process. A Ca/S ratio of 5 means that 50 kg of $CaCO_3$ is required to burn 100 kg coal. The cost of supplying $CaCO_3$ and recovering or treating the solid effluent stream is prohibitive. Unless this ratio can be reduced to near the stoichiometric rato (Ca/S=1), this method will not be implemented. There have been efforts to overcome this problem - for example; using finely pulverized $CaCO_3$ particles of about 10 micron diameter to create a large surface area for reaction, or by using an artificial desulfurizing agent such as portland cement particles[42] instead of $CaCO_3$, or by pretreatment of the desulfurization agent by NaCl.[43] These trials have not yet been successful. The reader may

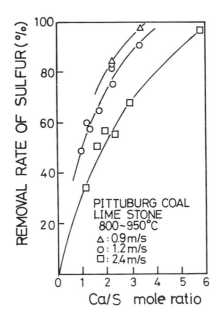

Fig. 3.15. Effect of Ca/S ratio on desufurization rate.[20]

understand that numerous problems have to be solved to develop direct desulfurization of fluidized bed coal combustion in the future.

3.3.4 The cost of desulfurization processes

The construction cost of the wet desulfurization process is plotted against the plant size expressed by the flue gas volume to be treated in Fig. 3.16. The construction cost is proportional to the flue gas volume to be treated to the order of 0.8. The construction cost of the desulfurization unit for a 1000 MW power plant is from 65 million dollars to 110 million dollars. In general, the construction cost of the wet desulfurization process is three times higher than that of the dry NO_x removal process using NH_3 and catalyst.

The actual construction costs of wet type desulfurization units constructed after 1982 are shown in Table 3.9. All of the processes listed in Table 3.9 are lime and gypsum processes. The average cost is around $100/kw which is twice or three times that of the NO_x removal process for a coal combustion facility. This is because the desulfurization process requires large scale facilities such as the absorbing tower compared to the NO_x removal process. The construction cost does not vary with the type of flue gas for the

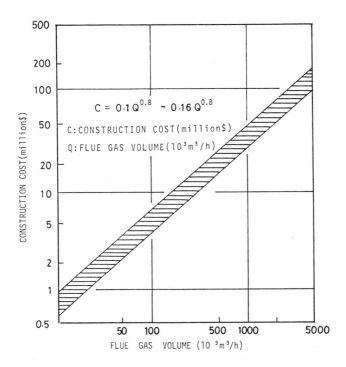

Fig. 3.16. Construction cost of wet deslfurization plant.[23)]

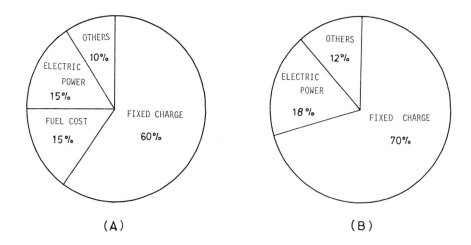

Fig. 3.17. Breakdown of the total annual cost of flue gas desulfurization[10] (A) after burner, (B) air-air heater

Table 3.9
Cost of desulfurization process[10]

Name of boiler	A	B	C	D
Fuel	Heavy oil	Heavy oil	Mixture of Coal and oil	Coal
Boiler power (MW)	85	13	600	700
Inlet SO_2 (ppm)	1500	1500	1000	600-700
Outlet SO_2 (ppm)	35	5	40	30-35
Reduction rate (%)	98	99.7	96	95
Inlet dust (mg/Nm^3)	180	150	150	30-150
Outlet dust (mg/Nm^3)	40	70-80	45	10-20
Reduction rate (%)	78	50	70	70-80
Construction cost ($/kw)	90	95	105	100

desulfurization process. That is, the costs for the coal combustion facilities C and D were the same as those of the heavy oil combustion facilities A and B.

The breakdown of the total annual cost is shown in Fig. 3.17A for the case of afterburners and in Fig. 3.17B for the case of using an air-air heater system to reheat flue gas. In both cases, fixed charges account for more than half the total cost. The cost for the electric power accounts for 15 to 18% of the total cost. The electricity is used primarily for fan power.

REFERENCES

1. Ogasawara, M. et al., Kikai Gakkai Ronbunshu, $\underline{39}$, 3427 (1973)
2. Baulch, D.L. et al., High Temperature Rate Data No.4., Dept. of Physical Chemistry, The Univ. of Leeds, England (1969)
3. Breen, B.P., Thirteenth Symposium (International) on Combustion, p391, The Combustion Institute (1971)
4. Ogasawara, M., et al., Kikai Gakkai Ronbunshu, $\underline{39}$, 3417 (1973)
5. Fenimore, C.P., Thirteenth Symposium (International) on Combustion, p373, The Combustion Institute (1971)
6. Iverach, D., Fourteenth Symposium (International) on Combustion, p767, The Combustion Institute (1973)
7. Sadakata, M. and J.M. Beer, Sixteenth Symposium (International) on Combustion, p93, The Combustion Institute (1977)
8. Nihon Kikai Gakkai, "Formation Mechanisms and Controls of Pollutants in Combustion Systems" Nihon Kikai Gakkai, Tokyo (1980)
9. Fenimore, C.P., Combust. Flame, $\underline{19}$, 289 (1972)
10. Takagi, T., et al., Nihon Kikai Gakkai Ronbunshu, $\underline{44}$, 4282 (1978)
11. Kato, K., et al., Nihon Kikai Gakkai Ronbunshu, $\underline{42}$, 582 (1976)
12. Fine, H.D., et al., Fuel, $\underline{53}$, 120 (1974)
13. Kato, K., et al., "Challenge to NO_x", Energy saving center (1976)
14. Turner, D.W., et al., AIChE Symposium Series, $\underline{68}$, 55 (1972)
15. Sadakata, M., et al., Eighteenth Symposium (International) on Combustion, p65, The Combustion Institute (1981)
16. Pershing, D.W. and J.O.L. Wendt, Sixteenth Symposium on Combustion, p389, The Combustion Institute (1976)
17. Pohl, J.H. and A.F.Sarofim, Sixteenth Symposium (International) on Combustion, p491, The Combustion Institute (1977)
18. Sadakata, M., et al., Kagaku Kogaku Ronbunshu, $\underline{10}$, 150 (1984)
19. Tokuda, K., Text of Short Courses of Chyugoku and Shikoku Branch of Japan Society of Mechanical Engineers, p1 (1981)
20. Aoyagi, M. and D. Kunii, Chemical (20) Aoyagi, M. azommunication, $\underline{1}$, 191 (1974)
21. Furusawa, T., et al., J. Chem. Eng. Japan, $\underline{11}$, 377 (1978)
22. Gibbs, B.M., et al., Sixteenth Symposium (International) on Combustion, p461, The Combustion Institute (1976)
23. Takahashi, K., Netsukanri to Kogai, $\underline{26}$, 12, 37 (1974)
24. Sadakata, M., et al., Kagaku Kogaku Ronbushu, $\underline{5}$, 111 (1979)
25. Wendt, J.O.L., et al., Seventeenth Symposium (International) on Combustion, p77, The Combustion Institute (1978)
26. Osaka Kagaku Gijutsu Center, "Chisso Sankabutsu ni yoru Osenjittai to Boshi Gijutsu no Genjyo", Kagaku Joho Sha (1973)
27. Myerson, A.L., Fifteenth Symposium (International) on Combustion, p1085, The Combustion Institute (1975)
28. Okigami, N., et al., Preprint of the Fourteenth Japanese Symposium on Combustion, p21 (1976)
29. Takahashi, K., et al., Mitsubishi Juko Giho, $\underline{17}$, 6, 929 (1980)
30. Lyon, R.K., Inst. J. Chem. Kin., $\underline{8}$, 315 (1976)
31. Sema, T., et al., Karyoku-Genshiryoku Hatsuden, $\underline{29}$, 219 (1978)
32. Ando, J., "Fuel Conversion and SO_x.NO_x Removal Technology", p185, Project News sha, Tokyo (1983)
33. Mistubishi Research Institute, "Research of NO_x Control Technology from Stationary Sources" Saitama Ken (1982)
34. Matsuda, Y., Kobe Seiko Giho, $\underline{30}$, 2, 34 (1980)
35. Tsujimura, M., et al., J. Chem. Eng., Japan, $\underline{16}$, 132 (1983)
36. Kagaku Kogaku Kyokai, "Sekitan Syubetsu Taiki Osen Huka Hyoka Cyosa Hokokusho" Kagaku Kogaku Kyokai, Japan (1982)
37. Masuda, S., Preprints of the 47th Annual Meeting of The Soc. of Chem. Engrs., Japan, Tokyo, p200 (1982)
38. Oshiyama, et al., Preprint of the 50th annual Meeting of The Soc. of Chem. Engrs., Japan, p219 (1985)

156

39. Okazaki, K., et al., Kagaku Kogaku Ronbunshu, <u>10</u>, 751 (1984)
40. Hedley, A.B., J. Inst. Fuel, Apr., 142 (1967)
41. Highley, J., Institute of Fuel, Sympo. Series, No.1, PAP/D (1975)
42. Albaneese, et al., Proc. 6th Int. Conf. on FBC, Vol.III, (1980), p1060
43. Shearer, J.A., et al., Environ. Sci. & Tech., <u>13</u>, 113 (1979)
44. Nihon Sangyo Kikai Kogyokai, "Sekitan Riyo Shisetsu Nado Haisyutu Jyokyo Jittai Chyosa Hokokusho" Nihon Sangyo Kikai Kogyokai (1983)

Chapter 4

MONITORING AND SIMULATION

YUKIO YANAGISAWA

4.1 CONTINUOUS MONITORING

As mentioned in earlier chapters, there are air quality standards for five
air pollutants in Japan, that is, sulfur dioxide (SO_2), carbon monoxide (CO),
suspended particulate matter (SPM), photochemical oxidants (O_x), and nitrogen
dioxide (NO_2). The measurement methods for these pollutants discussed in this
chapter are employed at more than 1,000 monitoring stations in Japan.

In addition to these pollutants, measurement methods for nitric oxide (NO)
and non-methane hydrocarbons (NMHC), which are measured at several hundred
monitoring stations, will be mentioned briefly.

4.1.1 Sulfur dioxide

Sulfur dioxide is produced by the oxidation of sulfur in fossil fuels during
combustion. The conductometric method is taken as the reference method for
SO_2 measurement in Japan. As substances which are electrolytes in aqueous
solution affect the conductivity of the solution, the observed change in the
conductivity of the solution will be the sum of the effects of all the ions in
the solution. If the concentrations of all other electrolyzing gases are
assumed to be either constant or relatively insignificant, the change in the
conductivity can be related to the SO_2 concentration.

After passing through a dust filter and a flow meter, an air sample is
introduced into an absorbing solution of hydrogen peroxide. Sulfur dioxide gas
reacts with hydrogen peroxide:
$$SO_2 + H_2O_2 = H_2SO_4 = 2H^+ + SO_4^{2-} \qquad (1)$$
The increased conductivity produced by the additional hydrogen and sulfate ions
is related to the sulfur dioxide concentration. The hydrogen peroxide solution
is acidified with 1×10^{-5} N sulfuric acid to reduce the interference from CO_2.
Air pollutants such as Cl_2, HCl, NO_2, H_2S, and HF produce positive errors in SO_2
measurements, while NH_3 produces negative errors. High concentrations of
ammonia gas are often found in industrial areas and farming regions. In such
areas, an ammonia scrubber made of ion-exchange membrane or oxalic acid pellets

is added prior to the SO_2 absorption to eliminate the NH_3 interference.

The pararosaniline wet chemical method is employed as a reference method in the USA. Sulfur dioxide in the air sample is absorbed in a potassium tetrachloromercurate solution and converted to a monochlorosulfonatomercurate complex. Pararosaniline and formaldehyde react with the complex to form pararosaniline methyl sulphonic acid which is an intensely colored dye. The absorption of the dye is measured spectrophotometrically at 560nm.

4.1.2 Nitrogen oxides

Six types of oxidized nitrogen are chemically stable, including N_2O, NO, N_2O_3, NO_2, N_2O_5 and NO_3. Nitrogen dioxide (NO_2) and nitric oxide (NO), which are primarily generated by combustion, are considered to be air pollutants. Nitrogen oxides (NO_x) by convention are indicated as the sum of NO and NO_2 concentrations. Nitrogen oxides in ambient air can be measured either by wet chemical or by chemiluminescent methods.

The use of Saltzman reagent, which is one of the wet chemical methods, is the reference method for measurements of NO_2 and NO in Japan. Nitrogen dioxide in the air sample is absorbed in the Griess-Saltzman azo-dye-forming reagent (a mixture of sulfanilic acid, N-(1-naphthyl)-ethylenediamine dihydrochloride and acetic acid) which develops a red-purple color. The amount of reduced NO_2 in the solution is determined spectrophotometrically by measurement at 550nm. Nitrogen dioxide reacts with the azo-dye-forming reagent as follows:

$$2NO_2 + H_2O = HNO_2 + HNO_3 \qquad (2)$$

$$2NO_2 + H_2N - \bigcirc - SO_3H + CH_3COOH =$$

$$CH_3COON_2 - \bigcirc - SO_3H + HNO_2 + H_2O + (1/2)O_2 \quad (3)$$

$$HNO_2 + H_2N - \bigcirc - SO_3H + CH_3COOH =$$

$$CH_3COON_2 - \bigcirc - SO_3H + 2H_2O \qquad (4)$$

$$CH_3COON_2 - \bigcirc - SO_3H + \bigcirc - NH(CH_2)_2NH_2 =$$

$$HO_3S - \bigcirc - N = N - \bigcirc - NH(CH_2)_2NH_2 + CH_3COOH \quad (5)$$

If reactions (2), (4), and (5) occur, 2 moles of NO_2 produce 1 mole of azo-dye and if reactions (3), (4), and (5) occur, 2 moles of NO_2 are converted to 2 moles of azo-dye. The conversion ratio of NO_2 molecules to azo-dye molecules is 0.5 in the first case and 1.0 in the second case. As both reactions occur simultaneously in actual measurement, the ratio is usually empirically determined in practice. The ratio was reported as 0.72 in

Saltzman's original paper, but the value of 0.84 is currently used in Japan.

NO does not react with the azo-dye-forming reagent, but can be measured by oxidising to NO_2 by passing through acidic potassium permanganate solution. In the continuous Saltzman monitor, nitrogen dioxide in the air sample is absorbed by the azo-dye-forming reagent after passing through a filter and a flow meter. The absorption of the developed color produced by the reaction between NO_2 and the reagent is measured to determine the NO_2 concentration in the air sample. The remaining air containing NO is introduced into an oxidation chamber. Finally it is bubbled through more azo-dye-forming reagent where the oxidized NO reacts to form the azo-dye complex. Average concentrations of NO_2 and NO are measured by replacing the azo-dye-forming reagent contained at hourly intervals. Sampling of NO and NO_2 and development of color are done simultaneously in the Saltzman method.

In the Jacobs-Hachheiser method or its modification, NO_2 in the air sample is collected in a sodium hydroxide solution for 24 hours and subsequently analyzed in the laboratory by adding a mixture of phosphoric acid, sulfanilamide and N-(1-naphthyl)-ethylenediamine dihydrochloride. The absorption of the resultant colored solution is measured at 540nm.

In addition to these wet chemical procedures for NO_2 analysis, a gas phase chemiluminescent method has been used widely in recent years. Fundamentally, the wet chemical procedure analyzes NO_2, while the chemiluminescent method measures NO concentration as follows:

$$NO + O_3 = NO_2^* + O_2 \qquad\qquad (6)$$
$$NO_2^* = NO_2 + h\nu \qquad\qquad (7)$$

NO in filtered air sample is drawn into the reaction vessel and rapidly mixed with O_3. Chemiluminescent reactions (6) and (7) take place in the vessel and the intensity of the emitted light is measured by a photo-multiplier tube. For NO_2 analysis, the air sample containing NO and NO_2 is introduced into a converter to reduce NO_2 to NO. The reduced gas is then directed into the reaction vessel. Thus NO_x concentration is measured and NO_2 concentration can be calculated by subtracting the concentration of NO from that for NO_x.

4.1.3 Carbon monoxide

Carbon monoxide is produced by incomplete combustion. The carbon monoxide concentration in ambient air can be measured by non-dispersive infrared absorption or by a gas chromatographic method.

The non-dispersive infrared absorption method is the Japanese reference method. Molecules of different elements such as CO absorb infrared radiation at specific wavelengths, so non-dispersive infrared spectroscopy can be used for measuring CO. Infrared radiation is passed through two cells, a sample cell and a reference cell. Pure nitrogen gas is contained in the reference

160

cell, while CO in the air sample is pumped through the sample cell. The CO in
the air sample absorbs some of the infrared radiation at a specific wavelength
while the remaining infrared energy passes through to a dual cell detector
located behind the sample and reference cells. The dual cell detector is
filled with pure CO so that it is sensitive only to the infrared radiation at
the absorbing wavelength. The detector cells are separated by a thin metallic
film. The infrared beams passing through the sample cell and the reference
cell are separately absorbed by each cell of the detector. The detector on the
sample cell side receives less energy than that on the reference cell side due
to the removal of energy by CO in the air sample. The thin metallic film is
displaced to compensate for the difference in pressure of pure CO gas on both
sides caused by the inbalance of the intensity of the impinging infrared beams.
The displacement causes the change in capacitance which generates an electrical
signal.

The gas chromatographic method with a flame ionization detector (FID) can
also be used to measure CO in ambient air. Volatile organic compounds are
measured by the FID by introducing samples into a hydrogen flame burning in
air. Proportional changes in an induced electric field across the flame are
measured as the volatile compounds burn in the flame. Carbon monoxide, which
is not detected by the FID, is first reduced to methane in a catalytic column
and then detected by the FID after it has been separated from other compounds
in the sample by a separation column.

4.1.4 Photochemical oxidising agent (Ozone)

The neutral, buffered, potassium iodide method (NBKI) is used as the
reference method for oxidising agents in Japan. The absorption of oxidising
substances, mainly ozone, in the neutral buffered potassium iodide solution
yields iodine by the following reaction:

$$2 \, KI + H_2O + O_3 = I_2 + 2KOH + O_2 \qquad (8)$$

The absorption of iodine at 365 nm indicates the concentration of the oxidising
agents in the air sample.

In a continuous oxidising agent monitor. The filtered sample reaches the
absorption vessel through a CrO_3 oxidizer where sulfur dioxide in the air
sample is oxidised to sulfuric acid. Sulfur dioxide interferes with the
oxidising agent measurements by reducing the iodine produced by reaction (8).
In the absorption vessel, the air sample and potassium iodide solution flow in
a counter-current direction. The absorption of the potassium iodide solution
before and after contact with the air sample are compared and the difference
indicates the concentration of oxidising agents in the air sample.

The solution is repeatedly used after removing iodine by means of an
activated charcoal filter. Nitrogen dioxide and nitric oxide which are

oxidised by the CrO_3 oxidiser produce a positive error in the oxidising agents measurements.

The chemiluminescent analytical procedure is based on the chemiluminescent reaction of ozone with ethylene. Ethylene and ambient air containing ozone are introduced into a mixing vessel where the ozone reacts quantitatively with the ethylene to emit light, which is detected by a photomultiplier tube.

4.1.5 Suspended particulate matter

Suspended particulate matter is defined as suspended particles of diameter less than 10 μm. Particles smaller than 10 μm are respirable and remain suspended in the atmosphere for a significant period of time. The reference method for measuring the suspended particulate matter specifies the use of a low volume sampler to draw air at a flow rate of 20 l/min through a glass fiber filter for 24 - 48 hours. The mass concentration of the suspended particulate matter is calculated in $\mu g/m_3$ from the mass of collected particles and the volume of air sampled. A cyclone or a cascade impactor is used to exclude particles larger than 10 μm from the air stream prior to the fiber filter.

Errors in this method mainly come from 1) weighting errors, 2) non-uniform air flow and 3) non-uniformity of the separation of fine and coarse particles. A difference in the water content in the filter before and after the sampling is one of the basic errors encountered in weighing. The filters should be allowed to reach equilibrium at the same temperature and humidity prior to each weighing. If the filters are stored for a long time after sampling, mass may be lost due to evaporation of volatile substances. Static charges sometimes cause positive or negative errors in the mass measurement of lightly loaded filters. Therefore, any static charge on the filter should be neutralized with a Po^{210} source. A sharp decrease in air flow may occur during sampling if the particulate matter is oily or wet. The air flow rate should be checked frequently or controlled electronically. Non-uniformity of the separation of fine and coarse particles results in large deviations of the mass concentration in the presence of coarse particulates, since the mass of a particle of unit density is proportional to the cube of its diameter.

Suspended particulate matter can be measured by methods other than gravimetric measurement. The attenuation of beta radiation can be applied to the mass concentration measurement. Direct reading instruments for real time measurement include the light scattering method and the piezo-balance method. These methods are also the reference methods in Japan within the range where they show linear relation with the gravimetric method. The scattered light intensity of a single particle is a function of its particle diameter (d), refractive index and the wavelength (x) of the light used. For particles

162

which are small in diameter d compared with the wavelength x, the scattering intensity is directly proportional to d^6 and inversely proportional to x^4. With increasing particle diameter, its dependence on the particle diameter becomes less. If the characteristics of the sample particles, such as diameter distribution, refractive index and absorption efficiency of light, are reproducible, the light scattering method may be employed for ambient air monitoring after calibration against the gravimetric method. In the piezo-balance method, particles are pumped to a quartz crystal surface and deposited on it by electrostatic precipitation. The mass change of the crystal in an oscillator circuit changes its resonant frequency; the rate of frequency change reflects particulate mass concentration in the air sample. In applying this method to ambient air monitoring, loss of sensitivity due to high particle loading on the crystal surface and interference of absorbed water vapor should be taken into account.

4.1.6 Non-methane hydrocarbons

Various kinds of hydrocarbons are found in the atmosphere. Some of these are carcinogens and/or take part in photochemical oxidation.

Methane is a natural atmospheric gas exceeding 1 ppm which is released by the activity of methane producing bacteria, so only non-methane hydrocarbons are considered to be air pollutants. Many techniques using gas chromatography with a flame ionization detector (FID) have been developed for total non-methane hydrocarbon analysis and for specific hydrocarbon components.

Two types of GC/FID configurations have been used in Japan for automated analysis of ambient non-methane hydrocarbons; one is a differential method and the other is a direct method. In the differential method, the concentration of non-methane hydrocarbons is determined by subtracting the methane concentration from the concentration of total hydrocarbons (THC). The air sample is first introduced directly into the detector for the THC analysis, then sample of methane provided from a separation column is fed to the detector by a switching valve. Oxygen can interfere with the differential method. Oxygen and hydrocarbons in the air sample are introduced into the FID at the same time. These react to produce CO and CO_2 to which the FID is insensitive.

In the direct method non-methane hydrocarbons are separated from oxygen prior to entering the detector. As the separation column separates many components of the air sample according to their molecular weights in general (for example, inorganic compounds, methane and heavier organic components) many peaks of non-methane hydrocarbons are detected if the separation column feeds directly into the detector. If the carrier gas flow direction is reversed after the elution of methane, a plug of non-methane hydrocarbons is obtained at the opposite end of the separation column. By reversing the direction of the

carrier gas flow and by switching the connections to the separation column and
the detector, methane and non-methane hydrocarbons are analyzed directly. The
oxygen interference is thus avoided.

4.2 PASSIVE MONITORING

Spatial and temporal variations of air pollutant concentrations may be so
great that monitoring stations must be carefully sited in order to provide data
representative of their region. How are the representative locations
determined? How many monitoring stations are required to obtain full knowledge
of the air quality? The potential number of continuous monitors in operation
is limited by the costs of installation and maintenance although the continuous
monitoring methods described in the previous section are well developed.
Simple and inexpensive monitoring devices have been developed for simultaneous
measurements of air pollutant concentrations at many locations over long
periods of time. Even if these simple devices are less accurate than the
continuous monitors, they are very useful for providing an overview of the air
quality in an area of interest.

A passive monitor which can measure air pollutant concentrations without a
pump can provide simultaneous pollution measurements at many locations. The
application of the passive monitor is not limited to outdoor measurements.
People spend most of their time indoors, so the importance of indoor air
quality has become a significant public health issue in recent years. As
indoor air quality is primarily determined by the emission rate from indoor
pollutant sources, the air exchange and removal rates, and by outdoor pollutant
concentrations, air quality can vary widely from house to house. It is
therefore necessary to collect large amounts of data in order to obtain
statistically reliable exposure estimates. The passive monitor is particularly
well suited for large scale indoor and personal exposure measurements as well
as for outdoor measurements because it is structurally simple, silent and
inexpensive.

The main difference between passive and active (continuous) monitors is the
means by which pollutants are transferred from the atmosphere to the collecting
material. In the active monitor, pollutants in the air sample are drawn into
the collecting material by a pump, while pollutants are transferred by
molecular diffusion in the passive monitor. Pollutants collected by the
passive monitor are often analyzed by the same chemical procedure as the active
monitor, so the diffusion process is an essential part of the passive monitor.
If the diffusion rate or the sampling rate of the passive monitor is well
characterized, the pollutant concentrations can be quantitatively measured by
the passive monitor. I will describe the theoretical background of the
diffusion process to obtain quantitative results and then introduce several

widely used devices.

4.2.1 Theoretical analysis of the passive monitor

(i) Analogy of the diffusion process with electric resistance. The
diffusion process is described by Fick's law. The concentration, C $(mole/cm^3)$,
of the air pollutant of interest with respect to the one-dimensional position,
x (cm), and time, t (s) becomes:

$$\frac{dc}{dt} = \frac{d}{dx} (D \frac{dc}{dx}) \qquad (9)$$

where D is the diffusion coefficient.

The eddy diffusion coefficient in turbulent gas flow ranges from 100 to
10000 (cm^2/s), while the molecular diffusion coefficient is of the order of 0.1
(cm^2/s). Therefore, it is a reasonable assumption that a concentration
gradient exists only in the region of molecular diffusion around the sorbent of
the passive sampler. Under a steady state condition, integration of equation
(9) with boundary conditions of X = O, C = Co, and X = L, C = C_a gives:

$$N = (D/L) (C_a - Co) \qquad (10)$$

where Co is the concentration at the surface of the sorbent, L indicates the
thickness of the region of molecular diffusion and C_a is the concentration
outside the region. N is the mass flow rate per unit area, which is often
called the mass flux. If N is thought of as a current, equation (10) is
similar to Ohm's law. The difference in concentration (Ca - Co), which is the
driving force of the flow, is comparable to the voltage difference.

Mass Flux   Current

Concentration   Voltage   (11)

The proportional coefficient of current and voltage is resistance. In our
case, resistance is expressed as follows:

$$R = L/D \qquad (12)$$

The unit of R for mass transfer is (s/cm). The reciprocal of R, then, has the
same units as velocity. When we expose an absorbent of area A (cm^2) to the air
for a period t (s), the amount of absorbed air pollutant M (mole) becomes:

$$M = N * A * t = (A/R) * (C_a - Co) * t \qquad (13)$$

The units of A/R are (cm^3/s) which are the same as for the flow rate of the
active sampler. The area, A, and the sampling period, t, are the operational
variables, so characteristics of the diffusion process involve the resistance R
shown in equation (13).

(ii) Model of the passive sampler. There are usually three regions around
the sorbent of the passive monitor where air pollutants can diffuse by
molecular diffusion (Fig. 4.1). This implies that there are three types of
resistance in the process of air pollutants diffusing from the air to the
sorbent. Air pollutants collected by the sorbent must pass 1) a boundary layer

around the interface of the air and the passive monitor (R1), 2) a stagnant region produced by a diffusion barrier (R2) and 3) a boundary layer at the sorbent (R3).

These resistances connect in series. By analogy with electrical resistance, the overall resistance (Ro) of the diffusion becomes:

$$Ro = R1 + R2 + R3 \qquad (14)$$

The reciprocal of Ro is often called an overall mass transfer coefficient (Kog = 1/Ro). If a very small amount of the air pollutant of interest is absorbed, it is a reasonable assumption that Co in equation (13) is nearly equal to zero, equation (13) then becomes:

$$M = (A/Ro) * C_a * t = Kog * A * C_a * t \qquad (15)$$

which allows us to easily calculate the pollutant concentration during the sample exposure period (t).

(iii) <u>Descriptions of diffusion resistance by physical parameters</u>. Unless a chemical reaction occurs at the boundary layer in the gas phase region, R1 could be described by the following equation:

$$R1 = b/D \qquad (16)$$

Here, b is the thickness of the boundary layer and g stands for gas phase. In the same manner R2 becomes:

$$R2 = L/(D * v) \qquad (17)$$

where L and v are the length of the diffusion barrier and the void fraction of the barrier, respectively.

If the reaction between the air pollutant of interest and the absorbent is first order, irreversible and rapid, with reaction rate of k (1/s), then the

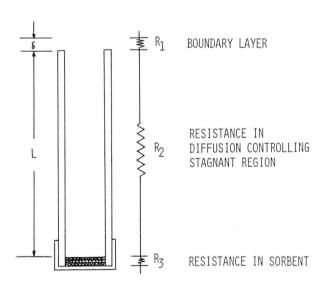

Fig. 4.1. A model of passive sampler.

third resistance becomes:

$$R3 = m/(k * D_L)^{1/2} \qquad (18)$$

where m is Henry's constant and D_L is the diffusion coefficient in the liquid phase.

(iv) <u>Effects of environmental factors on physical parameters</u>. Surface wind velocity, temperature and relative humidity are the three major environmental factors affecting the physical parameters.

Surface wind velocity (WV) has an effect on the thickness of the boundary layer b. If the air stream is laminar and incompressible, the thickness of the boundary layer near the leading edge of a flat plate can be described by the distance from the leading edge and the kinetic viscosity. In most cases, air flow indoors and outdoors is not laminar; therefore, we cannot predict the thickness of the boundary layer. It should be examined experimentally.

The diffusion coefficients and the chemical reaction rate constant are functions of temperature. Kinetic theory shows that the diffusion coefficient in an ideal gas is proportional to $T^{3/2}$ where T indicates absolute temperature. In a real gas mixture, the exponent of T is slightly larger than 3/2. The theory to predict the gas phase diffusion coefficient at a specific temperature is well developed. For example, if the Lenard-Jones potential parameters for the binary gas mixture are known, the diffusion coefficient is calculated from the equation derived by Hirschfelder et al.[2] On the other hand, development of the theory to estimate the diffusion coefficient in the liquid phase is insufficient. The reaction rate constant increases exponentially with elevation of temperature following Arrhenius' law.

If the relative humidity affects the water content of the sorbent, then the diffusion coefficient in the liquid phase and the reaction rate constant may be changed. The exact relation between them is not clear yet.

Overall resistance to the diffusion process in the passive monitor could be described as functions of these environmental factors:

$$Ro(WV, T, RH) = b(WV)/D(T) + L/D(T)$$
$$+ m(T)/(k(T, RH) * D_L(T, RH))^{1/2} \quad (19)$$

Only the length of the diffusion barrier, L, can easily be controlled (eqn. 19). For very large values of L, we can suppress the variation of the first and third terms due to change in the environmental conditions. However, if the second term is very large, the sensitivity of measurements which are proportional to the reciprocal of Ro, that is, Kof, is lowered. Therefore, we have to determine an appropriate length for the diffusion barrier. Of these environmental factors, the influence of the surface wind velocity on the overall resistance has been well examined empirically.

4.2.2 <u>Lead peroxide candle method</u>

The lead peroxide candle method[3] developed in 1934 is a semi-quantitative
method for ambient sulfur dioxide measurement. In this method, the ambient
sulfur dioxide concentration is not expressed in parts per billion but as the
sulfation rate [mg SO_3/(day x $100cm^2$ PbO_2)]. Nevertheless, this method provides
a useful historical overview of sulfur oxide pollution. For example, Fig. 4.2
shows sulfur oxides concentrations in some urban and industrial areas in Japan
since 1957. Although the monitoring method is semi-quantitative, the results
indicated well the progress of industrialization and the worsening of air
quality.

The underlying principle of the method is to measure the amount of sulfate
produced by the reaction :

$$SO_2 + PbO_2 = PbSO_4 \qquad\qquad (20)$$

An activated paste containing lead peroxide is homogenized in gum tragacanth.
This is coated on cotton gauze which is then wrapped around a porcelain
cylinder to form a candle. The candle held in a shelter is exposed to polluted
air for one month to absorb SO_2. After exposure, the cotton gauze is soaked in
sodium carbonate solution to dissolve the lead sulfate. The lead sulfate
filtered from the lead peroxide solution is acidified with hydrochloric acid.
After removing the carbonate ions, barium chloride solution is added and then

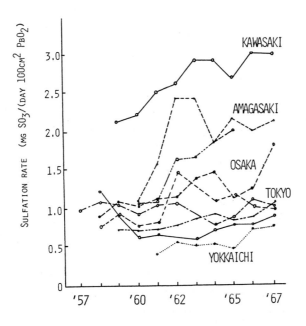

Fig. 4.2. Sulfur oxide concentration in '60s measured by
lead peroxide candle method.

168

the resulting barium sulfate is weighed.

The sulfation rate is calculated as:

Sulfation rate [$mgSO_3/(day \times 100 \ cm^2 \ PbO_2)$]

$$= (W1 - W2) \ 3 \ (80/233) \times (100/a) \times (1/n)$$

$$= 34.3 \times (W1 - W2)/(a \times n) \qquad (21)$$

where W1 and W2 are the weights of $BaSO_4$ in the sample and the blank, respectively. 'a' is the area of PbO_2 exposed to the air and n is the exposure period.

Further studies are required for monitoring the sulfur oxide concentration quantitatively by this simple, inexpensive method.

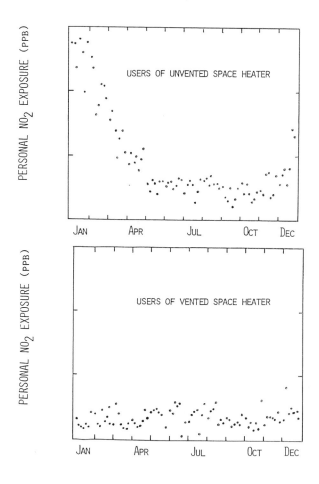

Fig. 4.3. Seasonal change of personal NO_2 exposures of users of unvented or vented space heaters.

4.2.3 Filter badge and palmes tube

The filter badge[5] and the Palmes tube[6] were developed for quantitative measurements of outdoor and indoor NO_2 concentrations and personal exposures to NO_2. For example, Fig. 4.3 shows the seasonal change in daily averages of personal NO_2 exposures measured by the filter badge.[7] A housewife and her neighbor living in a residential area in Tokyo were exposed to considerably different levels of NO_2 though outdoor NO_2 concentrations around their houses were the same. They used different types of space heaters. The Palmes tube is simpler in configuration, but less sensitive than the filter badge. I will explain the details of the filter badge here; the Palmes tube is described elsewhere.

The filter badge consists of three parts: a badge case, an absorbent sheet and a diffusion controlling mat (Fig. 4.4). The badge case has an opening to the air on one side. The absorbent sheet is made from a cellulose fiber filter paper containing a triethanolamine solution to absorb NO_2 gas. The diffusion controlling mat is a filter of hydrophobic fiber made of a fluorine containing polymer. Since the filter has an average pore size of 5 μm, the transfer of gas through the mat appears to be by molecular diffusion; thus the diffusion velocity controls the absorption rate.

After exposing the filter badge to the atmosphere, the absorbent sheet is put into a glass-stoppered cylinder and soaked in azo-dye-forming reagent. The azo-dye-forming reagent is a mixture of sulfanilic acid, concentrated phosphoric acid and N-(1-naphtyl)-ethylenediamine dihydrochloride solution. After allowing 40 min for complete color development at 25 - 30°C, the absorbance is measured at 545 nm.

The performance of the filter badge was examined by using a wind tunnel. When the absorbent sheet was directly exposed to the standard NO_2 gas in the wind tunnel, the absorption rate at a wind velocity of 4.0 m/sec was 2.7 times as great as the absorption rate at 0.15 m/sec. The absorption rate might be

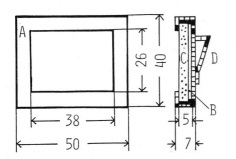

A: BADGE CASE
B: ABSORBENT SHEET
C: DIFFUSION CONTROLLING MAT
D: CLASP

Fig. 4.4. Filter badge for measurement of nitrogen dioxide.

enhanced by turbulent mixing at high wind velocity. The difference in the
absorption rates decreased as more layers were applied; however, at the same
time the absorption rate itself decreased. The optimum number of layers was
determined using the criteria that the effect of wind velocity should be
sufficiently suppressed, and that the sensitivity should be adequate.

The effect of the relative humidity on the absorption rate was also
examined. The absorption rate varied about 20%, with the relative humidity
ranging from 40% to 80%. The overall mass transfer coefficient was highest at
a relative humidity of 60%, but its variation due to relative humidity was less
than that due to wind velocity.

The filter badge method was compared with the Saltzman continuous monitor by
changing the sampling period from one day to seven days. Nitrogen dioxide
concentrations measured with the filter badge method were nearly equivalent to
the results obtained from the Saltzman method (Fig. 4.5). According to these
comparative tests, the filter badge can remain effective after 7 days'
exposure. It may be possible to expose for up to one month.

4.3 ATMOSPHERIC MODELS

What is the most cost effective way to maintain acceptable air quality? Air
quality control requires a lot of money, labor, and significant technical
development. These are very controversial political, economical and
technological issues. There are several alternatives for maintaining adequate
air quality; for example, a change of energy sources, installation of pollution
control equipment in automobiles and industrial plants, relocation of
industries, etc. Simulation modeling of the present environmental air quality

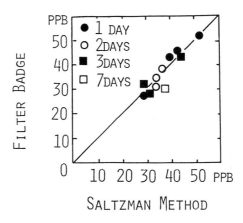

Fig. 4.5. Comparison of filter badge and Saltzman method.

and of future trends is a useful way to determine how to meet air quality standards best.

The behavior of pollutants emitted from specific sources is a complicated function of meteorological and source emission conditions. This behavior can be physically described by a diffusion equation using meteorological conditions as parameters. The meteorological conditions, however, can fluctuate so quickly and widely that we cannot feed raw meteorological data directly into the model, even using a very large computer. One must simplify the meteorological and source conditions into several categories. A theoretical explanation of a dispersion model and the categorization of meteorological and source emission conditions will be briefly described in the following sections.

4.3.1 Dispersion model

The concentration of pollutant released from a stack on a flat surface, is given by equation (22) assuming a steady state (Fig. 4.6).

$$c\,(x,\,y,\,z) = \frac{Q}{2\pi s_y s_z U}\,\exp(-\frac{y^2}{2s_y^2})$$

$$x\,(\exp(-\frac{(z+H)^2}{2s_z^2}) + \exp\,(-\frac{(z-H)^2}{2s_z^2}))\quad(22)$$

This equation is commonly used to calculate the concentration, $C(g/m^3)$, of gaseous or particulate pollutants of small diameter at a point $(x,\,y,\,z)$ in a buoyant plume from an effective stack height, H, which is the sum of physical

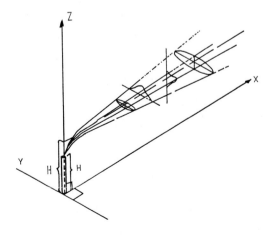

Fig. 4.6. Coordinated system for Gaussian dispersion of plume.

stack height and plume rise. This equation, the so-called Gaussian plume
equation, is derived with the following assumptions.

The first assumption is that the spatial profile of the average pollutant
distribution has a normal (Gaussian) distribution with a standard deviation of
s_y horizontally and s_z vertically. Both are determined by the meterological
conditions. Secondly, the mean wind velocity, U (m/s), is high enough to
ignore the diffusion effect in the downwind direction. Thirdly, pollutants,
once discharged from a stack, are conserved and are reflected completely rather
than being absorbed by the earth's surface. The final assumption is that the
pollutant emission rate, Q (g/s), is uniform and continuous for a longer period
than the travel time to any specific downwind position.

The actual profile of the plume, which is governed by the vertical
distribution of temperature and wind does not always fit the Gaussian
distribution as shown in Fig. 4.7,[9] but the plume model is still useful for
calculating an average concentration over a relatively long period.

If the mean wind velocity, U, is zero or very small (U less than 1m/sec),
the diffusion effect cannot be ignored in comparison with the advection effect.
Dispersed pollutant concentrations emitted from an instantaneous source with
low mean wind velocity are estimated using the puff equation.

$$c(x, y, z) = \frac{Q'}{(2\pi)^{3/2} s_x s_y s_z} \exp\left(-\frac{(x-ut)^2}{2s_x^2} - \frac{y^2}{2s_y^2}\right)$$

$$\times \left(\exp\left(-\frac{(z+H)^2}{2s_z^2}\right) + \exp\left(-\frac{(z-H)^2}{2s_z^2}\right)\right) \quad (23)$$

Here, t (s) is the time elapsed since a puff emission and Q' (g) is the mass
emitted from the instantaneous source. The pollutant concentration at the
particular point is described by the model as the superposition of many puffs
discharged before that time.

The plume and puff equations are basic model equations, so many derivative
equations are employed for specific conditions.

4.3.2 Parameters of the dispersion model

The parameters used in eqns. (22) and (23) to determine the pollutant
concentration at a particular point (x, y, z) must be related to the stability
of the atmosphere and the source emission conditions.

(i) Stability of the atmosphere. If a parcel of dry air moves freely upward
in a hydrostatically stable environment and expands slowly without exchanging
heat with its environment (i.e. adiabatic expansion), its temperature decreases
0.98 °C per 100 m of elevation. This adiabatic rate of temperature decrease,

the adiabatic lapse rate, is obtained from the hydrostatic equation (eqn. 24) and the first law of thermodynamics (eqn. 25).

$$\frac{dP}{dz} = -\rho g \qquad\qquad (24)$$

$$0 = C_p dT - \frac{1}{\rho} dP \qquad\qquad (25)$$

The observed rate of temperature change with height is called the environmental (temperature) rate. If the environmental rate of temperature decrease is the same as the adiabatic lapse rate, then an adiabatically displaced parcel is said to be in neutral equilibrium as it is moved upward.

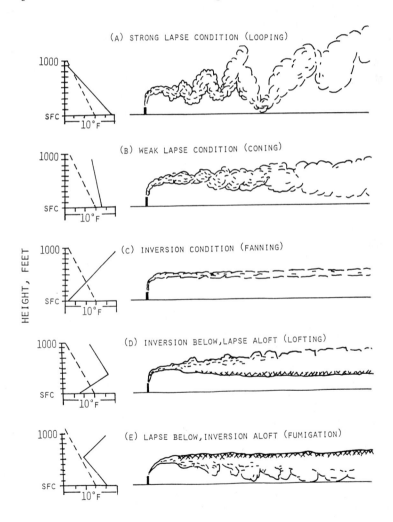

Fig. 4.7. Stack gas behavior under various conditions of stability.

174

When the environmental temperature rate decreases faster than the adiabatic lapse rate, then an air parcel moving upwards becomes warmer and less dense than the surrounding environment. The parcel is in unstable equilibrium and accelerates upward, powered by buoyancy forces. On the other hand, if the environmental temperature decreases at less than the adiabatic lapse rate (or even at a negative rate), the parcel is in stable equilibrium and is forced back to its starting height by (anti) buoyancy forces.

When an air parcel at temperature T is brought adiabatically from a pressure P to sea-level pressure Po (100 KPa), the temperature of the parcel becomes its potential temperature which is often used to express the vertical temperature profile. By substituting (1/O) in eqn. (25) with (1/O) = RT/P derived from the equation of state for the atmosphere and by integrating from the sea-level pressure Po to the pressure at any level, the potential temperature is calculated as follows:

$$T_p = T * (Po/P) R/Cp \qquad (26)$$

The vertical gradient of the potential temperature (dT_p/dZ) is approximated by $(dT/dZ) + a$, where a indicates the adiabatic lapse rate. Therefore (dT_p/dZ) indicates the equilibrium conditions. When (dT_p/dZ) is zero, it is said to be the neutral condition. If (dT_p/dZ) in a layer is negative, the layer is unstable; if it is positive, the layer is stable.

A typical environmental temperature profile (Fig. 4.8) is determined by the earth's surface characteristics, the amount of incoming solar radiation and the wind velocity. Normally temperature decreases with height. If temperature in-

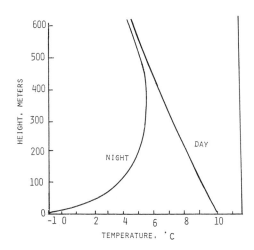

Fig. 4.8. Typical environmental temperature profiles.

creases with height at a particular location, then the area is said to be experiencing an "atmospheric temperature inversion", or simply "inversion". Nighttime inversion of the temperature profile sometimes occurs, and this is due to the absence of radiation.

As already shown in Fig. 4.7, the temperature profile controls the amount of thermal turbulence and consequently the extent of plume and puff dispersion. In addition to the thermal turbulence, fluctuations of instantaneous and average wind speed and direction are major factors in the dispersion process. Three-dimensional measurements of these fluctuations of the air are needed to determine the dispersion parameters for eqns. (22) and (23). Unfortunately, a data base of such measurements may be lacking for the area of the intended model calculation.

Instead of relying on such detailed measurements of turbulence, Pasquill[10] developed a simple scheme for estimating the axial standard deviations of dispersion by classifying atmospheric stability in terms of simple and inexpensive measurements of surface wind velocity and intensity of solar radiation. Table 4.1 shows Pasquill's stability classes in which classes A through C represent the unstable condition, class D indicates neutral conditions, and classes E through F are the stable conditions. "Strong insolation" corresponds to a solar altitude greater than 60' with clear skies. "Slight insolation" means a solar altitude of 15' to 35' with clear skies. If 5/8 to 7/8 of the sky is covered with broken, middle-level clouds at the "strong insolation" level, incoming radiation is expected to reduce to the "slight insolation" level when the sky is covered with low broken clouds. Thus, solar altitude and the amount of clouds determine the daytime stability

TABLE 4.1
Stability classes[11]

Surface wind speed [m/s]	Solar Insolation (daytime)			Cloudness (night)	
	Strong	Moderate	Slight	>4/8 low cloud (thinly overcast)	<3/8 cloud
< 2	A	A-B	B		
2	A-B	B	C	E	E
4	B	B-C	C	D	D
6	C	C-D	D	D	D
> 6	C	D	D	D	D

A : Extremely unstable conditions   D : Neutral conditions
B : Moderately unstable conditions   E : Slightly stable conditions
C : Slightly unstable conditions   F : Moderately stable conditions

Turner, D.B., "Workbook of Atmospheric Dispersion Estimates", US EPA (1970)

class. The nighttime stability class is determined only by the amount of clouds.

A modified table (Table 4.2) is used in Japan in which measured solar radiation greater than 50 [cal/(cm^2 x hr)], between 49 and 25 [cal/(cm^2 x hr)] correspond with "strong insolation", "moderate insolation" and "slight insolation", respectively.

(ii) Standard deviations of plume dispersion. Fig. 4.9 shows the standard deviations of the plume dispersion, Sy and Sz, as functions of downwind distances and stability classes. These functions were derived experimentally. The experiments resulting in Pasquill's curve were performed under the following conditions: uniform terrain with the release of pollutants from near ground level and with measurements of pollutant concentrations at downwind distances of less than 1 km. Although the observations were performed at downwind distances less than 1 km from the source, the standard deviations at distances further than 1 km were estimated by extrapolation of the curve.

Briggs (1973)[13] summarized a similar set of experiments of dispersion standard deviations done by the Brookhaven National Laboratory, the Tennessee Valley Authority and Pasquill. The sets of curves and formulas for both open-country and urban conditions were developed by interpolating these observations in order to eliminate the uncertainty of extrapolation of Pasquill's curves.

If measurements of turbulence are available, then it is preferable to estimate the standard deviations of the plume dispersion from the standard deviations of wind direction fluctuations. Despite the recommendation by Hanna et al (1977)[14] to use turbulence measurements for estimating the standard

TABLE 4.2
Modified table of stability classes used in Japan[12]

Surface wind speed at 10m [m/s]	Day Solar Radiation [cal/cm^2 hr]			Day and Night Cloud Amount	Night Cloud Amount	
	> 50	49-25	< 24	8-10	5-10	0-4
< 2	A	A-B	B	D	G	G
2-3	A-B	B	C	D	E	E
3-4	B	B-C	C	D	D	D
4-6	C	C-D	D	D	D	D
6 <	C	D	D	D	D	D

A : Extremely unstable conditions   E : Slightly stable conditions
B : Moderately unstable conditions   F : Moderately stable conditions
C : Slightly unstable conditions   G : Extremely stable conditions
D : Neutral conditions

deviation of the plume dispersion, Pasquill's curve is still popular because it is easy to use.

Under calm conditions, the axial standard deviation of the puff dispersion model is not a function of the downwind distance, but rather a function of the time elapsed since a puff release. The standard deviations are assumed to be proportional to the elapsed time t [sec];

$$sx = sy = \alpha * y \qquad\qquad (27)$$

$$sz = \gamma * y \qquad\qquad (28)$$

The proportional constants, α and γ, are empirically determined according to the stability classes (Table 4.3).

(iii) <u>Effective plume height</u>. The effective plume height is the sum of stack height and estimated plume rise. This is an important factor in determining the maximum pollutant concentration at ground level where most people breathe. Plume rise occurs due to the upward momentum of the stack effluent at the outlet and the upward force of buoyancy. The initial upward movement of the stack effluent is governed by the forces of momentum and friction. The buoyancy force operates continuously on the plume until it is at equilibrium with its surroundings; therefore, the plume rise also depends on the atmospheric stability and the surrounding mean wind velocity.

There are numerous formulas for predicting plume rise based on empirical and/or theoretical considerations. The functional form of the theoretical equations, whose coefficients come from experimental data, are derived from the

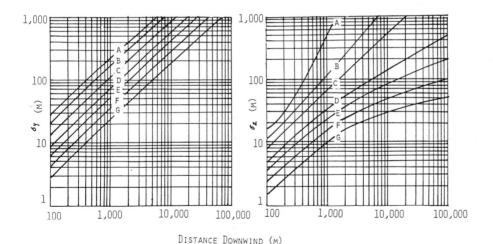

DISTANCE DOWNWIND (M)

Fig. 4.9. Horizontal and vertical dispersion standard deviations as function of downwind distance from source by Gifford (1961).[12]

conservational laws of heat and momentum. However, atmospheric motion is too complex to include all of the variables which may affect the plume rise in the rather simple model equations. Empirical equations can be more accurate than the theoretical equations for specific conditions. When empirical models are applied to different conditions, some parameters may need to be adjusted. The most popular plume rise equations are after Moses and Kraimer (1972) and found in their textbook[9].

Earlier work predicting plume rise was performed by Holland (1953), whose formula included two terms concerning the momentum and the buoyancy forces. Various studies have indicated that this equation underestimates the plume rise by a factor of 2 or 3.

Morse and Carson developed the empirical equation accounting for atmospheric stability, in which the effect of buoyancy was expressed by the square root of the heat emission rate.

Briggs plume rise equations classified by heat emission rate and potential temperature gradient are currently used in many applications.

(iv) Vertical profile of wind speed over the earth's surface. Surface wind velocity is usually measured at 15 m above the ground in Japan, a height lower than the typical stack height. A wind velocity profile in the atmospheric surface layer should be examined to obtain the proper mean wind velocity for use in the dispersion models. Wind velocity generally increases with elevation due to the highly variable frictional effects of the earth's rough surface. Three equations for predicting the wind velocity at a specific height will be discussed. The first two are based on physical phenomena and the third is

TABLE 4.3

Dispersion parameters for puff equation[12]

Stability class	Wind speed 0.4 [m/s] $\sigma_x = \sigma_y = \alpha t$,		0.5-0.9 [m/s] $\sigma_z = \gamma t$	
	α	γ	α	γ
A	0.948	1.569	0.748	1.569
A-B	0.859	0.862	0.659	0.862
B	0.781	0.474	0.581	0.474
B-C	0.702	0.314	0.502	0.314
C	0.635	0.208	0.435	0.208
C-D	0.542	0.153	0.342	0.153
D	0.470	0.113	0.270	0.113
E	0.439	0.067	0.239	0.067
F	0.439	0.048	0.239	0.048
G	0.439	0.029	0.239	0.029

empirically drawn.

If a constant shear stress with elevation is assumed, then the mean wind velocity profile in the surface layer of several tens of meters is:

$$U = (U_o/k) \ln(Z/Zo) \qquad (29)$$

Here, k is the Karman constant (k = 0.4). The friction velocity, U_o, is related to the surface shear stress (So) and air density (ρ) as follows:

$$U_o = (So/\rho)^{1/2} \qquad (30)$$

U_o is usually determined from the wind velocity profile.

This logarithmic velocity profile formula should be used only for neutral stability conditions, while for non-neutral stability conditions a log-linear form is given:

$$U = (U_o/k) (\ln(Z/Zo) + a * Z/L) \qquad (31)$$

The Monin-Obukhov stability length, L, is a function of heat transfer rate at the surface, which is difficult to obtain.

Therefore, the power law velocity profile equation, which is empirically derived, is used in many cases.

$$U = U_1 * (Z/Z_1)^p \qquad (32)$$

where U_1 is the observed wind velocity at a height Z_1. Values of exponent p ranges from 0.1 to 0.3 relating to the stability classes.[12]

4.4 ESTIMATION OF EMISSION

Air pollutants found in the atmosphere are discharged from a variety of different sources. These include natural processes and human activities. Emissions produced by human activities are the principal contributors to pollution in urban and suburban areas. The contributions to air pollution from these sources are generally placed in two categories: stationary sources and mobile sources.

4.4.1 Stationary sources

The time averaged emissions, from stationary sources identified with a plant or an installation fixed at a certain location, are primarily from fuel combustion, industrial processes and solid waste disposal.

Combustion fuels include petroleum oils (heavy oil, light oil, kerosene and naphtha), coal, coke, natural gas, liquid petroleum gas and wood. The industrial processes include metals smelting, petroleum refining, mineral products processing and chemical processes. The solid waste disposal processes

include incineration and agricultural burning. Organic solvent evaporation
from painting, gasoline retailing and residential combustion from cooking and
heating are miscellaneous sources.

The emission sources are identified as point sources and area sources
depending on their physical scale. Point sources are often large, single
sources of pollutants emitted from the tall stacks of power plants for example.
Area sources, which are treated differently from point sources in model
calculations because of their scale, however, contribute substantially to air
pollution in urban and suburban areas. These area sources are numerous small
industries, commercial buildings and residences.

Sulfur oxides, nitrogen oxides, carbon monoxide, hydrocarbon compounds and
particulate matter are considered primary pollutant species from these sources.
In addition, toxic subtances such as hydrogen chloride and mercury vapor, which
are sometimes found due to waste incineration processes, are included as air
pollutants.

Sulfur oxides are released into the atmosphere by the oxidation of sulfur in
coal or other fuels during combustion processes such as electric power
generation, smelting of sulfur bearing ores, use and manufacturing of sulfuric
acid, paper production, waste disposal processes, etc. Sulfur dioxide is the
primary component of the sulfur oxides. It is emitted mainly from liquid and
solid fuel combustion. Emissions can be estimated using the mass balance
equation and assuming that the sulfur in the fuel is converted to SO_2. The
accuracy of the estimate depends on the accuracy of the fuel sulfur content
determination and on the fuel consumption rate. The sulfur content of coal and
crude oil varies widely from approximately 0.1% to 7%, according to the
geological source of the fuel. Sulfur content also varies in each distilled
fraction of crude oil. Heavier crude oil fractions contain more sulfur.
Japanese standards for sulfur content in heavy oil and kerosene are listed in
Table 4.4. Pre-treatment to remove sulfur is required to meet the standards.
The average sulfur content of crude oil imported into Japan was 1.4% in 1983.
The capacity for pre-treatment of heavy oil was about 80 million cubic meters,
adequate for the domestic heavy oil consumption. In model calculations, the
stack gas removal of sulfur dioxide is also taken into account. The 1983
removal capacity of SO_2 was 140×10^6 Nm^3/hr for about 1400 air pollution
control devices.

Stationary sources of carbon monoxide emission in urban areas are normally
quite small in comparison with transportation sources. Combustion with
insufficient oxygen which sometimes occurs in cooking and heating by city gas
or charcoal can produce large amounts of carbon monoxide.

Nitrogen oxides, including nitric oxide (NO) and nitrogen dioxide (NO_2), are
emitted from fuel combustion, production and use of nitric acid, explosives

production and other industrial processes. Formation of nitrogen oxides in a combustion process is more complicated than formation of sulfur oxides because they are produced from nitrogen gas in the air as well as from nitrogen compounds in the fuel. The rate of formation of nitrogen oxides derived from atmospheric nitrogen, sometimes called thermal NO_x, is primarily influenced by the flame temperature. Thermal NO_x production may be determined from the ratio of fuel to air, fuel type and the burner type. Estimation of nitrogen oxides emission based on the fuel consumption rate is therefore less accurate than that of sulfur oxides. Specific operating conditions of appliances as well as fuel consumption rates are required to estimate NO_x emission. Ambient NO_x is usually considered to be conserved in the model calculations, but the ratio of NO_2 to NO_x is variable. Nitric oxide is primarily produced at the point of combustion and discharged from a source. In the atmosphere, nitric oxide is photochemically oxidized to nitrogen dioxide, a strong oxidant which is considered to cause adverse health effects. Because ambient nitrogen dioxide concentrations are the subject of air quality standards in Japan and other countries, the environmental nitrogen dioxide concentration should be estimated by the air quality models. The methods used to evaluate photochemically produced nitrogen dioxide will be discussed in the following section.

Emissions of volatile hydrocarbons from stationary sources are caused by evaporation from storage areas, by solvent extraction processes, and by consumer gasoline distribution, etc. Hydrocarbon emissions from combustion are normally quite small because of the almost complete combustion of the fuel.

Particulate emission from stationary sources results from combustion processes, grinding operations and from other minor processes. Emission rates of combustion particles vary widely depending on fuel type, ash content of the fuel, temperature of the combustion, air flow rate to the combustion and humidity as well as combustion equipment conditions. These emissions can be

TABLE 4.4

Japanese standards for fuel sulfur content

	Class	Sulfur content (wt%)
Kerosene	1	< 0.015
	2	< 0.50
Heavy oil	A	< 2.0
	B	< 3.0
	C	< 3.5

largely eliminated if adequate controlling techniques are applied, such as, cyclones, filters, electrostatic precipitators and wet scrubbers. Emissions from non-combustion processes are produced by chemical manufacturing, petroleum refining, metal processing, etc. Particulate formation by atmospheric reactions is also important in evaluating acid deposition, and so on.

Size distribution and chemical composition of particulate matter are essential in assessing the human health impact. Among the effects on the respiratory system are gross toxicity from heavy metals, carcinogenesis from organics and direct damage by deposition of granular and corrosive materials. The deposition efficiency of particulates in the pulmonary system varies with particle size. As the particle size decreases, particles are more likely to reach the pulmonary region and remain in the lungs; therefore the fraction of fine particles should be monitored to evaluate health effects. In Japan, the mass concentration of suspended particulate matter of diameter less than 10 μm is measured.

It is unrealistic to measure the actual emissions from all air pollution sources. Emission rate estimates, are generally based on fuel consumption rates and/or production rates which are validated by on-the-spot inspections. This is a practical means of compiling an emission inventory. The first step in constructing the emission inventory is to collect basic information from all sources. The basic information consists of five items: 1) identification of a particular factory; 2) information on the manufacturing processes; 3) air pollution control equipment; 4) range of operating conditions; and 5) smoke and air pollutant emissions at the operating conditions.

The factory identification includes name, address, telephone number, category of the factory and name of the person responsible for air pollution control. The information on the manufacturing process includes the process name, product name, and characteristics of the fuel, burners and stacks. Fuel information for each facility includes the type and amounts used per year, and the contents of sulfur, nitrogen and ash. As for burners and stacks, the type and rating size of burners, and the height and location of stacks are reported as well as the capacity and efficiency of pollution control equipment and the name and type of device (i. e. electrostatic precipitator, scrubber, fabric filter, etc.) Operating conditions include typical production rates, fuel consumption rates and operation periods and schedules of the facilities. The emission rate of smoke, its temperature and oxygen content as well as the emission rate of NO_x, SO_x and dust are reported.

After collecting these data in the area of interest, on-the-spot inspections are required to confirm their accuracy. It is desirable to do the on-the-spot inspection on all of the large scale sources, while for the area sources, a certain percentage of facilities should be the subject of inspection. Emission factors of pollutants from various types of fuel and facilities can be obtained based on the basic information and on-the-spot inspection data.

The emission inventory of the region is compiled using the emission factors, fuel consumption rate and production rate. If the pollutant concentration data at the outlet of the stack are available, the emission rate is calculated by:

Emission rate [kg/hr] = pollutant concentration [ppm]

$\quad$ x dry gas discharging rate [Nm^3/hr]

$\quad$ x molecular weight [g] x (1/22.4) x 10^{-6} $\quad$ (33)

When the emission factors are used, the emission rate is:

Emission rate [kg/hr] = emission factor [kg/kcal]

$\quad$ x fuel consumption rate [kg/hr]

$\quad$ x calorific value [kcal/kg] $\quad$ (34)

For sulfur oxides emission, the sulfur content of the fuel instead of the emission factor can be used for the emission rate calculation:

Emission rate [kg/hr] = fuel consumption rate [kg/hr]

$\quad$ x sulfur content [wt%] x 10^{-2} $\quad$ (35)

4.4.2 Mobile sources

Transportation, on land, sea, and in the air, contributes air pollution burdens which match stationary source emissions. The principal pollutants emitted during transportation are carbon monoxide, nitrogen oxides, sulfur oxides, hydrocarbons and particulate matter. Metal aerosols originate from fuel treatment additives, such as lead, and fuel impurities. Discussion here will focus on vehicle emissions which account for a large fraction of urban air pollutants. The magnitude of vehicle emissions is estimated by constructing an emission inventory using emission factors and traffic flow volumes in a specific region.

(i) Traffic flow. Vehicle emission factor differ with vehicle class, so the traffic flow must be measured for each class. The Japanese Ministry of Construction uses 8 vehicle categories in standard road traffic surveys: 1) light passenger car; 2) passenger car; 3) bus; 4) light truck; 5) compact truck; 6) freight-passenger car; 7) heavy duty truck; and 8) special purpose vehicle.
These 8 classes are sometimes collapsed into 6 classes by combining classes 4 and 5, and classes 7 and 8.

In model calculations, highways and intercity roads, where traffic volumes are usually large and vehicle speed is relatively high, are treated as line sources of air pollutants, while community roads within cities and towns are considered to be area sources.

The traffic flow volume can be measured or estimated in various ways. The most accurate but labor intensive way is to count the number of vehicles passing a specific location mechanically or manually. Appropriate counting intervals are needed to reliably measure diurnal, weekly and seasonal average traffic flows. However, it is not realistic to observe traffic flow on all roads in the region of interest. The alternative is to estimate traffic flow from at least two aerial photographs which are taken at specific intervals. The aerial photographic resolution should be adequate to identify vehicle classes. We have to be careful not to count parked vehicles which sometimes comprise more than 80% of the vehicles in the urban aerial photographs.

Traffic flow on community roads can be estimated from socio-economic parameters, such as type of land use, and population and road density. Toll tickets may be used for counting traffic on toll roads, tunnels and bridges.

Using these methods, traffic flow is obtained in the units of (number of vehicles x km/hr). For the line sources such as highways and intercity roads, traffic flow is calculated from direct observation:

Traffic flow = [number of vehicles per hour]

$$x \text{ [length of road]} \qquad (36)$$

and from the air photograph:

Traffic flow = [number of vehicles per 1 km of road]

$$x \text{ [driving speed] } x \text{ [length of road]}$$

$$(37)$$

For the area sources, traffic flow on community roads is calculated from the following equations based on the aerial photographs.

Traffic flow = [number of moving vehicles per area]

$$x \text{ [area] } x \text{ [driving speed]} \qquad (38)$$

The driving speed is calculated from the two aerial photographs taken at specific intervals.

(ii) Emission factors.

(ii-1) Regulations. Since automobile exhaust was identified as the major source of air pollution in urban and suburban areas, the regulation of exhaust gas has proceeded by encouraging technological developments. As the emission standards were intensified, so pollutant emissions from automobiles varied with their model year. In the early days of the regulation beginning in 1961 in California, simple, low cost technology was applied, for example, crankcase emission controls. Emission standards for exhaust gases were first enacted in 1966 in the U.S.A. and in Japan. Only hydrocarbons and carbon monoxide were regulated. The control of nitrogen dioxide, which required more technological development, started in 1971 in the U.S.A. and in 1973 in Japan. In Japan, NO_x emissions of 1978 model passenger cars were reduced by 90% of their 1973 levels.

The emission standards are prescribed for specific test cycle modes which must reflect the actual emissions. Emissions vary considerably with different driving conditions, that is, long or short trips, stop and go driving in urban traffic and high speed traveling on highways, etc. It is almost impossible to include all of the driving conditions in the emission tests. The standard test cycle modes were developed to represent the typical traffic patterns in urban areas where automobile exhaust is a major source of air pollution.

A 10-mode test cycle used in Japan represents a daytime traffic pattern in urban areas. Distance traveled per test cycle is 0.664 km and average driving speed is 17.7 km/hr. After warming up the engine, the NO_x emission test is performed on a dynamometer according to the 10 mode test cycle. Since 1975, an 11-mode test cycle which simultates commuter traffic conditions from a suburban area to the town center was added to the NO_x emission test. As it simulates early morning or late evening driving conditions, the 11-mode test is done without warming up the engine.

(ii-2) Typical driving pattern. As the 10-mode and 11-mode test cycles were developed for regulatory purposes, they do not always represent the typical traffic pattern in a specific region. Although the easiest way to do the emission inventory is to use the 10-mode or 11-mode test cycles as representative of the driving pattern in the area of interest, it is often necessary to approximate the typical driving patterns in the region for the model calculations.

The steps used to determine the typical traffic pattern are as follows:

1) Select the representative roads in the region by road type, number of traffic lanes, traffic flow volume, etc. as criteria.

2) Decide the observation times, that is, on weekdays and weekends at peak and off-peak times, and so on.

3) Drive a test car equipped with a driving pattern analyzer which can record driving speed, driving modes (gearbox position), brake operation, engine rpm, etc.

4) Analyze the observed driving pattern data to determine the typical driving patterns. Extraction of the typical driving patterns is performed by classifying the data according to: a) time fraction of idling, acceleration, deceleration, and constant speed periods, b) acceleration, deceleration, and constant speed, c) trip length and number of modes between idlings, and d) average speed.

Fig. 4.10 shows examples of the typical traffic patterns found on various types of roads in urban areas.

(ii-3) Measurement of emission. Once the typical driving pattern is determined, emission rates of pollutants for the driving pattern can be measured in laboratories using the dynamometer. Test cars should be selected to reflect the chronological changes in emission standards.

186

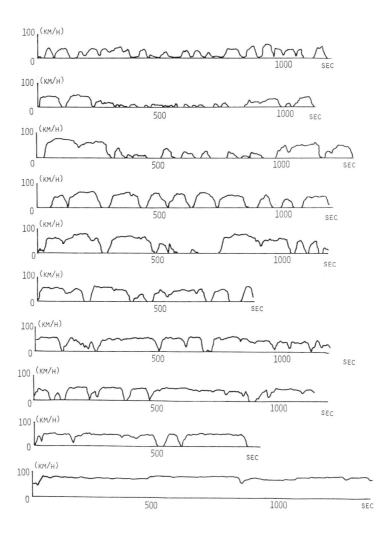

Fig. 4.10. Examples of driving patterns in urban area.

4.5 EXAMPLE OF COMPUTER SIMULATION

4.5.1 Subject of simulation

In the former sections, I briefly described the sub-models composing the simulation for reproducing the present environmental conditions or for predicting the future trend.   In this section, I will show an example of the simulation for ambient NO_2 concentrations.[16]   A project team was set up by local government including experts from universities, research institutes and local government departments.   They developed a simulation model which could reproduce the NO_2 concentration profile of the basic year (1978) and then use the model to predict the future NO_2 profile through 1985 by entering the predicted emission rates of nitrogen oxides.

The study region for this simulation is about 3,800 km^2, located north of Tokyo. The central and eastern parts of the region comprise two-thirds of the total area and is flat land while the western part is hilly. The southeast area has a high population density. There are about 5,000 facilities emitting smoke and the total road length is 47,000 km. There are about 1.6 million vehicles registered in the region or almost one per family.

Ambient NO and NO_2 concentrations are continuously monitored at 50 observation stations over the entire region and 9 additional stations are located along roads. Yearly averages of NO_2 and NO_x concentrations over the past 5 years was almost constant at about 23 ppb in the south and 18 ppb in the north.

Although ambient NO_2 concentrations were the primary subject of this study, the NO_x profile was modeled first, followed by the NO_2 simulation. Nitrogen dioxide is not considered to be a conserved component due to its formation from NO by photochemical reactions, while NO_x is assumed to be conserved in the simulation.

4.5.2 Input data

(i) <u>Meteorological data</u>. The initial year of the simulation was 1978. The fractional distribution of the wind direction, monthly averages of wind velocity and temperatures of the initial year were collected together with the averages for the past decade. We can conclude from these observations that the

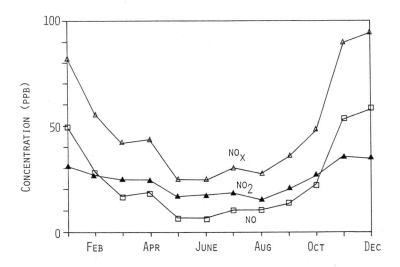

Fig. 4.11. Seasonal variations of observed nitrogen oxides concentrations.

initial year was not a meteorologically extraordinary year.

Frequency distributions of the stability classes were calculated from the meteorological data at 34 observation stations in the region. About half the meteorological conditions belong to stability class D (neutral condition), while G (very stable condition) is the second highest frequency class. According to the vertical gradients of potential temperature, nighttime was usually more stable than daytime, and wintertime was more stable than summertime. The observed vertical gradients of potential temperature lead to the high ambient NO_2 and NO_x concentrations in the wintertime as shown in Fig. 4.11.

Mean wind velocity in the upper layer was estimated based on the power law.

(ii) <u>Source emission data</u>. An inventory of NO_x emissions from stationary sources was made using measurements of stack gas and calculated emissions. Data was collected from more than 5,000 facilities in the region. The following equations were used to calculate NO_x emissions:

Waste disposal process:

Emission (kg/yr) = amount of waste (ton/yr) x
emission (1.04 kg/ton)

Cupola furnace:

Emission (kg/yr) = coke consumption (kg/yr) x
calorific value (kcal/kg) x
emission factor (4.31 kg/kcal)

Electric arc furnace:

Emission (kg/yr) = production (ton/yr) x
emission factor (0.779 kg/ton)

Other facilities:

Emission (kg/yr) = fuel consumption x calorific value
x emission factor

Total NO_x emissions from the stationary sources were about 18,000 ton/yr. NO_x emission from cement kilns located in the western part of the region accounts for over half the total emission of the stationary sources.

The NO_x emission inventory of mobile sources was prepared using the following procedures. Traffic flow, on highways or intercity roads, was obtained from observations of each road. Traffic flow on community roads was estimated by the following equation:

Y = 81.215 X1 + 309.812 X2 + 5.171 X3 + 94.803 X4
    − 2.590 X5 + 441.281   (R = 0.817)

where:

Y(number of cars x km/12h) = Estimated traffic flow
X1:(km^2) = Square of road length of width between 2.5 and
5.5 m

$X2:(km^2)$ = Square of road length of width between 5.5 m and
11.0 m

X3:   = Square root of population

X4:   = Number of manufacturing facilities

X5:   = Number of service facilities

This equation was derived from the aerial photography and the observations of traffic flow in some areas in the region.

NO_x emission factors for the various classes of vehicles at various driving speeds were obtained from the dynamometer test. The car age distribution was taken into account. Since the emission factors change with the driving speed, the average driving speeds on the highways were calculated by:

$$V = 0.741 \times Vm + 979 \times (WIDE/Q) + 6.61 \times (1/CROS)$$
$$- 4.94 \times TP1 - 2.70 \times TP2 - 13.8 \qquad (R = 0.841)$$

where:

$V(km/h)$	= average driving speed
$Vm(km/h)$	= regulated driving speed
$WIDE/Q(m \times h/\#)$	= reciprocal of traffic density
	= (road width (m)/traffic flow rate (#/h))
$1/CROS(km/\#)$	= reciprocal of traffic light density
TP1	= dummy variable
TP2	= dummy variable

(in the evening peak, TP2 = 2, otherwise TP2 = 0)

For the community roads, average driving speeds were estimated separately by type of area, for example, 17 km/hr in the business area and 43 km/hr for farmland. The total NO_x emission from all mobile sources was about 42,000 ton/y of which highways and intercity roads contributed 73%. The areas highly polluted by mobile source emissions were in the southeast and along the highways and intercity roads (Fig. 4.12).

The NO_x emission from miscellaneous sources such as gas stoves and space heaters in residences was also estimated from the fuel consumption and corresponded to 2.5% of the total NO_x emission.

The effective heights of the emission sources were estimated. For a high stack, the Morses & Carson's equation was used for windy conditions and the Brigg's equation was used for calm conditions. For the lower stacks, typical heights were used. Release heights of mobile exhaust for windy conditions were assumed to be the road height for highways and 3 m for community roads. For calm conditions, they were assumed to be 4 m for community roads and the road height plus 3 m for highways.

4.5.3 Calculations

The plume and puff equations were used for windy (>0.4 m/s) and calm (<0.4

190

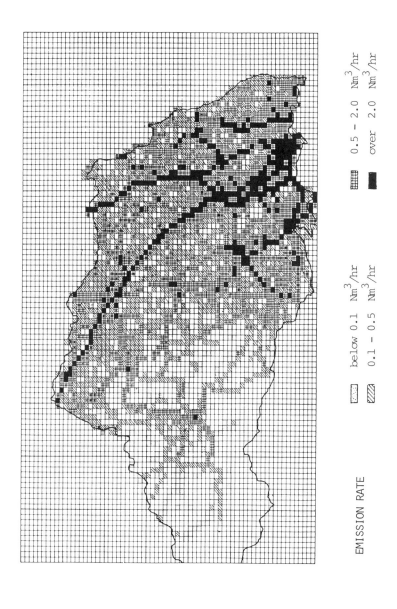

EMISSION RATE

below 0.1 Nm^3/hr

0.1 - 0.5 Nm^3/hr

0.5 - 2.0 Nm^3/hr

over 2.0 Nm^3/hr

Fig. 4.12. An example of spatial distribution of NO$_x$ emission from automobiles in a suburb of Tokyo.[16]

m/s) conditions. Stationary sources were classified according to their stack height point sources (stack higher than 20 m) and area sources (stack lower than 20 m). Mobile emissions from highways and intercity roads, and from community roads are considered line sources and area sources, respectively. Miscellaneous sources are treated as area sources.

Spatial and temporal scales of the calculation were determined by population density and temporal variation of ambient NO_2 concentrations. The study region, which is about 70 km from east to west and 60 km from north to south, was divided into 1 km squares in high population density areas and 2 km squares in rural areas. The total number of cells was 2076. Eight different time categories were set up and a yearly average was obtained from weighted averages of these time categories. The eight time categories consisted of 2 seasons with 4 periods in each day: winter (December through March) and summer (April through November), with morning, daytime, evening, and nighttime.

NO_x concentrations were calculated using a simulation model and the corresponding NO_2 concentrations were predicted by the following equation based on the calculated NO_x concentrations:

$$NO_2 = NO_x * (1 - a * (\exp(-kt) + b)/(1 + b))$$

where, a is the ratio of NO to NO_x at a release point (a = 0.85 in this case) and b is a suppression factor of NO oxidation to NO_2, which depends on the intensity of sunlight and the ozone concentration. In this case, b varies with

TABLE 4.5
Criteria for validation of simulation[12]

Rank of accuracy	Criteria
A	$A_O < \{(1/3)(Y-B_g)+B_g\}$, P = (0.8-1.2), r > (0.71), S'/Y < (1/4) or $A_O < \{(1/3)(Y-B_g)+B_g\}$, S'/Y < (1/5)
B	$A_O < \{(2/5)(Y-B_g)+B_g\}$, S'/Y < (1/4)
C	$A_O < \{(2/5)(Y-B_g)+B_g\}$, S'/Y < (1/3)

$A_O = (Y - X)$; Y = average of obserbed concentrations; Y(i) = observed conc. at i-th location; X = average of calculated conc.; X(i) = calculated conc. at i-th location; P = regression coefficient of observed on calculated conc.; r = correlation coefficient; $S' = \sqrt{\{Y(i) - A_O + X(i)\}^2 / (n-2)}$; B_g = back ground concentration {in this case $B_g(NO_2)$ = 0.002 ppm, $B_g(NO_x)$ = 0.003 ppm}

the time period of the calculation ranging from 0.3 to 0.55. The exponent, k, indicates the overall reaction rate of NO oxidation, which differs for different emission sources as follows:

$$k = 0.00618 \times U \times (O_3) \quad : \quad \text{stationary point source}$$
$$ = 0.0618 \quad \times U \times (O_3) \quad : \quad \text{stationary area source}$$
$$ = 0.100 \quad \times U \times (O_3) \quad : \quad \text{mobile, miscellaneous source}$$

where U (m/s) and (O_3)(ppm) are the average wind velocities and the background ozone concentrations.

The simulation was validated by comparing observed and predicted NO_x concentrations. The validation criteria are: 1) difference between observed and predicted average concentrations; 2) correlation coefficient between them; 3) regression coefficient of the predicted concentrations compared to the observed concentrations; and 4) the standard error of the predicted concentrations from the regression line where the regression coefficient is fixed at 1.0. The precision of the prediction is evaluated by 3 ranks according to the criteria (Table 4.5). Precision rank A is required for the yearly average concentration and rank C for the 8 time categories (Table 4.6).

The simulation of the ambient NO_x and NO_2 concentrations was highly accurate in all of the time categories. For example, yearly averages of predicted concentrations and observed concentrations at 34 stations in the region agreed well as shown in Fig. 4.13. The spatial distribution of the predicted yearly average of NO_2 concentration is shown in Fig. 4.14, in which high NO_2 concentration areas were found in the southeast, and polluted lines tended to be in the northwest. This suggested that automobile traffic was a major source of NO_2 pollution in this region as clearly shown in Fig. 4.12.

4.5.4 Prediction of future NO_2 concentrations

Since the simulation satisfactorily reproduced ambient NO_2 concentrations in 1978, future NO_2 concentrations can be predicted by entering estimated source emission data into the model.

TABLE 4.6
Desirable rank to be achieved by simulation at each time categories[12]

	Summer	Winter	Yearly average
6 am - 10 am	C	C	B
10 am - 4 pm	C	C	B
4 pm - 9 pm	C	C	B
9 pm - 6 am	C	C	B
Daily average	B	B	A

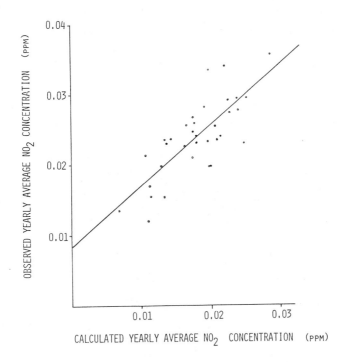

Fig. 4.13. Correlation of calculated and observed NO_2 concentrations[16].

NO_x emissions from stationary sources were estimated as follows. Emissions from major facilities were assessed from an industrial questionnaire polling their production plans. For minor enterprises, which were treated as area sources, estimated production growth rates for each business category or projected population growth in the region were used to predict future emission changes. Development plans for new industrial parks were also taken into account. The calculations indicated that NO_x emissions from stationary sources in 1985 were expected to increase by 33% over 1978 levels from 18 Kton/yr to 24 Kton/yr.

Estimates of mobile source emissions were composed of the predicted traffic flows on existing and planned roads. Emission factors were modified allowing for changes in age distribution of vehicles and chronological change of exhaust gas regulation. About 250 km of additional highways and community roads were planned to be in use by 1985. The traffic flow used in the 1978 simulation was re-allocated to the existing and planned roads by assuming that all the planned roads would be open for traffic during the target year. Growth rates of traffic flow were estimated by comparing the traffic flow in 1977 and 1980. Since the maximum capacity of traffic flow is physically limited, the growth

194

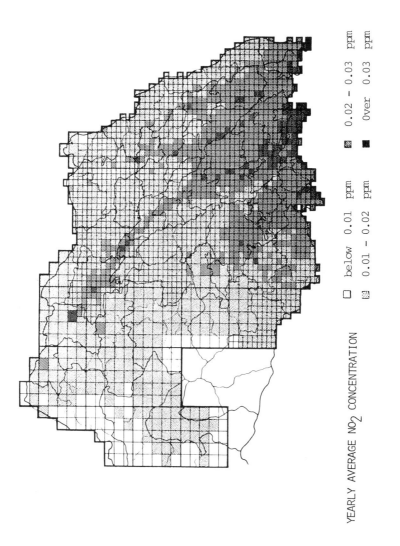

YEARLY AVERAGE NO₂ CONCENTRATION

□ below 0.01 ppm   ▨ 0.02 - 0.03 ppm
▩ 0.01 - 0.02 ppm   ■ Over 0.03 ppm

Fig. 4.14. An example of calculated NO_2 concentration distribution in a suburb of Tokyo[16].

rate of traffic flow on each road varies with the extent of traffic jams. When
the extent of traffic jams was less than 1, the traffic flow on an existing
road might increase by about 5% yearly. However, if the extent exceeded 1.8,
it was assumed the traffic flow could not increase any more. The expected
increase of traffic flow during the 7 years prior to 1985 was calculated for
each road by applying the growth rates. The traffic flow was projected to
increase by 30% from 43×10^6 (vehicle x km)/day (1978) to 56×10^6 (vehicle x
km)/day (1985).

The age distribution of vehicles is estimated by the survival curve of
vehicles in the region. Vehicle registration data was used to obtain the
survival curve but the data for vehicles over 10 years old was not available,
so the lifetime of all kinds of vehicles was assumed to be 13 years.

NO_x emissions from mobile sources in the region were calculated based on the
estimation of the traffic flow, the age distribution of vehicles, and
regulatory standards for exhaust gases. Despite an expected increase in the
traffic flow of 30% over 7 years, the NO_x emissions in the region were

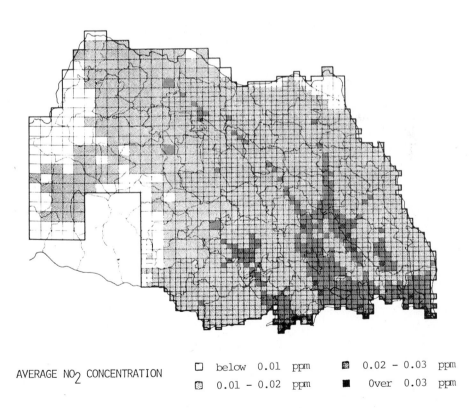

AVERAGE NO_2 CONCENTRATION

☐ below 0.01 ppm   ▨ 0.02 - 0.03 ppm

▤ 0.01 - 0.02 ppm   ■ Over 0.03 ppm

Fig. 4.15. NO_2 concentration predicted from estimated emission[16].

predicted to decrease by 24% due to the replacement of old vehicles with stringently regulated vehicles.

Total NO_x emission would be reduced by implementation of the regulations, but some areas which are along the heavily traveled roads or at the southeast edge of the region, would not achieve the NO_2 ambient air quality standard. (Fig. 4.15). There are 11 cells out of the 2076 of the simulation, where NO_2 concentrations are expected to exceed 30 ppb for the yearly average concentration. Feasible alternatives for reducing NO_x pollution to meet the air quality standard all over the region are still needed. If we can make a 50% reduction of mobile source emissions, the yearly average of NO_2 concentration in all of these cells would be lower than 30 ppb. A combined reduction by 40% of mobile source emissions and 50% of stationary source emissions would bring about the same result.

REFERENCES

1. Environment Agency (Division of Air Pollution Control), "Manual for continuous monitoring of atmospheric environment", Kogai Taisaku Gijutsu Doyukai (1986)
2. Hirschfelder, J.O., et al. "Molecular theory of gases and liquids", John Wiley & Sons, NY (1954)
3. Wilsdon, B.H. and McConnel, F.J., "The measurement of atmospheric sulfur pollution by means of lead peroxide", J. Soc. Chem. Ind., 53, 383-388 (1934)
4. Hori, M., et al., "Surveilance of atmospheric environment", Tokyo Daigaku Shuppankai (1984) (Japanese)
5. Yanagisawa, Y. and Nishimura, H., "A personal sampler for measurement of nitrogen dioxide in ambient air", Taiki Osen Gakkaishi, 15, 316-323 (1980) (Japanese)
6. Palmea, E.D., et al., "Personal sampler for nitrogen dioxide", Am. Ind. Hyg. Ass. J., 37, 570-577 (1976)
7. Yanagisawa, Y., et al., "Estimation of annual average of personal NO_2 Exposure from short period measurement", Taiki Osen Gakkaishi, 19, 292-299 (1984) (Japanese)
8. Yanagisawa, Y., et al., "Wind effect on adsorption rate of nitrogen dioxide passive sampler, palmes tube and filter badge", Proceeding of APCA Annual Meeting 86-37.7 (1986)
9. Bethea, R.M., "Air pollution control technology -- An engineering analysis point of view", Van Nostrand Reinhold Company, NY (1978)
10. Pasquill, F., "The estimation of the dispersion of windborne material", Mateorol. Mag., 90, 33-49 (1961)
11. Turner, D.B., "Workbook of atmospheric dispersion estimates", US EPA (Office of Air Programs), (1970)
12. Environment Agency (Division of Air Pollution Control), "Manual for total mass control of nitrogen oxide emission", Kogai Kenkyu Taisaku Center, (1982) (Japanese)
13. Briggs, D.A., "Diffusion estimation for small emission", ATDL Contribution File No. 79, Atmospheric Turbulence and Diffusion Laboratory (1973)
14. Hanna, S.R., et al., "Handbook on atmospheric diffusion", The Department of Energy, DOE/TIC-11223 (1982)
15. Saitama Prefecture Kankyobu, "Survey of mobile air pollution sources", (1981) (Japanese)
16. Saitama Prefecture, "Report of the committee for control of air pollution with nitrogen oxides", (1983) (Japanese)

Chapter 5

SYSTEM FOR REGULATION

SABURO KATO

5.1 BASIC FRAMEWORK FOR AIR POLLUTION CONTROL

The legislative foundations of air pollution control policy were set in 1967 and 1970. The "Basic Law for Environmental Pollution Control", enacted in 1967, is a seven-page document that spells out general principles regarding the responsibilities of business, and of central and local government bodies in a comprehensive pollution control program aimed at protecting human health and conserving the living environment.

In December 1970, a special session of the Diet devoted almost exclusively to environmental issues revised 8 existing pollution control-related laws and established 6 new laws. The Air Pollution Control Law of 1968 was at that time revised, providing a solid legal basis for future air pollution control.

5.1.1 The unique role of ambient air quality standards

Ambient air quality standards are a policy goal, formulated pursuant to the provision of Paragraph 1, Article 9 of the Basic Law for Environmental Pollution Control, which sets forth the air quality desirable to be maintained for the protection of human health. Generally, the term "environment quality standards" as used in the Basic Law refers to the qualities of air, water and soil and the level of noise that are desirable to be maintained for the protection of human health and the conservation of the living environment.

Prior to the enactment of the Basic Law in 1967, emission control for individual sources was designed and applied on a case-by-case basis. Under these circumstances, the growing industrial activity in any particular area resulted in environmental degradation, even if each source of pollution complied with the emission standards. To remedy the shortcomings of the individual approach, the concept of establishing certain standards for environmental quality was incorporated into the Basic Law.

The ambient air quality standards formulated under this comprehensive approach were the policy goals for the protection of human health and the conservation of the living environment. To attain and maintain these goals of air quality, various effective administrative measures were undertaken, such as improving fuel quality, land use planning, facility layout planning as well as individual emission controls. In fact, the ministries and agencies concerned are requested by the law to make every possible effort to ensure the maintenance of the standards by implementing environmental pollution control measures in a comprehensive, effective and appropriate manner. For instance, in the field of air pollution control, closely related policies concerning energy, industry and transportation are generally developed while integrating environmental aspects into their own fields.

Environmental quality standards are based on the scientific studies of the effects of pollutants on human health and living environment under various exposure conditions. As such, the standards may be revised as new scientific knowledge can be obtained with respect to the effect and measurement method of existing and newly identified pollutants.

In Japan, as quality standards play a very important role in pollution control policy, the procedure for setting such standards deserves attention. The general procedure is as follows:

Prior to establishing ambient air quality standards, the Director General of the Environment Agency (the State Minister for the Environment) consults the Central Council for Control of Environmental Pollution on matters relating to the environmental conditions desirable to be maintained and on measurement methods for related pollutants.

In response to the inquiry, the Central Council appoints a Committee of Experts consisting of specialists in evaluating health effects and in measuring methods for related pollutants. The committee, in turn, gathers scientific data and information available relating to the pollutants in question, and after having evaluated and discussed the data and information, it draws up a set of criteria and proposes guidelines for presentation to the Central Council.

The Central Council reviews the criteria and guidelines presented by the committee with the aim of determining measures for attainment, and recommends to the Director General of the Environment Agency a set of environmental conditions that can serve as the basis for environmental quality standards. Based on the recommendations, the Director General announces standard values for environmental quality, methods of measurement, areas to which they apply and the period for achieving such environmental quality. Thus, environmental quality standards are established.

The ambient air quality standards so far established are summarized in Table 5.1. They have been established principally for the protection of human health.

Table 5.1

Ambient air quality standards

Sub-stance	Sulfur dioxide	Carbon monoxide	Suspended particulate matter	Nitrogen dioxide	Photo-chemical oxidant
	0.04 ppm	10 ppm	0.10 mg/m^3	0.04 ppm	0.06 ppm
	0.1 ppm	20 ppm	0.20 mg/m^3	0.06 ppm	
	Daily average of hourly values shall not exceed 0.04ppm, and hourly values shall not exceed 0.1ppm.	Daily average of hourly values shall not exceed 10ppm, and average of hourly values for eight con-secutive hours shall not exceed 20ppm.	Daily average of hourly values shall not exceed 0.10mg/m^3, and hourly values shall not exceed 0.20mg/m^3.	Daily average of hourly values shall be within the range of 0.04 ppm and 0.06 ppm or below.	Hourly values shall not exceed 0.06 ppm.

(left margin, rotated) Environmental Conditions

5.1.2 Emission controls for stationary sources

With the aim of meeting the air quality standards, emission control over stationary sources is enforced under the Air Pollution Control Law. Emission standards and fuel standards are enforced for "soot and smoke" emitting facilities, and the standards for structure, operation and management are applied for "particulates" emitting facilities.

The Air Pollution Control Law also provides for special measures in the case of accidental discharging of any of 28 specified substances, such as ammonia.

"Soot and smoke" are defined by the law as follows:

(1) sulfur oxides generated as a result of combustion of fuel;

(2) "soot and dust" arising from fuel combustion or electricity-use as a source of heat; and

(3) the toxic substances released or generated as a result of combustion, synthesis, decomposition or other treatment, that is, cadmium, and its compounds, chlorine and hydrogen chloride, fluorine, hydrogen fluoride and silicon fluoride, lead and its compounds, and nitrogen oxides.

Facilities which generate soot and smoke of a certain size or larger and which are installed at factories or office buildings are defined as soot- and smoke-emitting facilities and, as such, they are subject to emission standards.

Different regulatory measures are prescribed for sulfur oxides, soot and dust, and toxic substances. For the first two, facilities newly installed or added to existing ones in designated areas, where air pollution is already significant, are subject to special emission standards which are more stringent than the ordinary emission standards.

Emission standards prescribed by the government with respect to soot and dust and toxic substances represent the national minimum, and prefectural governments are empowered to establish their own standards by virtue of an ordinance —— a by-law enacted by the local legislative body —— where the situation warrants it. If the Director General of the Environment Agency finds that a certain prefecture needs standards more stringent than the national minimum, he may recommend such standards to the governor.

Prefectures are not allowed to set more stringent sulfur oxide standards than the national standards, because the control of sulfur oxides is closely related to the national energy policy. Instead, the national standards for sulfur oxides reflect local conditions both in K-value control, and total mass control, as described below.

To ensure effective enforcement of emission controls, managers of soot- and smoke-emitting facilities are required to comply with the emission standards and to notify the appropriate regulatory agency of the installation of any new facilities or of any changes in the structure of existing facilities. Violators of these requirements are subject to penalties, and such violators may be ordered to change the proposed plan or to improve the structure or design of modified facilities. In addition, managers of soot- and smoke-emitting facilities are required to monitor and record regularly the quantity of soot and smoke their facilities release into the air. The prefectural governor is empowered to call for reports on the current state of soot- and smoke-generating facilities and may order a competent official or officials of his prefectural government to inspect the premises.

5.1.3 Emission controls for motor vehicle exhaust

The Air Pollution Control Law empowers the Director General of the Environment Agency to establish permissible limits of motor vehicle exhaust emissions. The following exhaust emissions from motor vehicles: CO, HC, NO_x, particulates and lead are designated as those which are liable to affect human health adversely. The Director General of the Environment Agency has established permissible limits for CO, HC, NO_x and diesel smoke. (a permissible limit for lead is not necessary in Japan, because since 1975 only lead-free gasoline has been used for gasoline-powered cars.)

The law also provides that the Minister of Transport should ensure the
attainment of the permissible limits by stipulating matters necessary for the
enforcement of exhaust emission control in the government order provided for in
the Road Transport and Motor Vehicle Law (enacted in 1951). The law demands
that any vehicle, which is to be used on roads, must pass an initial or
continuation inspection set by the Minister of Transport. Also, virtually all
mass produced motor vehicles get type-approval by the Minister of Transport
before appearing on the market. The law also obliges all motor vehicles to
satisfy the permissible limits of exhaust emissions in their initial or
continuation inspections or type-approval tests.

Following on from the early restrictions on motor vehicle exhaust emissions,
in 1975 tougher restrictions were put into effect for carbon monoxide,
hydrocarbons and nitrogen oxides for gasoline-powered passenger cars. As a
result of these restrictions, the levels of carbon monoxide and hydrocarbons in
motor vehicle exhaust emission have been reduced by more than 90% from those
when there were no restrictions. As for nitrogen oxides, emission levels were
also reduced by more than 90% because of the 1976 and 1978 restrictions.

In December 1977, the Central Council for Environmental Pollution Control
released a report on Long-Term Policy for the Establishment of Permissible
Limits for Motor Vehicle Exhaust Emission. In order to realize the targets as
soon as technically feasible, the Environment Agency evaluated and promoted the
development of pollution control technology through the Investigation Committee
for Motor Vehicle Pollution Control Technology, consisting of university
professors.

This led to the phase-I restrictions of nitrogen oxide exhaust from trucks
and buses, which were enforced in 1979. The phase-II restrictions were
subsequently introduced for light-weight and medium-weight gasoline cars in
1981, for heavy-weight gasoline cars, light trucks and indirect-injection-type
diesel vehicles in 1982 and for direct-injection-type diesel vehicles
in 1983.

5.1.4 Monitoring of air pollution

(i) Local air pollution monitoring networks. Environmental monitoring in
Japan serves as the basis for environmental policy. In fact, environmental
monitoring is an essential tool not only in assessing the quality of the
environment but also in formulating the environmental policy and evaluating the
effects of existing environmental measures. Because of their proven value, a
variety of monitoring activities are under way at both national and local
levels.

Due to the rapid development in monitoring, data-transmission and data
processing techniques, more and more sophisticated environmental policies are

being introduced and implemented with considerable success.

The Air Pollution Control Law, contains the following provisions.

[Article 22]

The governor of a prefecture shall continually monitor and survey the level of air pollution.

[Article 20]

The governor of a prefecture shall measure the density of motor vehicle exhaust in the air, on roads or in places surrounding roads where serious air pollution by motor vehicle exhaust occurs or is likely to occur on account of traffic congestion at the traffic intersections, etc.

[Article 24]

The governor of a prefecture shall make public the conditions of air pollution in the areas under his jurisdiction.

Based upon such provisions, local air pollution monitoring networks are being consolidated both by prefectures and by those designated cities that have also been authorized under the Cabinet Order to enforce the law. Table 5.2 shows the number of air monitoring stations operated by local governments.

The purposes of such monitoring stations can be summarized as follows:

1 To ascertain the state of compliance with the ambient air quality standards [SO_2, CO, SPM, NO_2, photochemical oxidants (O_x)].

Table 5.2

Number of air pollution monitoring stations operated by local governments (in 1985)

	General Air Pollution Monitoring	Automotive Emission Monitoring	Total
SO_2	1,647	54	1,701
NO & NO_2	1,321	295	1,616
CO	197	315	512
O_x	1,021	48	1,069
NMHC	306	142	448
SPM	680	65	745
Dustfall	1,478	–	1,478

2 To provide information allowing the necessary steps to
   be taken in case of emergency.
3 To monitor the effectiveness of regulation.
4 To manage air quality on a regional basis.
5 To watch specific sources of pollution, and to
   monitor the background conentrations of pollutant, etc.

As is indicated in Fig. 5.1, many major Japanese cities maintain a
telemeterized monitoring system. Under the system, fuel consumption, sulfur
content in heavy oil, and concentrations of NO_x and SO_x in flue gas as well as
ambient data are telemetered from major industrial plants and from air
monitoring stations to the monitoring center in the city, for control purposes.
In most cases telemeterized data are displayed to the general public.

(ii) <u>National air monitoring network (NAMN)</u>. National air pollution
monitoring stations and national environmental background air monitoring
stations have been established since 1965 with two aims: 1) clarifying the
nationwide state of air pollution caused by both currently regulated pollutants
as well as other substances and 2) gathering the raw data needed for setting
ambient air quality standards and formulating pollution control programs.

National air pollution monitoring stations are installed at 15 sites
throughout the country, each being equipped with various instruments for
monitoring sulfur dioxide, nitrogen oxides and other air pollutants. The data
obtained are analyzed to clarify the cause of air pollution.

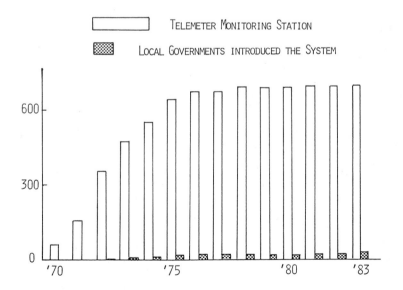

Fig. 5.1. The number of monitoring stations and the number of local
goverments having introduced the monitoring system.

National environmental background air monitoring stations are located at eight places for the purpose of understanding ambient air conditions in unpolluted areas on the major plains of Japan. These environmental air monitoring stations are equipped with instruments for measuring hydrogen fluoride and ozone in addition to the normal equipment of national air pollution monitoring stations.

Besides these 23 stations, three national motor vehicle exhaust gas monitoring stations (ambient air) have been in operation in Tokyo since 1968. They monitor CO, SO_2, NO, NO_2, and particulate matter.

5.1.5 The establishment of the Environment Agency

(i) Background. The pollution control administration of Japan was markedly strengthened thanks to the establishment, in July 1970, of the Headquarters for Countermeasures for Environmental Pollution (headed by the Prime Minister) and to the subsequent enactment and consolidation of anti-pollution measures by the 64th (November - December 1970) and the 65th (December 1970 - May 1971) Diet Sessions. However, the wide distribution of pollution control functions among a number of ministries and agencies created serious bottlenecks in the enforcement of comprehensive anti-pollution measures.

In view of the above, Prime Minister Sato decided to establish an Environment Agency not only to control environmental pollution but also to promote administrative measures for the overall conservation of nature including better management of national parks and protection of wild life. As a preliminary step, an inter-agency Preparatory Committee for the Establishment of an Environment Agency, composed of the administrative vice-ministers of all the ministries and agencies concerned, was instituted under the chairmanship of Mr. Yamanaka, Director General of the Prime Minister's Office. The work of this committee rapidly led to the establishment of an independent agency for environmental protection and enhancement. The reasoning underlying this move may be summarized as follows:

  a. The responsibilities and concern of the Environment
     Agency should not be limited merely to pollution
     control, rather, the Agency's administrative
     jurisdiction should cover all spheres of environ-
     mental protection including nature conservation.
  b. Regulatory measures, such as the setting of
     standards, and the monitoring and surveillance of
     pollution, which have been spread over a number of
     ministries and agencies, should be concentrated
     under a single command, the Environment Agency.
  c. In view of the vital importance of scientific

<blockquote>
research and investigation relating to pollution
control, a National Institute for Environmental
Studies should be established.
</blockquote>

A law for the Establishment of the Environment Agency was approved by the Cabinet on 16 February 1971 and passed the Diet on 24 May. Under the Law, the Environment Agency came into being on 1 July 1971.

(ii) <u>The Environment Agency's responsibilities and the task of the</u> Air <u>Quality Bureau.</u> The Environment Agency is responsible for overall promotion of environmental protection and the following matters are under its jurisdiction.

[General]

These include the planning, drafting and promotion of basic policies relating to protection of the environment; overall coordination of the various branches of the government responsible for environmental protection; coordination of budgetary policies for expenditures related to pollution control; and centralized control of appropriations for research and development. The agency's administrative structure is designed to increase its effectiveness as an overall coordinator.

[Nature Conservation]

The agency has under its jurisdiction enforcement of the Nature Conservation Law, the Natural Parks Law, the Wildlife Protection and Hunting Law and the law relating to the Regulation of Transfer of Special Birds.

[Pollution Control]

Matters coming under the jurisdiction of the agency include establishment of environmental quality standards, enforcement of the Air Pollution Control Law, the Water Pollution Control Law and other laws relating to environmental pollution control.

[Director General of the Environment Agency]

The head of the Environment Agency is called the Director General and is appointed to the Cabinet with the rank of a Minister of State.

When the Director General deems it necessary for the protection of the environment, he has the power to request information or explanations from the heads of other administrative agencies. He (or she) is also empowered to make recommendations to them with respect to important matters. When the situation so warrants, he (or she) can recommend to the Prime Minister that steps be taken.

[Air Quality Bureau]

This bureau is responsible for establishing environmental quality standards and the enforcement of the various pollution control laws relating to pollution caused through air-air pollution, noise, vibration and offensive odour. The Air Pollution Control Division, for which the author worked from July 1981 to October 1984 as the head of the division, is charged with the administrative service relating to the establishment of emission standards, the proper use of fuel to control air pollution as well as the monitoring of air quality. The bureau also covers the control of noise, vibration and offensive odour. It is charged, in addition, with the enforcement of related laws, investigation of environmental pollution in related areas, and drafting of plans. In view of the gravity of pollution caused by automobiles, the bureau has also established an Automotive Pollution Control Division to attack on a broad front environmental pollution caused by automobiles. On 1 October 1978, the Office of Traffic Pollution Control was established to promote and coordinate overall countermeasures for traffic pollution.

5.1.6 R & D in the field of pollution control

R & D in the field of pollution control is very actively pursued at both public and private research institutions. It seems to me that the most important is the Environment Agency's National Institute for Environmental Studies (NIES), which was established in March 1974, in Tsukuba Academic City, which is about 60 km east of Tokyo. The institute was established to play the leading role in environmental research in Japan. It enables inter-disciplinary studies to be undertaken with the participation of outside experts from universities and other research institutes. It also provides large-scale experimental facilities for environmental studies, and conducts field studies.

Since the institute's inception, various efforts have been made to improve its organizational structure and facilities. The administration of research at the institute has recently been improved. Recent research projects in the field of air pollution are shown in Table 5.3.

While extensive research and study in these fields is conducted by various

Table 5.3

Recent study themes conducted by NIES

(a) Studies on Photochemical Reactions of Hydrocarbon-Nitrogen Oxides-Sulfur Oxides System (1980-1981)
(b) Experimental Study of the Effect of Combined Air Pollutants (NO_2, O_3 and SO_2) on the Living Body (1982-1986)
(c) Study of Wide Range Transport, Mixture and Deposition Process on Air Pollutants (1982-1985)
(d) Study of Air Purification Function by Plant (1982-1985)

research institutes of the government and private industry, the government has also undertaken basic research on the effects and mechanisms of pollution. In addition, it has conducted research on pollution prevention measures such as the establishment of various environmental standards, as well as on the development and assessment of pollution prevention technology. The government has also been encouraging development of large-scale, comprehensive technology such as flue gas desulfurization techniques. These have either high administrative priorities or use innovative techniques that are expected to contribute substantially to pollution abatement. For this purpose the government organizes large-scale project development teams including the private sector or subsidizes private business in their development efforts.

While carrying out such research and study activities, the government is required to establish close links between many research groups since today's research projects include many diverse areas of science and technology, and consequently require the close cooperation of people in various fields. Because of this, the Environment Agency is required by law to coordinate cost estimates of pollution prevention measures to be undertaken by government ministries and agencies. At the same time, it appropriates and administers the total costs of pollution prevention research and studies undertaken by both ministry research institutes as well as all costs of research projects contracted by government ministries and agencies.

Local government research institutes focus their activities on experiments and studies of matters closely related to the local environmental issues. The Environment Agency has taken measures to support their continued activities in this field, by giving financial or technical assistance.

5.2   REGULATION OF SO_x

Japanese experience in sulfur oxides (SO_x) control has been very unique and has proven to be very successful. In fact, the ambient levels of SO_2 throughout Japan have dropped drastically during the past decade or so. Nowadays more than 99% of all air pollution monitoring stations have met the ambient quality standard for SO_2, which is undoubtedly one of the most stringent standards in the world (Table 5.4).

Such achievements in reducing drastically the ambient levels of SO_2 have been made using a number of policy tools based upon the best available technology for the control of SO_x. Among them are K-value regulation, regulation of the sulfur content of fuel oil, and total emission control.

5.2.1 K-value regulation

Initially, the statutory emission control of sulfur oxides was applied to the concentration recorded at stack outlets under the Soot and Smoke Regulation

Table 5.4

State of compliance with sulfur dioxide environmental quality standards

Item			"Effective Stations"
Year	Total number	Satisfying stations	Rate of achievement (%)
1972	685	227	33.1
1975	1,238	992	80.1
1980	1,571	1,546	98.4
1981	1,586	1,569	98.9
1982	1,605	1,596	99.4
1983	1,613	1,603	99.4
1984	1,623	1,614	99.4

Law of 1962, which is the first air pollution control law ever enacted in Japan. In those days, the regulatory measures were designed to cope with spreading air pollution that was extending to an ever widening area. This was caused by sharp increases in the consumption of energy by the heavy and chemical industries which had kept Japan growing rapidly since the early 1960s. However, the law failed to check the spread of pollution in areas containing industrial complexes, let alone improve the ambient concentrations of sulfur oxides.

The realization of the gravity of the situation led to the institution of ambient air quality standards under the Basic Law for Environment Pollution Control of 1967 as stated before.

Seizing the opportunity when a sweeping amendment was written into the Soot and Smoke Regulation Law in 1968, subsequently known as the Air Pollution Control Law, the system of controlling the K-value was adopted. This method prescribes permissible limits for the quantity of sulfur oxides emitted according to the heights of smoke stacks. The K-value is given under the following formula:

$$q = K \times 10^{-3} \times He^2$$

where

q : hourly volume of sulfur oxides emitted (Nm^3/h)

K : constant given for each area

He: effective height of smoke stack (m)

Here, He is obtained according to the Bosanquet I formula described below:

He = Ho + 0.65(Hm + Ht)

Ho = real height of smoke stack (m)

$$Hm = \frac{0.795 \ (QV)^{1/2}}{1 + 2.58/V}$$

$$Ht = 2.01 \times 10^{-3} Q (T-288)(2.30 \log J + \frac{1}{J} - 1)$$

$$J = \frac{1}{(QV)^{1/2}} (1460 - 296 \frac{1}{T-288}) + 1$$

The K-value is determined in such a way as to control the maximum ground concentration contributed individually from all the facilities with various stack heights to a certain value, and it is calculated in accordance with the following formula which is based on the diffusion equation by Sutton.

The maximum ground concentration, C_{max}, on the principal axis to the leeward of a source of smoke is obtained according to Sutton's diffusion equation as follows:

$$C_{max} = 0.234 \frac{Cz}{Cy} \frac{Q}{uHe^2}$$

Here, on the assumption that the Sutton's diffusion parameter Cy is equated to Cz (the assumption is reasonable when the stability of the atmosphere is neutral) and the wind velocity u is 6 m/s, C_{max} is given as follows:

$$C_{max} = 0.234 \frac{Q}{6He^2}$$

where,

C_{max} : maximum ground concentration (3-minute value)(In this case, the reading of concentration is indicated in terms of 10^{-6}, rather than 1 ppm.)

Q : quantity of pollutants emitted in units of m^3/s at 15°C

Generally, the maximum ground concentration is often indicated in terms of hourly values, so that the given 3-minute value is converted into hourly values. According to Rolly's conversion rate for varying averaging time, by multiplying the given three-minute value by 0.15, the hourly value is obtained as follows:

[Hourly value C_{max}] = 0.15 x [3-minute value C_{max}]

Further, Q is translated into standard conditions (0°C, at the standard atmospheric pressure) called q.

$$q = Q \times \frac{273}{273 + 15} \times 3600$$

From the above,

$$q = 0.584 C_{max} \times 10^6 \times He^2.$$

In terms of ppm, the hourly value is represented by $C_{max} \times 10^6$.

$$q = 0.584 C_{max} He^2$$

where

q   : the quantity of pollutants emitted (Nm^3/h)

C_{max} : the maximum ground concentration (ppm)

He : the effective height of smoke stack (m)

The above equation serves as the emission standard and if $0.584\ C_{max}$ is assumed to be $K \times 10^{-3}$, then

$$q = K \times 10^{-3} \times He^2$$

This equation serves as the emission standard provided by the law.

The relationship between the K-value and the maximum ground concentration is represented by $K = 584\ C_{max}$, on the basis of which the K-value is determined. The relationships between the K-value and C_{max} that have been used so far are summarized in Table 5.5 below.

Table 5.5

K-value and maximum ground concentration

K-value	1.17	1.75	2.34	2.92	3.50	4.67	5.26	6.42
C max (ppm)	0.002	0.003	0.004	0.005	0.006	0.008	0.009	0.011
K-value	7.59	8.76	9.34	11.7	14.6	15.8	17.5	18.7
C max (ppm)	0.013	0.015	0.016	0.020	0.025	0.027	0.030	0.032

The K-value is established for each area and has been revised several times. Revisions were made to attain the prescribed ambient air quality standards for sulfur dioxide by the target year, taking into consideration the current state of air pollution in the given area, the overall source inventory for the soot- and smoke-emitting facilities and the projected increase in the consumption of fuels.

Specifically, the K-values were established by the following procedures. In this case, the findings of the latest survey of existing soot- and smoke-emitting facilities (which has been conducted nationally once every two years) served as the basis for computing such K-values.

(a) The total quantity of sulfur oxides emitted (Qo) for each area was estimated for the year when the emission standard (K-value) is to be established by calculating the following:

      Qo = r x Qs

where

r : the rate of increase in the area-wide
fuel consumption for the year over the
base year

Qs : the total quantity of sulfur oxides
emitted in the area for the base year

(b) Present state of air pollutants: The measurements
of ambient concentration of sulfur oxides during
the base year were used. If a given area maintained
a large number of monitoring stations, the average
concentration monitored at the worst two or three
stations was used.

(c) Target value for the ambient concentration: The
target value to be attained during a given year
represented one of the series of graduated levels
of concentration designed to help attain the
prescribed ambient air quality standards by the
target year.

(d) The permissible total quantity of sulfur oxides
for a given area (Q) was calculated according to
the following equation:

$$Q = \frac{\text{target value for the ambient concentration}}{\text{present concentration of sulfur oxides}} \times Qs$$

(e) The required rate of reduction (R) in the quantity
of sulfur oxides emitted was computed according to
the following equation:

$$R = \frac{Q}{Qo} \times 100$$

(f) Calculation of the value for the emission standard
(K-value):
First, the quantity of sulfur oxides expected to
be reduced for each facility when we assume a certain
K-value was calculated. Then, the quantities of
sulfur oxides reduced in individual facilities
were added up and thus the relationships between the
rate of reduction in the quantity of sulfur oxides
and the assumed K-value were obtained on the basis of
which the K-value corresponding to the given R
prescribed above was estimated.

Thus, on the basis of the K-value calculated for the given area in accordance with the above-mentioned procedures, the areas are now classified into 16 categories, with K-values ranging from 3.0 to 17.5. For certain areas where sulfur oxide pollution was serious in the past, stricter K-values (1.17, 1.75 or 2.34) are applied for new sources.

For instance, the K-value is 1.17 for metropolitan areas including Tokyo, Yokohama/Kawasaki, Nagoya and Osaka. The K-value is either 1.75 or 2.34 for local industrial cities which suffered in the past from relatively severe air pollution.

Assuming normal plant design and operation of a coal-fired power plant with a unit capacity of 1,000 MW, the maximum flue gas concentrations of SO_x is about 60 ppm in the case of a K-value equal to 1.17. In order to comply with this standard, low-sulfur coal with a sulfur content lower than 0.8% would have to be used and flue gas desulfurization (FGD) equipment with a rate of removal exceeding 90% would have to be installed. Similarly, flue gas concentrations of SO_x if the K-value is 17.5 should be around 1,250 ppm, which can be achieved by using coal with a sulfur content lower than 1.5% without installing FGD equipment.

SO_x emission checks of soot- and dust-emitting facilities are generally run on the basis of reports filed by the management of the factory and competent local government officials who may enter the premises of factories whenever they consider it necessary to verify the conformance to the standards. In certain areas, the managers of factories are required to install continuous emission monitors on their principal pollution sources, which are linked to a local monitoring center through telemeters. In case any factory fails to meet the prescribed emission standards, the local government is empowered to impose penalties on such managers. Normally, however, the local governments cause such factories to restore the compliance of their facilities.

5.2.2 Regulation of the sulfur content of fuel oil

In areas where small- and medium-sized space heaters substantially contribute to air pollution in winter, pollution control based on the K-value prescribed for such areas does not always prove to be effective. Falling into this catagory are the urban areas and, for such areas, fuel standards to control the sulfur content of available fuels are necessary. By nature, they are applicable only during periods when space heating causes heavier air pollution.

In Article 15 of the Air Pollution Control Law, it states:

"If the governor of the prefecture recognizes that serious air pollution of sulfur oxides occurs or is likely to occur in an area where sulfur-oxides-related soot- and smoke-emitting facilities are concentrated whose volume of fuel fluctuates according to season and that any person who emits sulfur oxides in the area uses in the facility any fuel which fails to meet the fuel standard, the governor may recommend such a person to observe the fuel standard within a prescribed period." further,

"If a person who receives a recommendation under the provision of the preceding paragraph does not obey the recommendation, the governor of the prefecture may order him to observe the fuel standard within a prescribed period."

The original fuel standard which was set in 1971 was up-graded in 1976 to a sulfur content ranging from 0.5 to 1.2%. This standard is applied to the factories and business offices located in the 14 areas which are specified under the Cabinet Order; Sapporo, Asahikawa, Sendai, Chiba, Tokyo, Yokohama, Kawasaki, Nagoya, Kyoto, Osaka, Kobe, Amagasaki, Hiroshima and Fukuoka.

5.2.3 Total mass emission control of SO_x

The control system for sulfur oxides has undergone a change from that of concentration control to that of K-value control. Nevertheless, both of these control systems had the following drawbacks:

(a) The system of K-value control, which aims at diffusing the soot and smoke by increasing the height of smoke stacks, may be conducive to improving the highly polluted spots, but it raises the possibility of eventual pollution over much wider areas.

(b) The proven overall behavior of pollutants in an area, where sources of pollutants are highly concentrated, does not conform to the diffusion theory which underlies the system of K-value control.

(c) In cases, where a large number of smoke sources are located over a wide area and where the pollution in individual segments of such an area combines with one another to produce a uniformly high concentration of pollution over the entire area, the answer lies not in increasing the height of smoke stacks but in curtailing the quantity of pollutants.

With a view to remedying such drawbacks, the system of total mass emission control was introduced by a June 1974 amendment to the Air Pollution Control Law and applied to those areas where ambient air quality standards cannot be met with the traditional emission control measures (K-value control in the case of sulfur oxides). This system is designed to ensure the attainment of ambient air quality standards rationally and systematically by curtailing the overall emission of pollutants in a given area to below the calculated permissible total load of pollutants. The method takes into consideration the particular conditions of the area, such as its meteorological and topographical conditions and distribution characteristics of pollutant sources.

Under this system, the government designates, by means of a Cabinet Order, the pollutants (called designated soot and smoke) and the areas (called designated areas) which are subject to control. The governor of the area designated by the Cabinet Order draws up a program for the reduction of total emission of designated soot and smoke, on the basis of which the governor establishes total mass emission control standards applicable to factories and business establishments (specified factories, etc.) which are larger than a certain size. In addition the program includes standards for fuel use (standards for sulfur contents) applicable to factories and business establishments other than the specified factories, etc.

At present, both sulfur oxides and nitrogen oxides are designated as "designated soot and smoke" under the system. Total mass emission control for sulfur oxides is currently applied in 24 areas including almost all major urban and industrial cities of Japan (Fig. 5.2). Together, these 24 areas account for only approximately 3.1% of the nation's land area. However, they account for 31% of the total population of Japan and for approximately 30% of the sulfur oxides emitted.

The term "total mass emission" as used in the context of the total mass emission control does not mean the environmental assimilative capacity; rather, it refers to the permissible total quantity of emission for a given area calculated in such a way as to meet the prescribed ambient air quality standards. For the purpose of the law, the concept of total mass emission is divided into the following four categories:

(1) The total quantity of designated soot and smoke generated as a result of and in the course of all business or other activities of man and emitted into a designated area (actual total emissions).

(2) The total quantity of designated soot and smoke emitted into the air from the soot and smoke emitting sources installed and operating at all specified facilities located within a given designated area (total emissions of all specified facilities).

(3) Such total quantity of designated soot and smoke concerning that referred to in (1) above as calculated by scientific methods in such a way as to satisfy the prescribed ambient air quality standards (targeted total emissions).

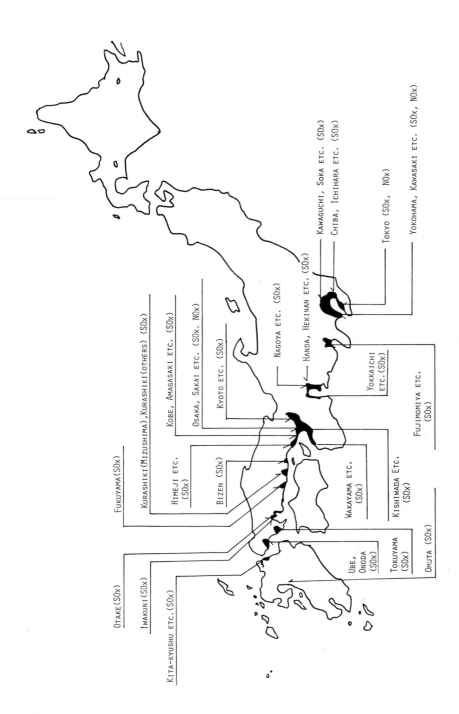

Fig. 5.2. The designated areas for the total mass emission control.

(4) The target quantity to which the total quantity
referred to in (2) above is to be reduced
(required emission reduction).

The total quantity referred to in (3) above corresponds to the permissible
total emission quantity for a given area, and it is calculated on the basis of
mathematical diffusion modeling.

An emission reduction plan typically provides for a target quantity (4) by
which the total quantity referred to in (1) is to be reduced to that referred
to in (3). The plan also specifies an attainment schedule and methods for
attaining the target emissions. According to such a plan, the prefecture
governor establishes standards for the total mass emission control. There are
two methods for determining such standards, but so far only the following
formula is used.

$$Q = aW^b$$

where,

Q : permissible emission quantity (Nm^3/h)

W : quantity of fuel used at specified factories

a : constant determined so as to attain the target
quantity of reduction

b : constant determined within $0.8 \leq b < 1$

It is also possible in certain cases, such as when a designated facility is
being enlarged or a new designated facility is being constructed, to apply a
special total emission standard which is more stringent than the standards
applied to existing facilities.

Fuel standards are also set for factories and businesses other than
specified facilities which force them to take appropriate control measures.
These standards apply throughout the year.

5.3 REGULATION OF NO_x

In 1973 Japan started regulating nitrogen oxides (NO_x). This was about 10
years after the first full-scale SO_x controls and coincided with the first oil
crisis. Despite the socio-economic difficulties caused by the oil crisis,
Japan started and continued strenuous efforts to abate NO_x pollution arising
from both stationary and mobile sources. Thanks to these measures ambient NO_2
levels have gradually and steadily declined throughout the country in recent
years. For instance, in Fig. 5.3, where data from 26 monitoring stations
reporting continuously since 1965 are shown, a slight upward trend at the
beginning has been replaced by generally flat figures in recent years. Similar
or more distinct improvement trends can be seen in Table 5.6.

These improvements were produced by advanced combustion technology and by
the denitrification of flue gas as well as by fuel conversion. Major aspects

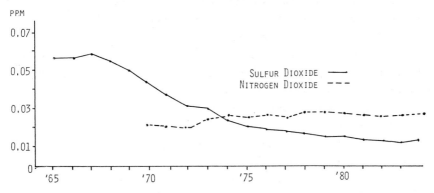

Fig. 5.3. Yearly average concentrations of sulfur dioxide and nitrogen dioxide.

of such technology are listed below.

(1) Low NO$_x$ combustion technique

    (i) Improvement of combustion conditions

        a) Decreasing air ratio

        b) Decreasing air preheating

        c) Decreasing heat load of combustion chamber

    (ii) Improvement of combustion techniques

        a) Using low NO$_x$ burners

        b) Two-stage combustion method

        c) Flue gas recirculation method

        d) Off-stoichiometric (Bias) combustion

Table 5.6

State of compliance with nitrogen dioxide environmental quality standards at general air pollution monitoring stations

Year	1978		1980		1982		1984	
	No. of stations	Ratio (%)	No. of stations	Ratio (%)	No. of stations	Ratio (%)	No. of stations	Ratio (%)
Over 0.06 ppm	75	7.6	44	2.8	25	2.0	43	3.3
Between 0.04 ppm and 0.06 ppm	233	23.8	288	24.4	267	21.4	283	21.7
Under 0.04 ppm	673	68.8	839	71.3	963	76.6	976	75.0
Total	981	100.0	1,169	100.0	1,245	100.0	1,362	100.0

      e) Improving combustion chamber design

      f) Water or steam injection

      g) Using fuel additives

(2) Denitrification of flue gas

As with SO_x control, the regulation of NO_x is based on several policy tools, which include:

    (a) setting national uniform emission standards for NO_x
        and strengthening of the standards in five phases;

    (b) total mass emission control;

    (c) regulation of motor vehicles.

5.3.1 Emission standards for nitrogen oxides

Nitrogen oxides are pollutants that demand close attention not only because they are harmful to human health but also because of their role in causing photochemical air pollution - so much so that measures designed to control nitrogen oxides have now completely replaced in importance those for sulfur oxides control.

Nitrogen oxides emission standards for facilities which emit smoke and soot were first formulated as regulations for uniform nationwide enforcement in August 1973 on the basis of the Air Pollution Control Law. The first regulations of 1973 were followed by successive measures to toughen the standards in December 1975 (second regulations), in June 1977 (third regulations) and in August 1979 (fourth regulations).

In September 1983, the latest revision (fifth regulations) was made in response to (1) the energy policy which promotes changes from oil to solid fuels such as coal which generate more nitrogen oxides, and (2) technical progress in combustion technology to reduce NO_x emissions. Emission standards for NO_x are very complex; they differ with the type of emitting facility as well as with the volume of flue gas and the date of installation of each facility.

5.3.2 Total mass emission control of NO_x

Nitrogen oxides emission control techniques for stationary sources include stack gas denitrification and low NO_x combustion techniques. The Environment Agency has been continuously following their development since 1975.

Recently, low NO_x combustion technology has been making remarkable progress, effecting considerable reductions of nitrogen oxide emissions by the use of two-stage combustion, low NO_x burners, etc.

Stack gas denitrification techniques have been applied not only to clean gases such as LNG, but also to dirty gases such as heavy oil combustion gas or even to coal combustion gas. The reliability of denitrification has been advanced by techniques such as improved catalyst beds and by solving the problem of acid ammonium sulfate deposition, etc.

Simple non-catalytic denitrification processes have already been put into practical use and have begun to offer an opportunity for process choice depending on the conditions of each facility such as cost efficiency, location, etc.

Total NO_x mass emission control was introduced along with these technological developments after the previous successful application of total SO_x mass emission control. Legally this was made possible by the revision of the enforcement ordinance of the Air Pollution Control Law in June 1981. Three areas of central Tokyo, Kanagawa and Osaka were chosen as "designated areas" for the system.

In these three areas, it was expected that environmental quality standards for NO_2 should be met by 1985 through reductions of 32.0% (Kanagawa), 26.9% (Osaka) and 19.3% (Tokyo) of nitrogen oxides emitted from specified factories by applying the total mass emission control.

The method of total mass emission control of NO_x is, in principle, the same as employed for SO_x. The only differences are as follows:

(1) Because in the case of NO_x, mobile sources such as motor cars are a major source of pollution, mere control of stationary sources does not suffice. Therefore, apart from the total mass emission control, tough measures against mobile sources such as reduction at source and drastic traffic control are necessary.

(2) In the formula to quantify the amount of permissible NO_x discharge from individual stationary sources, not only the formula of $Q = aW^b$ but also $Q = k \Sigma (CV)^\ell$ is used, here,

Q : Permissible amount of nitrogen oxides emission (unit - cubic meters per hour as converted to the values at a temperature of 0°C and a pressure of 1 atm).

W : Total amount of raw materials and fuels consumed by all soot- and smoke-emitting facilities related to nitrogen oxides in a specified industrial plant, etc., (unit - kiloliters per hour as converted to an amount of heavy oil).

a : Constant prescribed by the prefectural governor so as to achieve the emission reduction target.

b : Constant prescribed by the prefectural governor
within the range of not less than 0.80 to less
than 1.0 taking into consideration the state of
distribution by scale of the specified industrial
plants, etc., and the actual conditions of
consumption of raw materials fuels within the
designated area concerned.

C : Facility coefficient prescribed by the prefectural
governor for each type of soot- and smoke-emitting
facility related to nitrogen oxides.

V : Amount of gas emission of each soot- and smoke-
emitting facility related to nitrogen oxides
at a specified industrial plant, etc.
(unit - 10 thousand cubic meters per hour as
converted to the values at a temperature of
$0\,^\circ C$ and a pressure of 1 atm).

k : Reduction constant prescribed by the
prefectural governor so as to achieve the
emission reduction target.

ℓ : A constant prescribed by the prefectural
governor within the range of not less than
0.80 to less than 1.0 taking into consideration
the state of distribution by scale of the
specified industrial plants, etc. and the
nitrogen oxides emission characteristics, etc.
within the designated area concerned.

5.3.3 Regulation of motor vehicles

Nitrogen oxides emitted from motor vehicles have been regulated since 1973
for gasoline- or LPG-powered motor vehicles and since 1974 for diesel-powered
vehicles. A target standard of average emission of NO_x: 0.25 g/km for
gasoline- or LPG-powered cars was set in the interim report of October 1972 by
the Central Council for Environmental Pollution Control. Regulations
approaching this goal were implemented in 1975, 1976 and 1978. The 1978
standard is the most stringent standard in the world.

As a result, the amount of nitrogen oxides emitted from gasoline or
LPG-powered passenger cars was reduced by more than 90% from those levels prior
to regulation. As the number of motor vehicles conforming to the 1978
regulation increases, the exhaust NO_x emission rate from passenger cars is
expected to decrease.

Also, in order to eventually tighten regulations on exhaust gases from trucks and buses, the Central Council for Environmental Pollution Control reported on 26 December 1977, after about two and a half years of studies, on the long-term prospects of reducing the allowable limits of automotive exhaust gases.

Regulations for the first stage targets in accordance with the report became effective in 1979. Also, in order to enforce regulations as soon as possible for the second stage targets indicated in the report, the Investigating Committee for Motor Vehicle Pollution Control Technology was established to assess and review the current development of technology for reducing automotive exhaust gases and to promote technological development.

In response to the first report of the Motor Vehicle Control Technology Committee which was published in April 1979, the second phase regulations on light- and medium-weight gasoline-powered passenger cars were authorized for the 1981 regulations in August 1979. The enforcement began in January 1981 for light-weight gasoline-powered passenger cars and for medium-weight gasoline-powered passenger cars from December 1981.

Again, in response to the second report (published in May 1980), the second-stage regulations on heavy-weight gasoline-powered vehicles, light-weight trucks and indirect injection diesel vehicles were authorized for the 1982 regulations in September 1980. Enforcement started in January 1982 for heavy-weight gasoline-powered vehicles, light-weight trucks and indirect injection diesel passenger cars and in October 1982 for indirect injection diesel vehicles other than passenger cars.

Furthermore, based on the third report (published in May 1981), the second stage regulations for direct-injection diesel vehicles were proposed for 1983. Notification was issued in August 1981, and implementation began in August 1983. After that, the second stage regulations applied to all types of vehicles.

At present, the concentration control applied to diesel passenger cars is the same as that applied to trucks and buses. However, based on the upward trend in the number of diesel-powered passenger cars in recent years, an evaluation study indicated that a change from concentration control to emission load control was needed. Although a target value for emission load was proposed in May 1981 by the committee, the target was meant to be an administrative target to strengthen the regulations. Technical evaluation aimed at achieving the target in a short period is about to proceed.

Because it will take several years for the replacement of aged vehicles by low-pollution vehicles, nitrogen oxides regulations for trucks, buses, etc. will probably not prove effective until around 1985 for the 1979 regulations and around 1990 for the phase-2 regulations.

Other countermeasures as well as vehicle exhaust controls are required for

NO_x air pollution reductions, such as traffic control or improvements of road structures as well as drastic changes in urban transportation modes.

5.4 REGULATIONS OF PARTICULATES, HYDROCARBONS, AND OTHER TOXIC SUBSTANCES
5.4.1 Soot and dust and other particulates

Particulate matter in the ambient air is divided into two classes; dustfall and suspended particulate matter. Suspended particulates fall into two categories: suspended particulate matter less than 10 μm in diameter and other suspended particulates. Environmental quality standards, however, have been set only for suspended particulate matter less than 10 μm diameter.

The sources of such particulate matter are found in various areas, including industrial activities, such as factories or workshops, as well as motor vehicle traffic and naturally, such as soil matter raised by the wind. The Air Pollution Control Law regulates the particulate matter emitted from industrial activities in factories or workshops. This controlled particulate matter is classified into two categories under the law; one is "soot and dust" generated by combustion of fuels or other substances, or by using electricity as a heat source, and the other is "particulates" emitted or dispersed by crushing, grading or other mechanical operations or piling. The Air Pollution Control Law and other regulations also control the particulate matter emitted by motor vehicles such as black diesel smoke.

(i) Regulations against soot and dust. Emission standards for soot and dust are specified for each type and size of dust emitting facility. More stringent specified standards are stipulated for newly installed and expanded facilities in regions where clustered facilities create severe air pollution.

The partial amendments in the regulation for the implementation of the Air Pollution Control Law were promulgated in May 1982. The emission standards for soot and dust were strengthened to cope with changes in energy utilization, to keep pace with major developments in emission control technology and to contribute to the further control of suspended particulate matter.

The gist of the revision is as follows.

    (a) The utmost emphasis was laid on revising emission standards for coal-burning boilers. The allowable limits were reduced by nearly halving the pre-revision values for boilers burning heavy oil and other liquid fuels.

    (b) Standards for other facilities were also strengthened. The emission standards on other facilities discharging soot and dust were wholly revised. In general most emission limits were reduced to about 50% below the pre-revision levels. The new special emission standards, covering new facilities installed in nine highly polluted areas, including the 23 wards of Tokyo, were set at levels which can only be achieved by adopting sophisticated soot- and dust-control technology, which is now spreading. These standards were also strengthened to about 50% below the pre-revision levels.

(c) A standard oxygen concentration adjustment formula for soot and dust was introduced where its use was deemed appropriate in the light of the mechanisms whereby soot and dust are generated. This measure was taken to prevent polluters from diluting gas emissions to meet the standards and also to ensure fairness in enforcing controls.

(d) New emission standards for soot and dust were set for seven categories of facilities generating smoke and soot, including coke ovens and electrolytic furnaces for aluminum smelting. No emission standards for soot and dust had previously been in force on these facilities.

(e) This revision was put into effect on 1 June 1982. The new standards were immediately applied to new facilities. Previously existing facilities were spared the enforcement of the standards until 30 June 1984.

(ii) <u>Countermeasures against particulates.</u> Standards covering the structure, use, and management of particulate-generating facilities, such as conveyors and crushers were established in 1971.

In view of the increased use of coal and other solid fuels it is anticipated that the standards will be strengthened a little bit further.

(iii) <u>Countermeasures against suspended particulate matter.</u> Since the ambient air-quality standard for suspended particulate matter was established in January 1972, the compliance ratio for the standard remained exceedingly low until 1980. Although the rate has begun to rise in recent years (63% in 1983), it is still far from satisfactory. The establishment of countermeasures was begun in 1981. A 4-year investigation and survey was started to obtain results regarding the controls at the emission source, influence of emissions on the environment and results of improvement of the environment obtained by the implementation of countermeasures.

(iv) <u>Countermeasures against black diesel smoke.</u> Regulations regarding black smoke emitted from diesel-powered vehicles were put into effect in 1972 for new cars, and in 1975 for cars already in use.

Because of the recent upward trend in the number of diesel-powered vehicles, surveys were started in 1980 on actual pollution along roadsides caused by diesel exhaust gases and their effects on human health.

The recent increase in the number of vehicles with studded tires in winter has prompted the Environment Agency to conduct a survey on the environmental impact of dust generated by studded tires.

5.4.2 Countermeasures against photochemical air pollution and regulations of hydrocarbons

Photochemical air pollution is caused by a series of very complicated reactions in which the secondary pollutants of photochemical oxidants, consisting mainly of ozone, are generated from a mixture of air, NO_x, and HC irradiated by sunlight. During every summer since 1970, cases of tangible health damage have been observed. These are characterized by symptoms of irritated eyes, sore throats and sensations of suffocation, most likely caused by photochemical air pollution.

The government established the "Conference for Promotion of Photochemical Smog Control Measures," consisting of representatives of 12 government ministries and agencies in June 1972 in order to advance effective and comprehensive measures against air pollution by photochemical oxidants. In July of that year it reported "Promotion of Photochemical Smog Control Measures" which was a series of interim measures to be executed quickly and basic measures for long-term implementation. The conference decided on "Guidelines for Photochemical Smog Control" to establish more specific measures in April 1975. The Environment Agency has taken action and has conducted a series of surveys and investigations according to these suggestions. It established environmental quality standards for photochemical oxidants in May 1973. Incremental measures have been taken by the agency to tighten the regulation of NO_x emissions from factories, business establishments and automobiles and of HC emitted from automobiles.

The local authorities have adopted emergency guidelines for photochemical oxidant excesses in accordance with Article 23 of the Air Pollution Control Law. They issue photochemical forecasts, warnings or alarms according to observed concentrations of photochemical oxidants and weather conditions.

(i) Present state of photochemical air pollution. Warnings of photochemical oxidant excesses are issued when the hourly values of photochemical oxidants exceed 0.12 ppm and when polluted conditions are expected to continue based on meteorological observations. Warnings were issued on a total of 171 days in 16 prefectures during 1985, which was a significant increase over the period from 1979 to 1982. In those years, less than 100 warnings were issued during each

year because of low temperatures in summer and long lasting rainy seasons
(Table 5.7).

The breakdown of days with warnings by month for 1985 is one day in April,
19 days in May, 28 days in June, 64 days in July, 45 days in August, 13 days in
September and one day in October. The number of warnings were largest in July
and August reflecting meterological conditions favoring oxidant formation.

There have been no oxidant alarms issued since 1979. (An alarm is issued
when the hourly values of oxidant concentration exceed 0.24 ppm and this
condition is likely to continue based on meteorological conditions.)

(ii) Photochemical air pollution forecasts and emergency countermeasures.
To obtain the meterological data necessary for the judgement of issuing
emergency reports (warnings and alarms), the Environment Agency conducts
weather observations every summer in 10 locations of four regions, Tokyo Bay,
Ise Bay, Osaka Bay and Seto Inland Sea where the photochemical air pollution is
a problem. This meteorological information is shared with local authorities.
Meteorological conditions which are likely to threaten photochemical air
pollution are forecast and analyzed by the Meteorological Agency at eight air
pollution meteorological centers, 11 meteorological centers and 11
meteorological stations. These forecasts are reported to local government.
The local governments issue warnings or alarms based on this information
together with data from their own monitoring stations in accordance with local
guidelines for emergency measures against photochemical oxidants. They may
also request voluntary efforts to reduce the emission of air pollutants from
stationary sources and voluntary restraint of non-emergency car use. They also
provide public information and health care for residents.

(iii) Promotion of research and study on photochemical air pollution.
Photochemical air pollution is a very complicated phenomenon with diverse
aspects. Surveys of photochemical pollution cover a wide range of fields
including: mechanisms of photochemical reactions; meteorological effects such
as transport and diffusion; and emission of causal pollutants. Predictive
models of photochemical air pollution incorporate these factors as well as the

Table 5.7
Number of days with warnings issued and reported victims (1979-1985)

Year	1979	1980	1981	1982	1983	1984	1985
Number of days with warnings issued (days)	84	86	59	73	131	135	171
Number of reported victims (persons)	4,083	1,420	780	446	1,721	5,822	966

effects of secondary pollutants on human health and of photochemical oxidants on vegetation. Surveys conducted to date have already revealed much about the nature of this difficult problem.

Laboratory research is being conducted in parallel exploring the mechanisms of photochemical reactions - photooxidation reactions in the ambient atmosphere are studied using movable smog chambers. Photochemical reactions of the HC - NO_x - wet air system are studied using large smog chambers located at the National Institute for Environmental Studies. This research is steadily accelerating our theoretical understanding of the details of photochemical reactions. Such efforts are allowing more accurate prediction of smog processes.

On the other hand, observation of the upper atmosphere is being conducted by using pilot balloons and radiosondes. Analytical studies of the relationships between pollutant concentrations and meteorological conditions on the ground surface and of the contributions of meteorological conditions to photochemical air pollution are also in progress, since knowledge of photochemical pollution in the actual environmental atmosphere is very important.

Researchers have developed a physicochemical model which can quantitatively reproduce concentrations of photochemical oxidants occurring in smog events. This model is based upon photochemical reaction models obtained from the above-mentioned studies. Data on pollutants and meteorological states in the upper atmosphere, data on the emission of primary pollutants and data on surface meteorological conditions are provided by daily monitoring. The research, which was started in 1975, has allowed increasingly accurate prediction of photochemical pollution occurring during particular summer days in the Tokyo Bay region. These achievements will support the emergency reporting system allowing improved control of regional photochemical air pollution.

(iv) Control of hydrocarbon emissions.

a. Control of hydrocarbons emitted from stationary sources

The importance of controlling HC, emitted from stationary sources has been pointed out in the "Guidelines for Photochemical Smog Control in the Future" reported both by the Conference for Promotion of Photochemical Smog Control Measures in April 1975 and in the report of the Central Council for Environmental Pollution Control in August 1976.

The Environment Agency established an expert study group for reviewing HC control of stationary sources in November 1979. The agency has conducted surveys on HC emissions and has evaluated emission control techniques since then. It adopted "The Promotion of Countermeasures for HC to Prevent Photochemical Pollution" based on the results of the survey of July 1982 in order to strengthen the control of HC emitted from stationary sources. The report evaluated the present state of HC emitted from stationary sources and emission control techniques and determined the direction of the measures to be taken.

The Environment Agency, in July 1982, requested local government authorities and related organizations to promote measures for emission control, and in March 1983, requested them to collect and organize data on stationary HC sources. It is anticipated that HC emissions from stationary sources would be much more effectively controlled by the use of such data.

b. Control of hydrocarbon emission from motor vehicles

Controls of HC emissions from motor vehicles consist of regulations on: 1) blow-by gas (an unburnt mixture of gas and air, which is emitted from the space between the piston and the cylinder; its major components are HC) from gasoline- and LPG-fuelled motor vehicles in 1970; 2) fuel vapor in 1972; and 3) HC emitted from the exhaust pipe of diesel-powered vehicles in 1974. Regulations for passenger cars, light- and medium-duty gasoline-fuelled vehicles and light cargo vehicles were all tightened in 1975.

As a result, the amounts of HC emitted from regulated passenger cars were reduced by 92% compared to preregulated cars (Fig. 5.4). The amounts of HC emitted from light- and medium-duty gasoline-fuelled vehicles, light cargo vehicles, heavy-duty gasoline-fuelled vehicles and diesel-powered vehicles were reduced by 65%, 52%, 52% and 10%, respectively, compared to those under no regulations.

5.4.3 Emission standards for toxic substances

In addition to NO_x, the Air Pollution Control Law designates the following four groups of substances as toxic substances generated from soot- and smoke-emitting facilities and stipulates control of their emission levels; (1) cadmium and its compounds, (2) chlorine and hydrogen chloride, (3) fluorine, hydrogen fluoride and silicon fluoride, and (4) lead and its compounds.

Standards are set for each of the four groups of toxic substances only, and

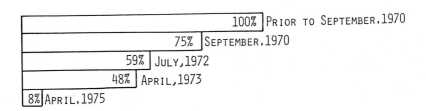

Fig. 5.4. Regulation of hydrocarbons emitted by passenger cars.

are applicable to a very limited number of soot and smoke emitting facilities. For instance, in the case of cadmium and its compounds, the emission standard is 1.0 mg/Nm^3, and as for lead and its compounds, the standard is 10 - 30 mg/Nm^3, depending on the type of furnace.

5.4.4 Regulation of carbon monoxide

Carbon monoxide (CO) emitted from automobiles was first regulated in 1966. Emission levels have been progressively reduced since then. Full-scale controls for three major pollutants (CO, NO$_x$, HC) were applied to gasoline- or LPG-powered vehicles in 1973, and to diesel-powered vehicles in 1974, both of which strengthened the CO standards. Thanks to the remarkable progress in engine technology including devices such as three-way catalysts, more stringent CO standards were applied to light/medium duty gasoline-powered passenger cars in 1975. This has reduced emission levels by 90% compared to the level of non-regulated vehicles.

This is reflected in the decline of average annual CO values recorded at 15 motor vehicle exhaust monitoring stations which have been taking measurements at roadsides continuously since 1971. Annual average values have fallen each year from a level of 6.0 ppm in 1971 to a level of 2.5 ppm in 1984 (Fig. 5.5). All the 293 roadside stations throughout the country met the ambient quality standard for CO in 1984.

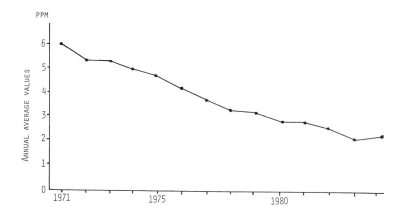

Fig. 5.5. Changes in annual average concentrations of CO.

5.5 UNIQUE EFFORTS BY LOCAL GOVERNMENTS AND INDUSTRY

In Japan, the fight against pollution was initiated and advanced rapidly by certain local governments where pollution problems surfaced in the early days and needed to be solved urgently without waiting for the eventual enactment of nationwide legislation. During this process, local governments devised a variety of effective instruments, some of which were later codified by the central government. Among them are: (1) the setting of stricter emission standards by the local government, and (2) the setting of emission standards by the local government for some pollutants which are not subject to control by national laws.

Japanese industry in general has also responded to the need to improve the environment in very positive ways. They have shown grave concern for environmental protection by concluding agreements with local governments leading to the stricter implementation of various environmental regulations.

Major factories in Japan must now have, by law, their own special departments for pollution control supported by highly educated and skilled personnel. The government conducts an annual national examination to certify competent persons for pollution control work in industry.

In this section such unique systems at both the local government level and in industry will be discussed.

5.5.1 Legislation by local governments

Administratively the Japanese Islands are divided into 47 prefectures and each prefecture is made up of municipalities (cities, towns and villages). In total we have some 3,250 municipalities across the country. "Local governments" are either prefectural or municipal. Each prefecture and each municipality, regardless of its size, must have its own legislative body, all members of which are directly elected by local people. Under the constitution of Japan, any legislative body of the prefecture or municipality can enact an "ordinance (by-law)", but the contents of these must conform with national laws.

Environmental problems, in most cases, are first perceived as local problems with different aspects due to natural conditions such as topography and climate, and social conditions such as population structure and the extent of industrial development. Therefore the local government is almost always the first to face the problem and is charged with the task of solving it, or at least trying to solve it, especially when there are no applicable national laws.

Under such circumstances, the local government has always been in a position to take the initiative in the fight against pollution. To do so legally it has needed ordinances approved by its legislative body. For instance, in Tokyo, as

early as 1949, the Industrial Pollution Control Ordinance was enacted and
various measures based on the ordinance were taken, although the measures were
not strong enough in many respects. This action by the Tokyo Metropolitan
Government was followed by similar legislative actions in the Osaka Prefecture
in 1950, the Kanagawa Prefecture in 1951 and in many other prefectures and
municipalities later on. By now, all prefectures and all major municipalities
have enacted very effective pollution control ordinances. To implement
measures embodied in the ordinances and measures required by national laws,
most local governments have set up special departments for pollution control.

As of 1 October 1985, prefectural governments have a department (division)
or a section (office) responsible for pollution control variously named,
together with pollution monitoring centers, pollution research institutes and
similar organizations. In addition, health centers have also been involved in
environmental administration together with the Agriculture and Forestry Offices
and prefectural offices. Prefectural offices have a total of 7,054 personnel
in charge of pollution control.

As of 1 October 1985, the number of municipal governments which had a
department (division, section, office) responsible for pollution control was
155. Municipal governments which provided a group responsible for pollution
control numbered 473. Municipal governments which had only full-time officials
responsible for pollution control numbered 368, the total of these amounted to
30.5% of all municipal governments. In addition, the number of municipal
governments which had either a pollution monitoring center or a pollution
research institute was 49. The number of municipal full-time personnel in
charge of pollution control was 6,268.

Ordinances enacted by local governments for environmental conservation can
be largely classified into the following four categories: 1) ordinances for
pollution control; 2) ordinances for environmental conservation; 3) ordinances
for nature conservation; and 4) other ordinances concerned with environmental
conservation (including ordinances for environmental impact assessment).

Ordinances for pollution control indicate that the basic attitude of the
local government toward pollution control is important for systematically
promoting practical measures for pollution control in local areas. All
prefectures have enacted ordinances for pollution control.

Ordinances for environmental conservation are basic regulations for local
governments to achieve integrated environmental conservation. As of 1 October
1985, seven prefectures and one ordinance-designated city have such ordinances.

Ordinances for nature conservation indicate the basic guidelines for local
governments to conserve the natural environment, and have been enacted by all
47 prefectures.

Other ordinances for environmental conservation include ordinances for natural parks, controlling quarries and conserving prefectural land. They also include ordinances for maintaining green space in the environment, ordinances for the taking of subterranean water, ordinances for the control of scattered empty cans and ordinances for the prevention of eutrophication of lakes. In addition, ordinances for environmental impact assessment have recently been appearing.

As such, it may be safely said that the state of enactment of ordinances by local governments is extensive and satisfactory, but it seems to me more important to note again that in Japan the ordinance is not just a copy of a national law but it supplements it or even provides stricter control of pollution. In the case of air pollution control, in Article 4 of the Air Pollution Control Law, it states as follows:

"1. In case any prefecture recognizes that the existing emission standards prescribed under Paragraphs 1 and 3 hereof with respect to soot and dust and toxic substances are inadequate to protect public health or conserve the living environment from the natural and social conditions in a part of its area, it may establish by a prefectural ordinance in accordance with the provisions of the Cabinet Order, a stricter emission standard with respect to such pollutants generated by soot- and smoke-emitting facilities in the part of the area, which supersedes the maximum permissible limits under the provision of Paragraph 1 of the preceding article.

2. The prefectural ordinance referred to in the preceding paragraph shall clarify the range of such an area.

3. If any prefecture establishes an emission standard under the provisions of Paragraph 1, it shall notify in advance the Director General of the Environment Agency."

In Article 32 of the same law, it is also stated that

"The provision of this law shall not prevent the local governments from instituting necessary regulations by ordinances on the emission into the air of substances other than soot and smoke generated by soot- and smoke-emitting facilities, the emission into the air of soot and smoke generated by facilities other than soot- and smoke-emitting facilities, and the discharge or

scattering into the air of particulates generated,
discharged or scattered by facilities other than
particulates emitting facilities."

Thanks to these articles in the law, in Japan local governments are very well
equipped with legislative powers.

5.5.2 Concluding pollution control agreements with industry

Apart from legislative power, local governments came up with one more very
unique and effective tool to constrain pollution, viz. through agreements with
the private companies concerned. This control system by way of "agreement" was
first introduced when the city of Yokohama was about to sell its newly
reclaimed offshore land in Isogo to two electric power companies which had
intended to build their thermal power plants on the land to meet the
ever-increasing demand for power supply in the high economic growth period of
the 1950s.

The city of Yokohama, in the negotiation process of selling its reclaimed
land as a site for the location of power plants, put forward to the companies a
number of conditions for pollution prevention, which were far more stringent
than the current regulations under both national laws and local ordinances.
Because the site was so close to residential areas, nearby residents had
strongly demanded that the city take a hard line on this issue. There was very
strong public opinion supporting the city as well as citizens' movements which
were rampant in those days. After heated and serious negotiations, the city
succeeded in getting the companies to accept the conditions in the form of an
agreement in late 1964, which was signed by the mayor and the presidents of the
two power companies.

Legally this agreement was neither a law nor an ordinance. It was just a
gentlemen's agreement concluded between the mayor and the representatives of
private companies. But in effect, it functioned like a legally binding
agreement and it forced the companies to take all necessary pollution control
measures as promised. For example, the agreed emission control levels for the
Isogo Thermal Power Plant of Electric Power Development Co., Ltd., one of the
signatories to the agreement, are shown with other relevant information in this
matter in Table 5.8.

As the case of Yokohama turned out to be a big success, this "agreement
system" spread rapidly to other parts of Japan including almost all types of
new industrial development, viz. the location, relocation or expansion of
plants.

Factories and other business premises which have concluded agreements of
pollution prevention number 25,658 as of 1 October 1984 showing an increase of
1,531 over the previous year.

[For information about the Isogo Plant]

1. Address   : Shin-Isogo, Isogo-ku, Yokohama
                         City

2. Output   : Unit No. 1   265,000 kw
                         Unit No. 2   265,000 "

3. Month and year of : Unit No. 1   May 1967
   start of commercial
   operation   Unit No. 2   September 1969

4. Land area   : Total area 121,290 m^2
                         (Including coal stock yard
                         of 20,700 m^2)

5. Power product   : Gross 3,732 x 10^6 KWH
                         (Fiscal year 1982)

                         Net   3,366 x 10^6 KWH
                         ("   )

6. Capacity factor   : 80.4%

7. Fuel
     Main fuel
        Coal   Consumption quantity:
                             1,353 x 10^3 t
                             (Fiscal year 1982)

        Mining site   Calorific value:
                                  6,200 kcal/kg

        Hokkaido
        Kyushu (Miike coal) Sulfur content:
                                  less than 0.6%

     Auxiliary Fuel
        Heavy and light oil Consumption quantity:
                             42 x 10^3 kl/2 unit/year
                             (Fiscal year 1982)
                             Calorific value:
                                  9,700 kcal/l
                             Sulfur content:
                                  less than 1.0%

8. Water
     Industrial water   Approx. 3,000t/Day
                             (Average)

     Re-use   Approx.   500   "
     (from Wet FGD)   (ditto)

9. Ash disposal

Ash disposal		212×10^3 t/2 unit/year
		(Fiscal year 1982)
Ash quantity for		202×10^3 t/year
re-use		(ditto)
	Cement raw material	105×10^3 t/year
	Cement mixture material	93×10^3 "
	Raw material for	4×10^3 "
	fertilizer of potassium	
	silicate	
Reclamation		10×10^3 "
		(Fiscal year 1982)

10. Gypsum

Product	44×10^3 t/year
Quantity for re-use	44×10^3 "

The number of agreements concluded on pollution prevention has continued to increase probably because 1) agreements on pollution prevention enable the concerned parties to take the proper measures suitable to the geographical conditions and social situations of the local communities and 2) managers of plants are likely to encounter obstacles durng operation unless they obtain the consent of local residents when selecting sites.

The details of agreements on pollution prevention are as follows. The most frequently listed pollution is water pollution. A total of 51.5% of the establishments maintaining agreements include water pollution in their control programs.

Table 5.8

Comparison of strictness by control systems

	Agreed upon levels	National/Local regulation levels
SOx	60 ppm	K = 3.0 ⟶ 200 – 240 ppm TMEC 100 ppm
NOx	159 ppm	480 ppm TMEC 184 ppm
Soot and dust	0.05 g/Nm^3	0.4 g/Nm^3

Note: TMEC stands for Total Mass Emission Control Prescribed by the Kanagawa Prefectural Government

These agreements on pollution prevention have been increasing recently, and are often concluded with local residents participating as one of the parties along with local governments, or alternatively as observers. Such agreements numbered 1,419 as of 1 October 1984, and agreements on pollution prevention made between citizen's groups and industries numbered 3,131.

Agreements on pollution prevention which provide for: 1)restriction of operation; 2)compensation for pollution caused by establishments; 3)liability without negligence; and 4)compensation or spot investigation to ensure the effectiveness of the agreements are increasing in number.

5.5.3 Efforts made by industries

The rapid and remarkable improvement in Japan's environment was brought about by a number of factors, such as increasingly stringent legislation, rigorous implementation by both national and local governments, strong support from the general public and mass media, legal actions in courts of law and structural changes in the industrial structure and energy supply systems. But it is without doubt that Japanese industry as a whole responded very positively to the threatening crisis in the environment in the 1960s and early 1970s, and without such active participation on the part of industry, the environment would now be far less agreeable for the Japanese.

(i) Investment in pollution control facilities. Private business has made enormous investments in the installation of pollution-control equipment and process change. Pollution control investments showed a downtrend after hitting a peak in 1975, but from 1980 they have grown gradually (Fig. 5.6). Installation of primary pollution control equipment began with the introduction of direct heavy-oil-desulfurization equipment followed by indirect heavy-oil-desulfurization equipment. Heavy-oil-desulfurization devices were rapidly installed from the latter half of the 1960s, and now most oil refineries are equipped with them. Installation of stack-gas-desulfurization equipment made rapid headway from the latter half of the 1960s, though the installation rate had somewhat slowed down in the latter half of the 1970s. Such extensive adoption of desulfurization equipment contributed substantially to the decline of sulfur oxide levels in the ambient air (Fig. 5.7).

The installation of stack-gas-denitrification equipment also progressed rapidly from the latter half of the 1970s (Fig. 5.8).

(ii) Technological development for pollution control. Since the 1960s the Japanese private sector has made every effort to apply scientific and technical advances in environmental protection, whether they are of domestic or foreign origin. In fact a number of technical seeds were imported from the United States and Western Europe but, in many cases, it is in Japan where such technology has been developed to levels of highly reliable and efficient

236

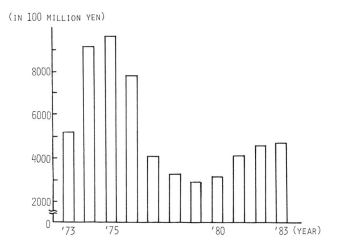

Fig. 5.6. Trends of pollution control investments by major private enterprises.

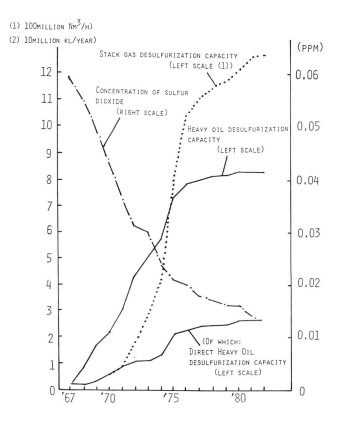

Fig. 5.7. Desulfurization capacity and concentration of sulfur dioxide.

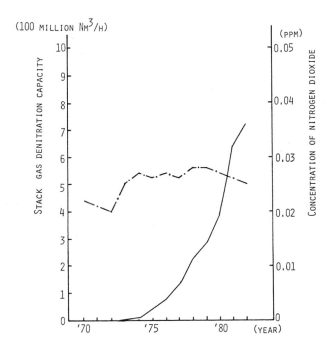

Fig. 5.8. Denitrification capacity and concentration of nitrogen dioxide.

commercial use. Such examples can be seen in a variety of technical fields such as automatic and continuous monitoring devices for air pollutants, telemetering techniques, desulfurization of fuel oil as well as flue gas, three-way catalysts used for motor vehicles, boiler combustion techniques and denitrification of flue gas.

Japanese industry has taken a decisive role in the development and implementation of all these advanced techniques. In this way, further promotion of technological innovation and its commercialization for higher levels of pollution control will continue in Japanese industries.

(iii) Establishment of the pollution control systems in factories. In order to prevent industrial pollution, it is also essential to improve pollution control systems in industrial plants. For this purpose, the Law for the Establishment of Organization for Pollution Control in Specific Factories was enacted in June 1971 to oblige entrepreneurs, from September 1972, to appoint pollution control superintendents to manage operations for pollution control in specific factories. These pollution-control managers must be equipped with specialized knowledge and skills for pollution-control. About 19,000 specific factories have built up their pollution-control systems with such specialists. In 1976, vibration-control managers were newly added.

The statistics of pollution-control superintendents and pollution control managers, from prefectural surveys show that, as of the end of March 1982, pollution-control superintendents numbered about 11,500 and the number of proxies was 11,000. Pollution-control managers, etc. numbered about 21,000, while proxies numbered 19,500.

GENERAL REFERENCES

1. Environment Agency's annual reports entitled "Quality of the Environment in Japan"
2. Environment Agency's Report submitted to the OECD Environment Committee's study on the environmental policies of Japan, entitled "Environmental Policy of Japan", July 1975
3. Air Pollution Control Division, Air Quality Bureau, Environment Agency, "The Outline of Air Pollution Control in Japan" January 1985
4. Saburo KATO, "Fifteen years under the Air Pollution Control Law (in Japanese)" Environmental Research Quarterly (published by Environmental Research Center) No. 47, February 1984

Chapter 6

THE POLLUTION-RELATED HEALTH DAMAGE COMPENSATION LAW

MICHIO HASHIMOTO

6.1 INTRODUCTION

Enacted on 10 October 1973, Japan's Pollution-Related Health Damage Compensation Law[1] established a much needed, pollutor-financed, nationwide compensation system for victims of designated illnesses caused by air and water pollution. While many nations, including Japan, have laws to control the emission
of substances toxic to the environment, only Japan has a comprehensive program
to provide financial and other aid to pollution victims. This chapter presents
Japan's four major pollution incidents during the 1950s and 1960s, the litigation based on these incidents, pollution legislation prior to the Compensation
Law, and the legislative history, mechanics, and an assessment of the Compensation Law.

During the 1950s and 1960s, Japan was absorbed with economic recovery.
Government, industry, and the scientific community were largely unprepared for
and unconcerned by the pollution illnesses which began to appear in the 1950s.
In 1955, a local scientist in the village of Fuchu in Toyama prefecture on
Honshu was the first to correctly diagnose itai-itai disease (cadmium
poisoning), an illness which had been endemic since 1910. In 1956, physicians
reported a new disease of unknown etiology in the vicinity of Minamata Bay in
Kumamoto prefecture on Kyushu. Not until 1968 did the Ministry of Health and
Welfare officially recognize that the so-called Minamata disease is caused by
ingestion of methylated mercury, a byproduct in the production of acetaldehyde.
In 1965, a second outbreak of Minamata disease was reported in the city of
Niigata in Niigata prefecture on Honshu. In 1961, residents of the city of
Yokkaichi in Mie prefecture on the Pacific coast of Honshu, the site of a large
complex of oil refineries and petrochemical and power plants, developed asthma,
emphysema, bronchitis, and other respiratory ailments.

It took a long time for attitudes towards pollution to change in Japan.
The victims were mostly poor, isolated, and inarticulate, and the pollutors
were callous and indifferent to their suffering. The development-oriented
government authorities had other priorities--to promote industry at all costs

and to make Japan internationally competitive. Perhaps this environment helps to explain why it took thirteen years after the initial outbreak for the Kumamoto victims of Minamata disease to decide to file suit against the Chisso Corporation.

In decisions which broke new ground doctrinally, the courts ruled in favor of the plaintiff-victims in all four cases, and awarded them damages. In the itai-itai case, the court held the defendant strictly liable under article 109[2] of the Mining Law.

In the Yokkaichi and the two Minamata disease cases, the courts held the defendants negligent. The courts found that the pollutors had a duty to use the most advanced techniques to detect and measure toxic substances in their industrial processes, and to conduct a program of continuous research on the possible hazardous effects of substances where risks were unknown. In addition, defendants had a duty to monitor the effects of such substances on the environment, use the most advanced technology to control these substances, and to terminate operations where necessary to avoid jeopardizing human health.[3]

Rendered between June 1971 and March 1973, the decisions were devastating to industry and contributed to society's acceptance of the notion that industry was responsible for the pollution it caused. Moreover, the trials were highly publicized, and they helped to arouse and mobilize the indignation of the citizens. The effect of the trials is most clearly manifested in the area of legislation. During the period of greatest national ferment over the trials, the government promoted the enactment of the strict liability amendments to the air- and water-pollution control laws,[4] and it passed the Pollution-Related Health Damage Compensation Law as a direct legislative response to the Yokkaichi decision.[5]

6.2 THE FOUR POLLUTION CASES

6.2.1 Minamata disease in Kumamoto prefecture

On 21 April 1956, pediatricians at the hospital attached to the Minamata plant of Chisso Corporation examined a six-year-old girl with symptoms of brain damage caused by unknown mechanisms. Physicians and townspeople at first called this perplexing affliction the "strange disease of Minamata." Government agencies and private groups conducted studies on the new illness to discover its cause and treatment, but definitive answers remained elusive for years. By 1977, the disease would afflict 910 people living in the coastal area of Minamata Bay.[6]

The victims of this most well-known of Japan's pollution diseases became the center of a national uprising against pollution.[7]

Minamata disease is a neurological disorder due to methylated mercury poisoning. It is very painful, causes tremors, and leads to severe, permanent

neurological and mental disabilities or death. Victims of Minamata disease
show symptoms similar to those of the Hunter-Russell syndrome, -- a disease
reported in Britain in 1940 which afflicted workers who handled various mercury
compounds.[8]

Because pregnant women poisoned by mercury transmit the toxin through the
placenta to their fetuses, many children born in Minamata during the mid- and
late-1950s were afflicted with the disease.[9]

Beginning in February 1946, Chisso Corporation discharged its waste water
containing methylated mercury through the Hyakken Channel into Minamata Bay.
Methylated mercury was a byproduct of Chisso's acetaldehyde production process,
which was produced for use in the manufacture of an acetic acid compound.
Gradually, the mercury settled in the bottom sediment and concentrated in the
tissues of fish and shellfish. The residents of Minamata became poisoned by
the mercury by eating the contaminated seafood.

It took many years for physicians and scientists to understand the etiology
of Minamata disease. During the hospital examination of the first case in
April 1956, it was learneed that there were two others with the same symptoms in
the patient's neighborhood. Alarmed by the seriousness of the outbreak, the
hospital reported the incident to the Minamata Health Center. Health officials
surveyed the area and found about forty afflicted patients. Family members had
been concealing individuals with the disease because they had been quickly
labeled as suffering from a communicable disease and the conventional belief
persisted that patients of communicable diseases should be hidden from sight.
The investigating officials also learned that large fish had floated to the
surface of Minamata Bay, and that cats which ate those fish became afflicted
with the same disease. One count taken by a house-to-house survey found that
50 out of 60 cats that lived in 40 patients' households died during 1953 to
1956. House cats usually died a couple of months before a member of the same
household was taken ill.[10]

Thereafter, on 28 May 1956, local health officials formed the Action Committee on the Strange Disease at Minamata. The Action Committee conducted a study
of the unknown disease and requested Kumamoto University Medical School to
investigate the matter. On 24 August 1956, the Medical School organized the
Minamata Disease Medical Research Team, consisting of doctors and other scientists from Kumamoto University Medical School. The Medical School suspected
industrial waste from Chisso, but it took several years to collect and analyze
the data.

In June 1957, Professor Takeuchi of the Kumamoto University Medical School
pointed to organic mercury as a possible causative agent.[11]

In February 1959, the Medical School began to monitor the concentration and
distribution of mercury in the fish, shellfish, and bottom sediment of Minamata

Bay. It was discovered that in September 1958, Chisso had changed the site of
its waste-water dump from the Hyakken Channel to the Yawata Pool, which leads
into the mouth of the Minamata River. In March 1959, six months later, the
first cases of Minamata disease began to appear in patients living near the
mouth of the river.[12] With this and other evidence, in July 1959, Kumamoto
University Medical School published its conclusions on the cause of Minamata
disease. It proposed the organic mercury theory, which later proved to be
correct.

Chisso immediately denied that its production process produced organic
mercury. In support of this contention, it noted that the catalyzer used in
its acetaldehyde manufacturing process was inorganic mercury, a harmless substance. Nevertheless, Kumamoto University Medical School continued its search
for the definitive cause of Minamata disease. In this effort, it was supported
by funds from Japan's Ministry of Education and the National Institutes of
Health of the United States Public Health Service. In 1960, Professor M.
Uchida of the Kumamoto University Medical School crystallized an organic mercury compound from an extract of shellfish in Minamata Bay and identified sulfur
in the alkylmercury. In September 1961, at the Seventh International Neurology
Assembly, Professor Uchida identified the chemical as a methyl mercury-
compound.[13] In October 1960, Professor K. Irukayama had taken a sample of
sludge from the waste water outlet of Chisso's factory and later identified
methyl mercury chloride (CH_3HgCl) in the substance.[14] Thus, methylmercury had
been found both in Chisso's waste water and in the fish eaten by Minamata
residents.

A number of other studies which produced different theories proceeded in
parallel with the investigation conducted by Kumamoto University Medical
School. After the first outbreak in April 1956, Kumamoto prefecture requested
the Ministry of Health and Welfare to monitor the spread of the disease. The
Ministry organized a study team headed by the dean of Kumamoto University
Medical School and the director of the prefectural health department. After an
initial study, the Ministry of Health and Welfare study team pointed to heavy-
metal poisoning as the suspected cause of the disease. In 1957, the Food
Sanitation Division of the Ministry of Health and Welfare took over responsibility for the case from the Control Division. In July 1957, it published the
manganese-selenium-thallium theory, which proposed that fish and shellfish
served as transmission media for these heavy metals. In July 1958, the director general of the public health bureau of the Ministry of Health and Welfare
ordered a scientific study based on the theory that industrial wastes contaminated the bottom sediment of Minamata Bay, which in turn contaminated fish and
shellfish and poisoned humans through unknown mechanisms. Again, Chisso denied
that this was the cause, noting that the amounts of manganese, selenium and

thallium in its waste water were below toxic levels. Later, the Ministry of Health and Welfare began to suspect mercury poisoning. On 12 November 1959, the Food Sanitation Council of the Ministry of Health and Welfare issued its report on the cause of the disease to the Minister of Health and Welfare. The report concluded that a type of alkylmercury compound in the fish and shellfish of Minamata Bay caused the disease. The report further concluded that indus- trial-waste effluent was probably the source of the alkylmercury contamination. However, the report did not contain any scientific proof of this theory due to restrictions on investigation set forth in the Food Sanitation Law. In a cabinet session, the Minister of Health and Welfare reported that the Minister of International Trade and Industry claimed that it was too early to point to alkylmercury discharged in industrial-waste effluent.

In 1964, the Ministry of Health and Welfare established the Division of Environmental Pollution Control. Professor H. Shiraki of the Kumamoto Univer- sity Medical School convinced the Division of Environmental Pollution Control[15] to take an interest in his research on the Minamata disease.

After discussing the matter, the Ministry of Health and Welfare decided to publish a monograph on Minamata disease research. The monograph was a compila- tion of all the studies and reports by members of the Kumamoto University Medical School Minamata Disease Medical Research Team from 1956 to 1963. It was funded by a new budget item contained in the 1965 fiscal budget.

The Economic Planning Agency had jurisdiction over matters under the Water Quality Conservation Law.[16] Nevertheless, it did not take jurisdiction of the Minamata disease incident under the authority granted by this statute because it was difficult to have new water zones designated for water pollution control purposes. However, in January 1960, the Economic Planning Agency organized the Minamata Disease Comprehensive Study Liaison Committee. While legislation limited the scope of permitted activities of the Ministry of Health and Welfare to medical research, the Liaison Committee did not have such limitations. Nevertheless, after only four sessions, officials dissolved the Liaison Commit- tee in March 1961. At its dissolution, the committee had failed to reach any conclusions.

Other groups with an economic interest in the outcome of the studies on the Minamata disease organized their own research efforts. For example, the Japan Chemical Industry Federation established a study committee to explore theories which would work against the alkylmercury theory.

Even Chisso conducted an internal investigation of the poisoning. It car- ried out secret experiments on cats and obtained toxicological results similar to the cerebellar findings of the Minamata disease pattern. However, Chisso[17] kept this information confidential and stopped the experiments.

Later, the Kumamoto court would point to Chisso's knowledge of its own guilt to void a patently unfair settlement agreement between Chisso and the Minamata victims. In other research carried out in 1962, Chisso identified CH_3Hg in the reactor drain of its acetaldehyde manufacturing plant, -- the same compound that had been identified by Professor Irukayama of Kumamoto University Medical School in 1960. Chisso also chose not to disclose the findings of this study.[18]

The suspected presence of mercury in Minamata Bay hurt the area's economy. In 1957, Kumamoto prefecture recommended a voluntary stop of sales of fish caught in Minamata Bay as a precautionary measure. When the presence of Minamata disease patients was confirmed in an area extending north of the City of Minamata, no one was willing to buy fish caught along the entire Shiranui coast. Members of the Minamata City Fishermen's Union as well as fishermen in neighboring towns could no longer engage in their livelihood. They demanded and received compensatory payments from Chisso Corporation.

Chisso also entered into settlement agreements with the victims of Minamata disease. On 15 August 1957, the victims formed the Mutual Aid Society of Patients of Minamata Disease and their Families in order to negotiate a settlement with Chisso. On 1 December 1959, the victims asked that the Conciliation Committee on Disputes Concerning Fisheries on Shiranui Coast, a group set up by the governor of Kumamoto prefecture, take up the problem of compensating the victims. On 31 December 1959, Chisso and the victims agreed on the terms of compensation. The agreement required Chisso to pay extremely small sums as sympathy money without admitting guilt. Article 5 of the agreement stated that "Even if it is determined in the future that Minamata disease is caused by water discharged from [Chisso's] factory, [the victims] shall make no further claim for compensation whatsoever."[19]

On 20 March 1973, the Kumamoto district court ruled that this provision was void as against public policy because, at the time the agreement was entered into, Chisso had known from its internal investigations, that its waste water contained methylated mercury.

6.2.2 Minamata disease in Niigata prefecture

In January 1965, Professor Tadao Tsubaki of the Niigata University Medical School Hospital diagnosed the Hunter-Russell syndrome in a 65-year-old patient. In April 1965, he confirmed the same diagnosis on a second patient. In view of these diagnoses, Professor Tsubaki initiated a clinical and epidemiological study in the downstream area of the Agano River basin in Niigata prefecture. He measured the alkylmercury content in hair and environmental samples. In May 1965 at the Kanto Neurology Society Meeting, Professor Tsubaki reported four cases of alkylmercury poisoning (one fatal). He also reported the findings to the Niigata prefectural government and characterized them as an outbreak of alkylmercury poisoning of unknown origins.[20] In June 1965, the prefecture reported these findings to the national government.

Several study teams were quickly organized to investigate the source of the mercury which had caused the poisonings. Niigata prefecture, Niigata University, and the Ministry of Health and Welfare organized the Niigata Prefecture Mercury Poisoning Research Center, later called the Niigata Prefecture Organic Mercury Poisoning Research Center. The Economic Planning Agency and the Ministry of International Trade and Industry began separate investigations. Also, the Science and Technology Agency formed an inter-ministerial study team comprised of itself, the Ministry of Agriculture, Forestry and Fisheries, and the Ministry of Health and Welfare. Within the Ministry of Health and Welfare, the Division of Food Sanitation studied the disease's epidemiology and the Division of Environmental Pollution Control monitored industrial plants which used mercury.

From the studies conducted in connection with the Kumamoto Minamata disease in the late 1950s and 1960s, it was known that alkylmercury contamination caused Minamata disease. Thus, the issue in Niigata prefecture was the source of the alkylmercury which caused the Niigata poisoning, and the several study teams concentrated on this question. This was a significant difference in approach between the Kumamoto and Niigata incidents.

The study teams proposed three theories on the source of the mercury which had caused the poisonings: (i) spillage related to the earthquake that rocked Niigata in June 1964; (ii) spillage from an upstream plant which used mercury; and (iii) spillage from a downstream plant which used mercury. The three theories caused serious scientific controversies. Towards the end of June 1965, teams from Niigata prefecture found high concentrations of mercury in fish, and issued an order prohibiting fishing along a length of 14 kilometers of the Agano River.

In March 1966, the Niigata Prefecture Organic Mercury Poisoning Research Center concluded that contaminated fish from the Agano River caused the alkylmercury poisoning associated with the Minamata disease. Meanwhile, on 24 March 1966, the Ministry of Health and Welfare released an interim report which identified the Kanose plant of Showa Denko Corporation, an acetaldehyde manufacturer, as the suspected source of mercury pollution. However, the report also said that the earthquake which shook Niigata on 16 June 1964 contributed to the contamination of the river fish by altering the course of the river and disrupting its riverbed. Thus, the judgement of the Ministry of Health and Welfare remained inconclusive due to a lack of concrete scientific evidence.

In May 1966, Professor Y. Takizawa of Niigata University, who had formed an independent study team, reported that his group had measured high levels of mercury in sludge and algae samples at the drainage site of the Kanose plant[21] and that he had identified methylated mercury in the samples.[22]

In 1966, the health department of Niigata prefecture confirmed the findings of Professor Takizawa. Showa Denko objected to the findings of Professor Takizawa and the interim report of the Ministry of Health and Welfare. In rebuttal, Showa Denko proposed that mercury pesticides caused the mercury pollution in the Agano River. It also proposed that the 1964 earthquake contributed to the pollution.[23]

A tidal wave caused by the earthquake had flooded sheds stored with agricultural chemicals. After a second earthquake hit Niigata in July 1966, Niigata prefecture conducted an on-the-spot examination of the disposal of soaked pesticides, and was assisted in this effort by an executive from the Kanose plant. Showa Denko retained Professor T. Kitagawa of Yokohama National University to develop and present the saline wedge theory of methylmercury contamination in order to support the fertilizer spillage theory.[24]

In December 1966, the Safety Engineering Society, chaired by Professor T. Kitagawa, organized a team to investigate the mercury poisoning.

On 20 April 1967, the Ministry of Health and Welfare study team issued its report. The report found that the concerned events constituted a second outbreak of the Minamata disease, that fish in the Agano River contaminated by methylmercury caused the incident, and that the methylmercury came from discharges into the Agano River from the acetaldehyde manufacturing process of the Kanose plant of Showa Denko. The ministry forwarded its report to the Council of Food Sanitation, an advisory body to the Ministry of Health and Welfare, for its review. But the council backed off from the conclusiveness of the ministry's report. In its own report, issued on 30 August 1967, the council said that the long and extensive pollution of the Agano River by waste water discharged from the Kanose plant provided the first basis for the disease's appearance. However, the council continued, most patients became ill during a limited period when the concentration of mercury increased rapidly, and the factors contributing to this rapid concentration are unknown at this time. The council's report became the official position of the Ministry of Health and Welfare.

There was disagreement among the ministries and agencies as to the correctness of the conclusions of the Ministry of Health and Welfare. In December 1967, in response to an inquiry by the Science and Technology Agency, the Ministry of Agriculture, Forestry, and Fisheries, and the Economic Planning Agency indicated that their teams officially agreed with the conclusions of the Ministry of Health and Welfare. However, the Ministry of International Trade and Industry took the position that the evidence was insufficient to identify a source for the mercury pollution in the Agano River. In March 1968, Showa Denko criticized the conclusions of the Ministry of Health and Welfare as biased.[25]

The Science and Technology Agency also was reluctant to confirm the conclusions of the Ministry of Health and Welfare. It drafted the findings of the interministerial study team, which were inconclusive with respect to an identification of the source of the pollution. The Science and Technology Agency report, released on 26 September 1969, became the official position of the government.

After the report was issued, the Ministry of International Trade and Industry issued directives to 49 industrial plants owned by 35 companies on mandatory measures to prevent mercury contamination.

6.2.3 Itai-itai disease in Toyama prefecture

In October 1955, at the 17th Assembly of the Japan Clinical Surgeon Society, Dr. Noboru Hagino and Dr. M. Kawano reported a disease of unknown etiology which had been endemic since 1910 in Fuchu and the surrounding area of Toyama prefecture. Characteristic symptoms were severe lumbar and femur pains, osteomalacia, splintering of bone tissue, disfigurement, posture deformation, crippling, and renal disorder. Death often resulted. The unbearable pain caused the Toyama victims to cry out itai-itai ("it hurts, it hurts"), from which the disease got its name.[26]

Victims had resided in the area for more than twenty years. Women aged 50 with a history of multiple pregnancies and lactation were especially susceptible.

An alluvial fan formed by the Jintsu River constituted the endemic area. This river irrigated the traditionally agricultural surrounding land. The Kamioka Mine of the Mitsui Mining Company was located about 50 kilometers upstream along the Jintsu River, and it had produced gold, silver, copper, and zinc since the 1890s. The mine had a long history of leaking wastes and effluent into the agricultural lands downstream. Because most victims were poor, hard-working farmers, for many years it was thought that the disease was the result of undernourishment and overwork. But in 1961, at the 34th Assembly of the Japan Orthopedic Society, Dr. Hagino and Professor K. Yoshioka hypothesized that chronic poisoning by cadmium contained in mining wastes and effluent caused itai-itai disease. The theory proposed that farmers living in the delta of the Jintsu River ingested cadmium by drinking the water of the Jintsu River and eating rice taken from paddies irrigated by it.

In 1963, the Ministry of Health and Welfare organized the Itai-Itai Disease Study Committee to review clinical and public health issues. The Division of Environmental Pollution of the Ministry of Health and Welfare formed a committee and reviewed all reports and references in Japan and abroad on the subject. It also examined environmental pollution at several zinc sites polluted by heavy metals. Its field study focused on environmental pollution caused by

trace metals in the air, water, soil, and biological media. In addition, the
Ministry of Education organized the Itai-Itai Disease Comprehensive Study Team,
which took an interdisciplinary approach. Finally, Toyama prefecture
established the Toyama Prefecture Special Local Disease Countermeasures Committee to study the matter.

In January 1967, the Ministry of Education study team issued its final
report on the etiology of itai-itai disease. The report concluded that cadmium
poisoning probably caused itai-itai disease. The Division of Environmental
Pollution of the Ministry of Health and Welfare continued its investigation and
reported that it had detected cadmium pollution in several areas and observed
signs of renal disorders and suspected cases of osteomalacia.[27]

In May 1968, the Ministry of Health and Welfare concluded that cadmium was
merely one of many contributing factors. In its report, the Ministry stated
that "Itai-itai disease is primarily attributable to the renal damage by
cadmium poisoning with subsequent osteomalacia, induced by multiple pregnancy,
lactation, hormonal disorder, aging, and calcium deficiency due to
malnutrition. Experts have not identified any source of cadmium pollution other
than the mining effluent of the Kamioka Mine of the Mitsui Mining Company."
The Minister of Health and Welfare reported these conclusions during a cabinet
session, and the government adopted them as its conclusions.

In January 1968, Toyama prefecture finally established a relief system for
patients of itai-itai disease. The system registered those undergoing diagnostic study and supplied patients with medical care at public expense. The
Ministry of Health and Welfare agreed to reimburse patients for their medical
expenses with funds from the Environmental Pollution Study Fund.

In March 1968, the study teams of Toyama prefecture, the Ministry of Health
and Welfare, and the Ministry of Education agreed on diagnostic criteria for
the disease. In addition, the Ministry of Health and Welfare issued provisional regulations requiring certain measures to be taken to prevent cadmium
pollution. Also, it organized a team to study the disease and its mechanisms
in more detail and, in particular, ways to prevent cadmium poisoning in the
early stages of renal damage. The ministry noted that there was a low risk of
a greater incidence of the disease because of two factors: (i) trends in the
onset pattern of the disease observed from data from the 1920s to the 1940s;
and (ii) the fact that local governments had built three dams along the Jintsu
River by 1968.

The Ministry of Education's Itai-Itai Disease Comprehensive Study Team
instituted nationwide surveillance of cadmium pollution in water, soil, and
foods, and conducted community health screenings. The team based these measures on the Ministry of Health and Welfare's provisional cadmium pollution-
control measures and the diagnostic criteria.

6.2.4 Air pollution in Yokkaichi

Japan's first petrochemical complex was located in the city of Yokkaichi in Mie prefecture. Commencing operations in 1959, the complex refined petroleum, produced petrochemicals, operated a power station using fuel oil with a high sulfur content, and manufactured titanium using sulfuric acid. Soon after the start-up, residents in Yokkaichi became very annoyed with the black smoke and soot from the new plant. Also, the fish caught along the shore of this small Pacific-coast city emitted a strong, oily smell and proved unmarketable. Beginning in 1960, local physicians noted an abnormal increase in the incidence of asthma, emphysema, bronchitis, and other respiratory ailments.

In a study sponsored by prefectural and city governments, Professor K. Yoshida of the Public Health Laboratory of Mie Prefecture University Medical School conducted a statistical analysis of the clinical records of patients in Yokkaichi from 1961 to 1968 using the national health insurance payment claims. Professor Yoshida examined the records of 30,000 patients residing in 13 districts in the city of Yokkaichi classified as polluted and non-polluted. In most disease categories, the study found no differences between patients from polluted and non-polluted areas. However, there were notable differences in four disease catagories: common cold, bronchial asthma, throat inflammation, and eye irritation. The results show that the number of visits per 100 persons (the incidence rate) in polluted districts was two or three times that of unpolluted districts, and that the incidence rate rose with increasing sulfur-dioxide concentrations. Elderly and very young children were more adversely affected than young adults.

Beginning in 1960, officials began to monitor air-pollution levels in the city of Yokkaichi using the PbO_2 candle method and deposit gauge. In addition, officials set up a sulfur-dioxide automatic air-monitoring device in the dis-pensary of a fishing village.[28]

The dispensary noted that 13 patients under its observation had developed asthma-like symptoms since the start of the air-monitoring program. The correlation between the sulfur-dioxide concentration and the development of asthma-like symptoms was as high as 0.88 percent. The dispensary observed a sharp increase in the number of onsets of asthma-like symptoms when the weekly average sulfur-dioxide concentration reached 0.1 to 0.2 ppm. In the village of Isozu, officials observed an abnormally high incidence of bronchial asthma among people over 50 years of age. In almost all of these bronchial asthma cases, onset began after 1959, the patients had low rates of positive reactions to house dust and other allergen tests, and the patients' family histories showed low rates of bronchial asthma.[29]

In 1963, the Ministry of Health and Welfare began a study of air pollution and its health effects in Yokkaichi and Osaka. The study used the British

250

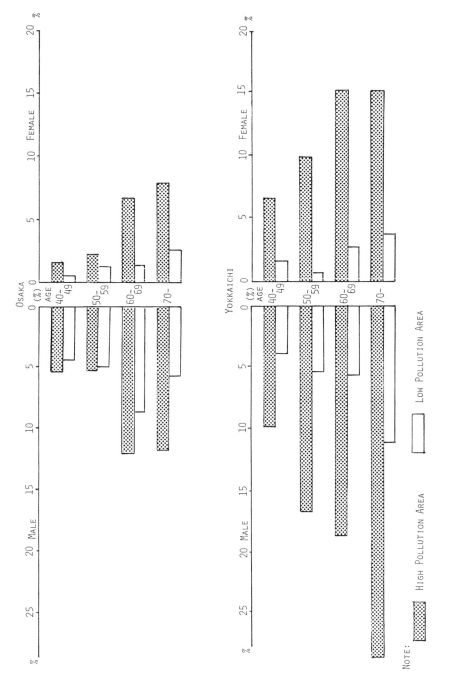

Fig. 6.1. Prevalence of respiratory symptoms classified by age and sex in Osaka and Yokkaichi, 1964.

Medical Research Council (BMRC) questionnaire survey method and pulmonary
function test developed by Vitalor (Fig. 6.1). The study monitored frequent
and continuous peaks of sulfur dioxide concentrations, with a maximum
concentration of 2.5 ppm/hr. It often recorded measurements of 1 ppm/hr, and
in special meteorological conditions it recorded 0.4 ppm/hr continuously. The
heights of the smoke stacks of the petrochemical complex were all below 60
meters. Officials observed a high concentration of sulfur dioxide in the
winter with a downwash phenomenon of 6 m/sec. In the central area of
Yokkaichi, officials observed a northwest wind in the winter and a southeast
wind with high peaks in the summer.[30]

In 1963, the Ministry of Health and Welfare and the Ministry of International Trade and Industry established the Kurokawa Commission, a multi-
disciplinary team of experts, to investigate the cause of the air pollution
problem and to prescribe comprehensive measures to control it. The Kurokawa
Commission considered the findings of the studies on air pollution and its
health effects and recommended minimum height requirements for smoke stacks and
the institution of special health care programs.

Meanwhile, the anti-pollution campaign gradually intensified in Yokkaichi,
and also in Mishima-Numazu where a second petrochemical complex was located.
Mishima-Numazu activists persuaded local landowners not to sell their land to
the advancing industries and began massive demonstrations against the proposed
complex. They rallied support with the slogan "No more Yokkaichi," and in 1964
they succeeded in closing the Mishima-Numazu plant.[31] The citizens' success
had grave implications for the siting of new complexes and for economic growth
generally. It persuaded the government to actively set to work on the formulation of a comprehensive pollution policy.

In 1965, the Ministry of Health and Welfare released the results of its
study of air pollution and its health effects in Yokkaichi and Osaka. After
many months of struggle, the residents of Yokkaichi persuaded Mie prefecture to
establish the Pollution-Related Medical Care Program to reimburse the medical
expenses of air-pollution victims whose bills were not completely covered by
national health insurance. However, air pollution in Yokkaichi worsened
between 1965 and 1967, and more serious cases of pulmonary disease appeared.
By 1969, the Medical Care Program had certified 600 patients.[32]

In 1967, the Ministry of Health and Welfare provided funds to the Pollution-
Related Medical Care Program for Yokkaichi on the condition that polluting
industries make contributions to the fund. Although on a small scale, the
program was effective, and in 1973 the air-pollution program of the Compensation Law was modeled in part after it. In 1965, officials succeeded in
gradually lowering the high sulfur-dioxide levels with the implementation of
the air-pollution-control recommendations of the Kurokawa Commission. In addi-

tion, Mie prefecture enacted an ordinance in 1972 which instituted a program to reduce sulfur. The ordinance set maximum permitted levels of sulfur emission as measured by mass.

6.3 LITIGATION

After years of inaction on the part of pollutors, the victims of Niigata[33], Kumamoto[34], Yokkaichi[35], and Toyama[36] took their grievances to the courts. In all four cases, the courts ruled in favor of the plaintiff-victims, and awarded them damages. The decisions in the four major pollution trials established the basic legal principles governing claims for compensation of health injuries from air- and water-pollution. They were devastating for industry. They established standards of care far more stringent than any government regulation at the time. The publicity attending the trials made pollution a national issue and hastened the government's implementation of new and needed pollution laws and regulations, including the Compensation Law.[37]

Table 6.1 presents information on the identity of the plaintiffs and defendants, the date the suit was commenced and the date judgement was rendered, the legal basis of the decision, and the amount of damages awarded. Many of the victims were unfamiliar with legal proceedings and only turned to the courts after all other avenues of relief failed. The Toyama (itai-itai disease) and Kumamoto (Minamata disease) victims each waited thirteen years before agreeing to file suit. Their trials each took another four years. The Yokkaichi (air pollution diseases) and Niigata (Minamata disease) plaintiffs took eight and two years, respectively, to file suit. Their trials took another five and four years, respectively.

On 12 June 1967, the Niigata Minamata disease victims were the first to file suit. The action against the Showa Denko Corporation was based on a theory of negligence under article 709 of the Civil Code. Article 709 states, "A person who violates intentionally or negligently the rights of another is bound to make compensation for damages arising therefrom." This was the first time a court was called upon to apply this provision to a pollution case.

In construing this provision, the Niigata court set a very high standard of care for chemical companies which may produce hazardous substances as by-products in their production processes. The court ruled that a chemical company had to use the best analytical techniques to determine whether its waste water contained any hazardous substances. Moreover, such a company "must take the strictest safety precautions to prevent even the slightest danger to humans and other living things." If danger to human health still remains, "curtailment or cessation of operations may be necessary."[38]

The plaintiffs faced a formidable challenge in proving causation. It was known by this time from the many studies done in Kumamoto that ingestion of

methylated mercury resulted in Minamata disease, and this fact was not in
dispute. The issue in Niigata was the source and mechanism of transmission of
the mercury. The defendants contended that the mercury did not come from their
plant but rather was part of the agricultural chemicals washed from storage
sheds in Niigata Port by a tidal wave following the Niigata earthquake of 1964.
The art of toxicology was not sufficiently advanced to permit a determination
of causation with scientific precision. But the court disposed of this problem
by resorting to statistical correlation. In effect, it ruled that the
plaintiffs had met their burden of proof by demonstrating a high statistical
correlation between the defendants' activity and the occurrence of the disease.
Specifically, the plaintiffs used epidemiological and statistical analysis of
mercury concentrations in different types of fish, percentages of contaminated
fish consumed, and differential studies of the incidence of Minamata disease
correlated with the type of fish eaten.

In rebuttal on the issue of liability, the defendants argued that they were
not negligent because they had complied with existing effluent standards.
However, the court dismissed this contention, stating that compliance with
administrative regulations shields a tortfeasor from administrative sanction
only, not civil liability.

The Kumamoto Minamata disease case also was devastating to Japanese
industry. This action was based on a theory of negligence under Article 709 of
the Civil Code. The court set a high standard of care. It said that if there
was doubt about the safety of a chemical plant's waste water, the plant must
immediately suspend operations and adopt the necessary maximum preventive
measures. "Especially with regard to the life and health of area residents,
the factory must exercise a high degree of care to prevent harm before it
happens."[39]

In assessing damages, the court rejected the plaintiffs' request for uniform
damages. It analyzed each plaintiff's circumstances to arrive at a fair and
reasonable amount. In doing so, the court considered loss of income even
though the plaintiffs' had only sought damages for emotional and mental
suffering. The court noted that if the plaintiffs' had claimed pecuniary
damages including loss of income, matters of proof would have been complicated
and the victims' relief delayed.

The Yokkaichi case, filed against the six companies in the petrochemical
complex, was brought on a negligence theory under the joint tort statute.
Article 719 of the Civil Code states in part, "If two or more persons have by
their joint unlawful act caused damage to another, they are jointly and
severally liable to make compensation for such damage; the same shall apply if
it is impossible to ascertain which of the joint participants has caused the
damage." The court applied the joint tort statute because the discharges of

Table 6.1

Summary of major pollution litigation

	Niigata Minamata Disease Case	Yokkaichi Air Pollution Case
Date case filed	1st; June 12, 1967 8th; January 19, 1971	September 1, 1967
Date of Decision	September 29, 1971	July 24, 1972
Court	Niigata District Court	Yokkaichi Branch Tsu District Court
Number of Plaintiffs (including deceased plaintiffs)	1st to 8th, 77 (56)	12 (9)
Defendant(s)	Showa Denko Kanose Plant	6 companies of the first Complex, Mitsubishi Kase, Mitubishi Yuka, Mitsubishi-Monsant Kase, Showa Sekiyu Yokkaichi, Chubudenryoku, Ishihara Sangyo
Theory of action	Civil Law; Article 709, (Torts)	Civil Law; Article 709, (Torts) Article 719, (Joint Torts)
Damages Awardes	270 million Yen (Mental Suffering)	88.21 million Yen (Mental Suffering, Loss of Income, Lawyers' Fees)

Source: Attachment to the Report of the Central Advisory Council of Environmental Pollution Control Measures; 1973

Itai-itai Disease Case		Kumamoto Minamata Disease Case
Trial Court	Appellate Court	June 14, 1969
March 9, 1968	Defendant; June 30, 1971 Plaintiff; September 6, 1971	
June 30, 1971	August 9, 1972	March 20, 1973
Toyama District Court	Kanazawa Branch Nagoya High Court	Kumamoto District Court
31 (14)	34 (14)	138 (45)
Mitsui Kinzoku Kyogyo (Kamioka Kogyosho)		Shin-Nihon Chisso (Acetaldehyde Manufacturing Carbide)
Mining Law; (strict liability) Article 109;		Civil Law; Article 709, (Torts)
57 million Yen (Mental Suffuring)	148.2 million Yen (Mental Suffering, Lawyers' Fees)	737 million Yen (Mental Suffering, Lawyers' Fees)

some of the defendants were insufficient in themselves to cause injury. In holding each defendant liable for the total damage done by the combination, even defendants with only minimal discharges, the court stressed the importance of the tainted association rather than the amount of individual emission.

The issue of causation presented daunting doctrinal problems to the plaintiffs and the court. The Yokkaichi diseases--asthma, emphysema, bronchitis, and other respiratory ailments--have multiple causes, such as smoking, in addition to air pollution in the form of elevated sulfur oxides levels. Expanding on the decision in the Niigata Minamata disease case, the court held that a level of statistical probability creates a legal presumption of causation. It relied on complicated statistical and epidemiological evidence to show that the defendants were the source of the pollution and that the pollution was transmitted to the victims. For example, it used charts of sulfur oxides levels by year, data on seasonal wind patterns affecting pollution discharges, and comparisons of hospital records for pulmonary disease in polluted and non-polluted areas.[40]

In assessing damages, the Yokkaichi court ruled that the court should calculate individual income losses. To do this, it resorted to a standard workers' scale of wages classified by age and gender. This wage scale was published annually by the national government as part of its collection of official statistics. This aspect of the Yokkaichi decision was far-reaching because the plaintiffs included fishermen and housewives who did not receive a monthly salary.[41]

The Itai-Itai Disease case filed against the Mitsui Mining Company was based on a theory of strict liability under Article 109 of the Mining Law.[42]

Under strict liability rules, the plaintiff need not prove that a defendant breached a duty of care in causing the plaintiff's injury. However, the plaintiff must still prove that the defendant caused the plaintiff's injury. In showing causation, the court admitted epidemiological evidence such as data showing that most patients were found only in the delta irrigated by water from the Jintsu River. This was an important ruling because factors such as nutritional deficiency, climate, overwork, and vitamin D deficiency substantially weakened the victims' proof of causation based solely on clinical and pathological evidence.

The appellate court affirmed the district court's decision in favor of the plaintiffs. Like the district court, it emphasized the importance of epidemiology in determining legal causation. In addition, the appellate court increased the damages awarded to the plaintiffs by the district court. In doing so, it noted that the plaintiffs had failed to plead pecuniary losses because of the difficulty of proof and the need for an early decision. The appellate court took this into consideration in reassessing damages for pain and suffering.

6.4   LEGISLATION

In the late 1960s and early 1970s, the government searched for an appro-
priate policy response to the mounting pollution crisis in Japan.   The Diet
enacted three pieces of legislation that were precursors to the 1973 Pollution-
Related Health Damage Compensation Law.   These were the 1967 Basic Law for
Environmental Pollution Control Measures, the 1969 Special Relief Law for
Pollution-Related Health Hazards, and the 1972 strict liability legislation.

6.4.1   The 1967 basic law for environmental pollution control measures[43]

The major policy goal of the Basic Law for Environmental Pollution Control
Measures was to require the government to devise a systematic, comprehensive
program to control pollution, and to require pollutors to pay their proportionate share of the government's costs.   While the specific mechanisms to achieve
these results were left to later legislation, this law set Japan on the course
towards pollution control.

Article 2 of the Basic Law defined environmental pollution as any situation
where air pollution, water pollution, noise, vibration, ground subsidence, or
offensive odours, arising over a considerable area as a result of industrial or
any other human activity, injured or damaged the health of humans or their
living environments.   The 1973 Compensation Law had its genesis in Section V of
the Basic Law, which addressed the settlement of disputes related to environmental pollution and relief for damages.   Specifically, Article 21 stated, "1)
The government shall establish a system for settlement by such means as mediation and arbitration.   2) The government shall establish a system for the
efficient implementation of relief for damage caused by environmental pollution."   Furthermore, Article 22 stated, "An enterprise shall bear all or part
of the necessary costs of the work undertaken by the State or local government
bodies to control pollution arising from the activities of such an enterprise."
The enactment of the Basic Law required the government to address the problem
of administrative jurisdiction of pollution issues.   This was necessary because
pollution matters were being handled piecemeal by fourteen ministerial agencies.[44]

That it took until 1967 for Japan to enact its first major piece of pollution legislation has been a subject of much criticism.   Twelve years passed
before the government acknowledged that the Minamata disease was pollution-
related.   At first it was called a "strange, unknown disease", then a kind of
food poisoning; only in the end did the government acknowledge that it was
methylmercury pollution caused by industrial water pollution.   An example of
the government's delay was its refusal to accept the findings of the Food

Sanitation Council of the Ministry of Health and Welfare in 1959 or the
Kumamoto University studies on the cause of the disease. In September 1965,
three years after the second outbreak of Minamata disease in Niigata prefecture, the government finally agreed with the conclusions of the Ministry of
Health and Welfare. The government was also slow in acknowledging the cause of
itai-itai disease--which came thirteen years after the first-reported incidence. For the asthma-like disease of the Yokkaichi case, the government took
five years after the public health studies were issued to acknowledge that the
cause was pollution-related.

The reason which the government always cited to buy more time was the lack
of solid scientific evidence. The author's degree of certainty with respect to
identifying the source of the pollution was 99% for the Kumamoto Minamata
disease, 80% for the Niigata Minamata disease, under 55% for itai-itai disease,
and just over 50% for the Yokkaichi air pollution-case. The author based these
assessments on his administrative experience in handling major pollution-
related health issues from 1961 to 1970. In the process of arriving at a
conclusion with respect to the source of the pollutants, the author continually
faced scrutinizing questions and criticism. Critics demanded to see hard
evidence of the cause and effect relation between the pollutants and the
disease as well as scientific proof identifying the source of the pollutants.
In this way, the rigors of scientific proof worked to provide a temporary
shield for the pollutors.[45]

The preparation for drafting the Basic Law began in 1965 when both houses of
the Diet organized Special Committees for Industrial Pollution Control. With
mounting social and political turmoil, the Diet was under great pressure to
take administrative action. Political power groups, the economic and industrial establishment, and the national and local governments were worried by the
closing of the petrochemical complex at Mishima-Numazu. Increasingly, the
government faced hostile questions in the Diet and in the media on pollution
issues. After the Basic Law was enacted, opponents debated whether the
Kumamoto and Niigata Minamata disease and the itai-itai disease cases came
within the scope of the definition of pollution in Article 2. The Ministry of
Health and Welfare finally addressed these questions in 1968 when it issued its
policy position with respect to the Minamata and itai-itai diseases. The
cabinet level policy positions were the top political decisions of the national
government. This was the first time the government reached an important policy
decision despite a lack of conclusive, scientific information.[46]

In accordance with the Basic Law, the Ministry of Health and Welfare subsidized the medical expenses of the Kumamoto and Niigata Minamata disease victims
with funds from its health research budget. However, after 1968, the Ministry
of Finance requested the Ministry of Health and Welfare to charge the indivi-

dual polluting enterprises with their proportionate share of the total medical
expenses. Until 1968, national health insurance benefits and the public expenditures of national and local government had paid these medical expenses.

6.4.2 The 1969 special relief law for pollution-related health hazards[47]

In October 1967, the Ministry of Health and Welfare completed drafting a
plan for the proposed victim relief system. The plan limited relief to medical
expenses suffered by certified victims living in designated areas. Even this
cautious proposal was rejected by other ministries as too generous. In
February 1968, the ministry remanded the matter to the Advisory Council for
Environmental Pollution Control Measures. The council, an advisory body to the
prime minister on environmental matters, proposed a relief system limited to
payment of medical expenses and funded in part by voluntary contributions from
industry. After further debate and amendment of the Advisory Council's recommendations, the Diet passed the Special Relief Law for Pollution-Related Health
Hazards during the 1969 session.

The Relief Law provided benefits for medical expenses, medical care, and
nursery care. Since 1961, the national health insurance and social security
programs have provided universal coverage in Japan. The Relief Law supplemen-
ted the benefits available to patients under these social insurance programs.
However, the benefits provided under the Relief Law did not include payments
for disability or pain and suffering.

The Relief Law set forth standards of eligibility for benefits. An applicant had to show that he was a victim of one of the following diseases: chronic
bronchitis, bronchial asthma, asthmatic bronchitis, pulmonary emphysema, and
their sequelae (the air pollution-related diseases) and Minamata disease, itai-
itai disease, and chronic arsenic poisoning (the water pollution-related
diseases). In addition, he had to show that he lived or worked for a
designated length of time in an area identified by the government as affected
by serious air- or water-pollution arising from industrial or individual activities.

There was a three-step procedure for certifying eligibility. First, a
physician diagnosed an applicant as having a designated disease. Second, the
Pollution-Related Health Hazard Certification Committee, established in each
prefecture by the governor, determined whether the applicant met the standards
for degree of exposure in a designated area. Finally, if all was in order, the
governor certified the applicant.

Under the Relief Law, government and industry contributed funds for the
payment of benefits. The national, prefectural, and local governments contributed half of the money for the relief fund in equal proportions, and the
Foundation for Cooperation with Environmental Pollution Control Measures con-

tributed the other half. Established by the Japan Federation of Economic Organizations (Keidanren), the Foundation for Cooperation collected voluntary contributions from private enterprises without government participation. In turn, the Foundation for Cooperation transferred the collected funds to the Environmental Pollution Abatement Corporation, which the Ministry of Health and Welfare and the Ministry of International Trade and Industry had jointly established in 1965. The government also deposited its share with the Environmental Corporation. The corporation then transferred the funds to the departments of local government administering the programs under the Relief Law.[48]

The air-pollution program of the Relief Law was based on the Yokkaichi program begun in 1965. In December 1969, the cabinet designated Yokkaichi, Nishiyodo-ku in Osaka, and the southern half of Kawasaki City, near Tokyo, as health-hazard areas. The worst air pollution in the past decade had been observed in these three areas.[49]

Although the Relief Law was essentially a limited, stopgap measure, it took the persistent, persuasive efforts of the Division of Environmental Pollution Control of the Ministry of Health and Welfare, established in 1968, to push the program through.[50]

6.4.3 Strict liability legislation of 1972

On 1 July 1971, the government established the Environment Agency and assigned it the task of preparing strict liability legislation. Strict liability is a concept which replaces traditional tort principles based on negligence. Under strict liability rules, a victim must still pursue his relief through a lawsuit, but he need only show that his disease was caused by specific pollutants discharged by the defendant; he need not also show that the defendant was negligent in permitting the pollutants to be discharged.

The Environment Agency's draft bill, prepared by March 1972, presented a very narrow application of strict liability. Defending its bill during the hostile reception, the government argued that the new legislation should be limited to new cases of pollution injury and then only to injuries caused by air and water pollution generated by industrial activity. Thus, the bill did not apply to the other forms of pollution defined in the Basic Law--soil pollution, noise, vibration, ground subsidence, and offensive odours. Accordingly, the bill sought to amend the Air Pollution Control Law of 1968 and the Water Pollution Control Law of 1970. An early draft of the bill included a presumption of causation, but economic and industrial groups strongly opposed this provision and in the end it was deleted. At about the same time, the Liberal Democratic Party and the Federation of Economic Organizations (Keidanren) organized a task force to draft their own strict liability law. The government's bill passed the Diet on 16 June 1972.

The new law included a provision requesting the government to establish a pollution-related health injury compensation system. Earlier, in April 1972, the Central Advisory Council of Environmental Pollution Control Measures had established a Special Subcommittee for Cost Bearing to conduct an inquiry into how costs should be borne for a pollution-related health injury compensation system. Thus, the strict liability law served as an important step in bringing about the Compensation Law.

6.4.4 Shift in pollution policy: 1965-1972

The Japanese government, and the Japanese people, underwent a drastic change in their attitudes towards pollution from 1965 to 1972. This shift in policy can be marked by a number of events. The second outbreak of Minamata disease, in Niigata prefecture, occurred in 1965. From 1967 to 1969, the victims of Japan's four major pollution cases filed lawsuits. Until final judgments were issued in the plaintiffs' favor from 1971 to 1973, the cases attracted much press and organized public support. In 1965, both houses of the Diet established a Special Committee for Industrial Pollution Control to help formulate proposals for the 1967 Basic Law for Environmental Pollution Control Measures. In 1968, the government finally acknowledged that Minamata disease and itai-itai disease were pollution-related. This signaled the beginning of the government's change in pollution policy. In 1969, the United Nations and the Organisation for Economic Co-operation and Development (OECD) each held sessions on the environment which helped to raise the level of concern all over the world. Japan endorsed the OECD's pollutor-pays-principle. In early 1970, President Richard M. Nixon attacked Japan for taking a trade advantage by not paying the costs of pollution control. In July 1970, Japanese newspapers reported cases of lead poisoning in Tokyo and high photochemical oxidant levels. Earlier, there had been reports of high levels of mercury and cadmium. This kind of press was instrumental in provoking strong public demand for stringent pollution controls. Also in July 1970, former Prime Minister E. Sato established the Pollution Control Headquarters, comprised of senior ministry officials, under his personal supervision. In the autumn of 1970, the Diet held a ten-week special session to consider fourteen pieces of pollution legislation. Despite the complexity of the bills, all fourteen were enacted. However, Prime Minister Sato was unable to deliver on his commitment for strict liability legislation during the special session. But the Environment Agency began an intensive examination of the strict liability proposals, and the Diet passed a bill in July 1972. Two days later, the court in the Yokkaichi case issued its decision giving a strict interpretation of Articles 709 and 719 on tort and joint tort liability.[51]

These developments in July 1972 shocked the industrial establishment, and

marked a turning point in Japan's pollution policy. Immediately after the
court issued its decision in the Yokkaichi case, State Minister O. Koyama,
Director General of the Environment Agency, called for the enactment of legislation to provide for a pollution-related health damage compensation system as
soon as possible. A nationwide consensus on the need for a compensation system
was rapidly crystallizing. The pollutors' heaven, which Japanese industri-
alists had enjoyed for nearly a century, had suddenly crumbled, and the indus-
trialists found themselves in a pollutors' hell.

6.5 THE POLLUTION-RELATED HEALTH DAMAGE COMPENSATION LAW

The major goal of the Pollution-Related Health Damage Compensation Law[52] is
to provide an administrative, non-judicial system of compensating victims of
environmental pollution. The law places the entire costs of the compensation
program, except for administration, on pollutors.

The legislative process in Japan is different from many other countries. For
important pieces of proposed legislation, the relevant ministry or agency of
the government appoints a citizens' advisory council in which academics, other
experts, and groups affected by the proposed legislation gather and negotiate
as needed to obtain a consensus. Thus, by the time a bill is presented to the
Diet for consideration, all the consensus-building groundwork has been done in
this forum.

Formerly an advisory organ to the prime minister, the Central Advisory
Council on Environmental Pollution Control Measures was transferred to the
Environment Agency when it was created in 1971. There, the Advisory Council
served the new agency's director general. There were about 30 active members
on the Advisory Council, consisting of representatives from academia; the
scientific community; polluting industries such as the automobile, iron, and
steel industries; the general public; citizens' organizations; local governments; and the press. The Advisory Council was charged with the task of
recommending legislation which would become the Pollution-Related Health Damage
Compensation Law. In 1972 and 1973, the Advisory Council conducted an extensive review of all the technical issues, prepared a report recommending general
policy positions for the proposed Compensation Law, and solicited comments from
interested parties. The Advisory Council submitted its recommendations in a
final report to the director general of the Environment Agency, which did the
actual drafting of the proposed Compensation Law, codifying the Advisory Council's policy recommendations. The Diet enacted the Compensation Law on 10
October 1973, and it became effective on 1 September 1974.

6.5.1 The recommendations of the central advisory council on environmental
pollution control measures

(i) An extra-judicial, administrative structure. The council argued that to require each victim seeking compensation for his health injuries to file a lawsuit in court would be too burdensome. Even with the new strict liability statutes, proving legal causation and damage in court would be too expensive, time-consuming, and risky. Also, even with the pro-victim Yokkaichi decision to serve as a persuasive precedent, an urban victim of an air pollution-related disease caused by multiple factors faced a heavy burden of proof with an uncertain outcome. Thus, the council recommended an extra-judicial, administrative structure to oversee compensation payments.

In addition, the council argued against integrating the compensation program with national health insurance or workmen's compensation. Integrating the compensation program with national health insurance would sever the link between the payment of compensation and the identity of the pollutors, thereby absolving pollutors of responsibility. Also, it would be unfair to non-pollutors to finance the compensation program from the general tax revenues. In addition, the council recommended that the compensation system pay for all medical expenses, not just as a supplement to that part of the expenses not reimbursed by national health insurance.[53]

(ii) Causation. The council believed that basic notions of fairness require a causal nexus between pollutant and victim before requiring pollutors to pay. Yet, science had not advanced to the point where it could prove this nexus with absolute certainty. Thus, in the interests of administrative expediency, and to relieve the terrible suffering of victims, the council adopted techniques of statistical probability and a rebuttable presumption of causation. The council refined the basic approach to causation developed in the pollution trials into a general methodology for disease, area and victim designation.

The council said, "Multiple factors contribute to pollution-related health damage. Thus, it cannot always be said with medical and scientific certainty that a given, single factor causes a particular disease. But for purposes of assigning liability in legal proceedings, it is satisfactory for plaintiffs to show a probability of causation. However, the showing of probability must be verified by epidemiological evidence on the degree of pollution and the incidence of disease."[54]

Different diseases have different degrees of specificity to a given pollutant. Minamata disease is specific to methylated mercury poisoning; no other pollutant or factor causes the disease. But the air pollution diseases (asthma, emphysema, bronchitis, and other respiratory ailments) have multiple causative factors, some of which are unrelated to industrial air pollution. Smoking is an example. Thus, the air pollution diseases are said to be non-specific. Itai-itai disease is semi-specific to cadmium poisoning.

The use of statistical probability using epidemiological data and a rebuttable presumption of causation are especially important for the non-specific diseases. The council said, "Each applicant for benefits under the compensation system must show the causal relation between a pollutant and his disease. This task is not difficult for diseases with specific causes, but for diseases with non-specific causes, such as obstructive pulmonary disease, the task is difficult. Thus, in order to have a system which also addresses non-specific diseases, the following presumption should be instituted: an individual will be presumed to meet the causation requirement if he can show an epidemiological causal relation between air pollution and the population group in the area. Thus, an individual need only meet three tests with respect to designated area, term of exposure, and designated disease. He will then be presumed to meet the causation requirement, unless there are special reasons which disprove causation for the individual applicant."[55]

In the course of arriving at the above formulation on causation, medical experts in the fields of pathology, experimental medicine, clinical medicine, and epidemiology often failed to agree on an approach. Nevertheless, lawyers argued that a complete consensus on the scientific evidence was unnecessary in view of the fact that the available evidence was limited. Lawyers asserted that, as long as the available evidence was considerable, the causation question could be resolved by resorting to principles of equity, unless there were specific reasons for objection. The court's opinion in the Yokkaichi case provided a crucial precedent for the compensation legislation.

(iii) Benefits. The council recommended the following seven categories of benefits: a medical treatment allowance (hospitalization and out-patient expenses), a disability allowance, a nurse allowance, a child victim allowance, a medical care allowance (miscellaneous and transportation expenses), a survivors' allowance, and a funeral allowance.

The most controversial of these was the disability allowance. The plaintiffs in the Yokkaichi and the two Minamata cases did not seek compensation for disability because of the difficulty of calculating lost future income and assessing life expectancy. Nevertheless, the Yokkaichi court sought to assess individual income losses by resorting to a standard scale of average wages differentiated by age and gender. The council adopted this approach, but recommended a disability allowance pegged at 80% of the Yokkaichi levels, to be paid monthly. Industry favored a lower rate, and the 80% level was considered an acceptable compromise. By comparison, workmen's compensation provides disability benefits at 60% of the employee's former wages, and the Automobile Accidents Compensation Law provides 60%-70%. Also, the council thought that 80%, rather than 100%, was justified especially in non-specific, air pollution diseases where there is a natural level of prevalence and incidence not caused by air pollution.[56]

For the medical care allowance, the council recommended a standardized table of reimbursable fees which doctors could charge. These fees are higher than the fees set under national health insurance. The council adopted the higher fees based upon a study conducted by the Japan Medical Association as authorized by the 1969 Special Relief Law. The study found that doctors spend more time with patients who are pollution victims due to the special problems related to their diseases.

In addition to the seven benefit categories, the council recommended the institution of health and welfare programs for victims. Under these programs, administrators would establish rehabilitation facilities in rural, unpolluted areas, assist in relocation, and help with the daily problems of victims. Each prefecture was to design a program suitable for local needs.

(iv) Financing compensation. The council's operating principle was that pollutors should finance the compensation program in proportion to their degree of contribution to pollution. Also, the mechanism for collection should be feasible, efficient, and well-managed.

To finance the air pollution part of the program (the so-called Class I diseases), the council studied two revenue methods for charging factories that emit pollutants--the fuel charge and the pollution-load levy. The fuel charge was a tax on the volume of fuel used by a factory. In the end, the council recommended the pollution-load levy--a tax on a factory's emissions of sulfur oxides. First, data presented at the Yokkaichi trial and independent government research indicated that sulfur dioxide was the principal cause of the victims' maladies. Second, sulfur oxides emissions could be easily calculated without having to make actual smokestack-top measurements, because these emissions are directly proportional to the percentage of sulfur in industrial fuel, the rate at which the fuel is burned, and the amount of stack-gas desulfurization that takes place. Finally, because the government possessed adequate data on industrial fuel consumption, sulfur oxides emissions could be monitored easily.[57]

Having a monitoring capability was important because the system relied on the accurate, self-reporting by industry.

The council further recommended that the amount of the pollution-load levy should be set to cover all estimated expenditures for benefit programs in the coming year. Each factory pays according to a graduated scale that takes into account several factors, including the amount of sulfur dioxide emitted from its stacks and the location of the factory. The council advised that the Compensation Law charter a quasi-public agency, the Pollution-Related Health Damage Compensation Association, to collect and disburse the funds.[58]

In addition, the council suggested that emission charges might replace direct regulation of emissions. It was thought that the charges would be an incentive for factories to install desulfurization equipment or switch to less-polluting fuels. However, this proposal was abandoned, and the program was labeled an emergency relief measure, not a new regulatory scheme.

Factories are not the only source of air pollution. Automobiles and other mobile sources contribute about 20% of Japan's total sulfur oxide and nitrogen oxides emissions. Thus, the council recommended that 20% of the program be financed by automobile owners. The council recommended that the Environment Agency select either a fuel tax or a vehicle tonnage tax. Administrators eventually selected the tonnage tax on the ground that collection costs would be minimized. At that time, there were more than 20 million vehicles in Japan. Also, vehicle owners already paid a tonnage tax, so it was an easy matter to reallocate part of the proceeds of the tonnage tax already being collected by the central government for purposes other than compensation.[59]

To finance the water pollution part of the program (Class II diseases), the council recommended a special levy on the four responsible companies, which would compensate victims directly. These companies were Chisso Corporation (Kumamoto and Kagoshima Minamata disease), Showa Denko (Niigata Minamata disease), Mitsui Mining Company (Toyama itai-itai disease), and Sumitomo Kinzoku (Shimane and Miyazaki chronic arsenic poisoning).

(v) Grievances. Finally, the council recommended the creation of a new administrative board to hear grievances arising under the Compensation Law. The council did not think it was appropriate for compensation grievances to be handled under the existing Administrative Grievance Examination Law. An applicant for benefits under the Compensation Law may challenge his certification decision, benefit level determination, and other matters. Pollutors may challenge the amount of their pollution-load levy.

6.5.2 The administrative system.

A victim who is certified as having a designated disease arising from his presence in a designated area for a specified length of time is eligible for benefits, and health and welfare programs.

(i) Designated diseases. Currently, the government has designated four air-pollution related diseases: chronic bronchitis, bronchial asthma, asthmatic bronchitis, pulmonary emphysema, and their respective sequelae. In addition, it has designated three water-pollution related diseases: Minamata disease (mercury poisoning), itai-itai disease (cadmium poisoning), and chronic arsenic poisoning.

Article 2 of the Compensation Law directs the prime minister to designate pollution diseases after consulting with the Central Advisory Council on Environmental Pollution Control Measures and the governors and mayors of the concerned prefectures and municipalities. Only diseases occurring in connection

with air- and water-pollution may be designated under the Compensation Law. The
other categories of pollution defined in the 1967 Basic Law for Environmental
Pollution Control Measures--noise, vibration, ground subsidence, and offensive

TABLE 6.2

Designated diseases, designated areas, and certified patients under the
pollution-related health damage compensation law, December 31, 1984

Category of Designation	Designated Disease	Designated Area	Local Government in Charge	Year Designated	Certified Patients
Class I	Chronic Bronchitis	Chiba	1	1974	755
Non-Specific Respiratory Disease	Bronchial Asthma	Tokyo	19	1974, 1975	35,229
		Yokohama	1	1974	934
		Kawasaki	1	1969, 1972, 1974	3,313
		Fuji	1	1974, 1977	895
		Nagoya, Tokai	2	1973, 1975 1978	5,873
		Yokkaichi, Kusu	2	1969, 1974	879 87
		Osaka	7	1969, 1974, 1975, 1977, 1978	31,078
		Kobe	1	1977	1,881
		Amagasaki	1	1970, 1974	5,288
		Okayama	2	1975	2,341
		Kitakyushu	1	1973	1,789
		Oomuta	1	1973	1,323
	Subtotal		40		91,665
Class II	Minamata Disease	Agano River, Niigata	2	1969	539
Specific Disease	Itaiitai Disease	Jintsu River, Toyama	1	1969	32
	Minamata Disease	Minamata Bay, Kumamoto	1	1969	1,086
		Kagoshima	1	1969	299
	Chronic Arsenic Poisoning	Sasagatani, Shimane	1	1974	9
		Toroku, Miyazaki	1	1973	102
	Subtotal		7		2,067
Grand Total					93,732

Source: Annual Report on the State of Environmental Pollution, 1984FY

odours--are not covered by the compensation scheme.

(ii) Designated areas. There are two types of designated area--Class I and Class II areas. In order for an area to receive Class I designation, the Cabinet must find that marked air pollution has arisen and that non-specific diseases due to the effects of such air pollution are prevalent. In Class II areas, a specific disease must be prevalent. Table 6.2 describes the present state of designated diseases and designated areas.

There is a two-step process for designating a Class I area. First, scientists measure the concentration of sulfur oxides in the proposed area to be designated. Second, health officials conduct a survey of health effects among the residents of the area.

There are several reasons why sulfur oxides are used as the measure of air pollution. While it is known that nitrogen dioxide as well as sulfur dioxide cause major health hazards in air-pollution related illnesses, by 1970, studies indicated a correlation between the concentration of sulfur dioxide and the prevalence of chronic bronchitis. Also, in 1972, the Yokkaichi court described the degree of air pollution in terms of sulfur dioxide. It noted a correlation between the concentration of sulfur dioxide and the prevalence and incidence of chronic bronchitis and asthma. Finally, the government had a well-documented, ten-year emission history of sulfur dioxide levels, suspended particulates, and deposit gauges, but very little on nitrogen dioxide. Thus, sulfur dioxide was selected as the measure of air pollution.[60]

The recommendations of the Central Advisory Council on Environmental Pollution Control Measures identify four gradations of sulfur dioxide concentrations based on a yearly average monitoring sample. These are: first grade, under 0.04 ppm; second grade, 0.04-0.05 ppm; third grade, 0.05-0.07 ppm; and fourth grade, over 0.07 ppm. Table 6.3 sets forth the gradations. If an area has a

TABLE 6.3

Gradation of air pollution by sulfur dioxide concentration for purposes of compensation area designation

Grade of Air Pollution	Ambient Concentration of SO_2 Measured by Electroconductivity Method	
	Annual Average	ppm
First Grade	0.02	0.04
Second Grade	0.04	0.05
Third Grade	0.05	0.07
Fourth Grade	0.07	

Source: Report of the Central Advisory Council for Environmental Pollution Control Measures, 1973

ten-year history of air pollution levels at the second, third, or fourth gradation, the analysis proceeds to the next step.

The second step in the area designation process is a health effects survey
developed by the British Medical Research Council (BMRC). Medical officials
interview area residents and ask them questions about their health, specifically regarding persistent coughing and phlegm. Officials also considered examining national health insurance records for this purpose, but they adopted the
BMRC survey because data using the survey had already been collected by 1973.[61]

The past surveys provided a benchmark for natural incidence and prevalence
rates. For example, the natural incidence of pulmonary emphysema for a forty-
year-old man might be one in one hundred. Using this data, administrators can
detect how far an area diverges from the natural incidence and prevalence
rates. The regulations specify three gradations: first grade, twice the
natural rate; second grade, two to three times the natural rate; and third
grade, four to five times the natural rate.[62]

Table 6.4 sets forth these gradations.

In deciding whether to designate an area, the Environment Agency then looks
at the pollution and disease gradations obtained from the two steps. An area
recording a third or fourth grade sulfur dioxide level and a second or third
grade chronic bronchitis prevalence rate is quickly designated. Areas receiving low scores are excluded. Also, when the pollution and disease levels in a
designated area drop below the set criteria, designation for that area is
withdrawn.[63]

This is how the administrative practice under the Compensation Law uses
statistical probability to create a rebuttable presumption of causation. In
determining the pollutant-disease nexus, the system operates on lesser levels
of certainty than scientific discipline would normally require. However, given
the dire need to do something about the suffering of pollution victims in 1973,
equitable principles won the day.

TABLE 6.4

Gradation of the prevalence rate of chronic bronchitis symptoms as measured
subjectively by the BMRC questionnaire method

Grade of Prevalence Rate	Base rate is the Natural Prevalence Rate for 40-50 year olds
First Grade	About Two Times
Second Grade	About Two to Three Times
Third Grade	About Four to Five Times

Source: Report of the Central Advisory Council for Environmental Pollution
Control Measures, 1973

One final note on designation. At the time the Compensation Law took effect on 1 September 1974, there were twelve areas designated and 14,355 patients certified under the 1969 Special Relief Law for Pollution-Related Health Hazards. These areas, corresponding to Class I areas under the Compensation Law, were located in twelve cities lying in eight prefectures. These areas and patients were redesignated and recertified, respectively, under the new Compensation Law. Class II areas and patients were similarly transferred.

(iii) Term of exposure. Once an area is designated, a victim seeking certification must meet requirements regarding term of exposure in the designated area. For example, a patient with pulmonary emphysema must show that he continuously lived, worked, or was otherwise present in a designated area for a term of three years, or, if his presence was not continuous, he must show cumulative presence of four-and-a-half years during a term of five-and-a-half years. The required term of exposure differs by disease and age. Table 6.5 summarizes the rules.

(iv) Certification procedures. Article 44 of the Compensation Law requires a prefectural or municipal government with a designated area to establish a Pollution-Related Health Damage Certification Committee. The Certification Committee is composed of ten doctors and five lawyers expert in pollution health matters. A victim who seeks benefits under the Compensation Law files

TABLE 6.5

Required terms of exposure for class I diseases

Designated Diseases	Continuous Exposure	Frame Period for Interrupted Exposure	Cumulated Term of Exposure for an Interrupted Case
Chronic Bronchitis and its sequelae	2 years (1 year for a person under 6 years old)	4 years (2 years and 6 months for a person under 6 years old)	3 years (1 year and 6 months for a person under 6 years old)
Bronchial Asthma and its sequelae	1 year (6 months for a person under 6 years old)	2 years and 6 months	1 year and 6 months (9 months for a person under a year old)
Asthmatic Bronchitis and its sequelae	1 year (6 months for a person under a year old)	2 years and 6 months	1 year and 6 months (9 months for a person under a year old)
Pulmonary Emphysema and its sequelae	3 years	5 years and 6 months	4 years and 6 months

Note: Article 2-1, Cabinet Order, based on Article 4-1-1, Pollution-Related Health Damage Compensation Law

an application and a report of a physician's diagnosis with the Certification Committee. The committee determines whether the applicant is eligible for certification, and if so, it evaluates the degree of the applicant's disability. This is necessary because the amount of the disability benefit varies with the severity of the patient's disability. At this time, the committee also determines the term of the patient's certification. For cases where the disability is irreversible, the certification is permanent; otherwise, it is temporary. However, certification can be renewed if the patient continues to suffer from his illness. Certification is retroactive to the date the application was filed.

(v) Benefits. The Compensation Law provides the following seven categories of benefits: a medical treatment allowance (hospitalization and out-patient expenses), a disability allowance, a nurse allowance, a child victim allowance, a medical care allowance (miscellaneous and transportation expenses), a survivors' allowance, and a funeral allowance.

The medical treatment allowance covers the entire amount of medical bills including the portion otherwise paid under national health insurance. The fees which physicians may charge are fixed.

The disability benefit is calculated by a standard monthly wage scale classified by age and gender with a factor for disability severity. As recommended by the Central Adevisory Council on Environmental Pollution Control Measures, the formula used to derive the table was 80% of the national average wage levels. The disability benefits in effect in Fiscal Year 1985 are set forth in Table 6.6. However, in setting the amount of benefits for a particular applicant, etiology factors unrelated to pollution may be considered.

TABLE 6.6

Standard scale of monthly disability allowance, FY 1985

Age Bracket	Sex	
	Male	Female
15 – 17	84.0	78.1
18 – 19	109.4	93.0
20 – 24	133.3	108.0
25 – 29	167.6	122.6
30 – 34	204.7	125.3
35 – 39	233.5	124.2
40 – 44	253.0	121.3
45 – 49	258.0	119.5
50 – 54	251.2	124.0
55 – 59	216.6	126.3
60 – 64	172.8	117.7
65 –	158.1	113.8

Source: Article 26, Pollution-Related Health Damage Compensation Law

Under the system, there are four degrees of disability, and a factor is assigned to each degree to calculate the amount of the disability allowance. See Table 6.7. Patients with a special grade classification receive an additional allowance for the services of a nurse. In Fiscal Year 1985, the nurse allowance was ¥36,500. The system of classifying a disability into four grades also applies to Class II diseases.

There is a child victim allowance. It is available for all four grades of disability in Class I, and for the congenital Minamata disease in Class II. In Fiscal Year 1985, the amount of the child compensation allowance was as follows: ¥52,700 for the special and first grades, ¥26,400 for the second grade, and ¥15,800 for the third grade.

The medical care allowance covers miscellaneous expenses for hospitalized patients and transportation expenses for out-patients. Table 6.8 sets forth the amounts.

The survivors' allowance is intended to compensate for damages and also to contribute to family life. The benefit provides monthly payments for a period of ten years after the patient's death to certain close family members. Table 6.9 sets forth the monthly survivors' allowance. Where there are no eligible survivors, a lump sum is paid to other survivors more distantly related to the deceased. The lump sum is equivalent to 36 times of the monthly allowance.

TABLE 6.7

Classification of grades for the disability benefit

Grade	Criteria & Guides	Factor
Special Grade	No labor capacity and daily life seriously restricted due to physical and mental conditions and under 24-hour nursing care.	1.0
First Grade	No labor capacity or prohibited from working; need for strict restriction of daily life due to physical and mental conditions.	1.0
Second Grade	Labor strictly restricted and daily life considerably limited due to physical and mental conditions.	0.5
Third Grade	Labor and daily life restricted due to physical and mental conditions.	0.3

Note: Article 10 of Cabinet Order, based on Article 26 of Pollution-Related Health Damage Compensation Law

TABLE 6.8

Medical care allowance, FY 1985

Classification	Conditions	Amount of Allowance
Hospitalized Patient	More than 15 days	28,500 Yen
	8 days to 14 days	26,500 Yen
	Less than 7 days	20,200 Yen
Out-Patient	15 days for class I area More than 8 days for class II	20,200 Yen
	4 days to 14 days for class I 2 days to 7 days for class II	18,200 Yen

Source: Article 40, The Pollution-Related Health Damage Compensation Law

The funeral allowance is allocated to the person who pays the victim's funeral expenses. The amount of the allowance in Fiscal Year 1985 was ¥466,000.

During each fiscal year, the Central Advisory Council for Environmental Pollution Control Measures reviews all the standard scales and revises them if warranted. This includes the disability allowance, child victim allowance, medical care allowance, and survivors' allowance. Also, a prefectural governor

TABLE 6.9

Monthly survivors' allowance, FY 1985

Age Bracket	Sex	
	Male	Female
0 - 14	56.3	56.3
15 - 17	73.5	68.3
18 - 19	95.7	81.3
20 - 24	116.7	94.5
25 - 29	146.6	107.3
30 - 34	179.2	109.7
35 - 39	204.3	108.6
40 - 44	221.4	106.1
45 - 49	225.8	104.5
50 - 54	219.8	108.5
55 - 59	189.5	110.5
60 - 64	151.2	103.0
65 -	138.3	99.5

Source: Article 17, Cabinet Order, based on Article 31, Pollution-Related Health Damage Compensation Law.

may suspend benefits in full or in part where a certified patient or the guardian of a certified child patient fails to follow a doctor's medical orders.

In addition to benefits, the Compensation Law requires the governor of a prefecture having a designated area to provide health and welfare programs. There are five such programs: (i) rehabilitation, (ii) patient relocation for medical treatment, (iii) equipment supply for home patient care, (iv) supervision and guidance for home patient care, and (v) other programs as necessary and appropriate for the promotion of the health and welfare of designated patients and to prevent the exacerbation of their diseases. These programs are based on the traditional duty of local governments to protect and promote the health and welfare of the residents in their jurisdictions.

(vi) <u>Interaction between the Compensation Law, national health insurance, and workmen's compensation.</u> These three statutes, and others, are independent programs. A victim of a pollution disease may select one, but only one, program in which to pursue his relief. Article 14 of the Compensation Law prevents double compensation where an applicant has already received relief under another law, including national health insurance, workmen's compensation, and 24 other programs designated by Cabinet Order. Similarly, Article 13 prevents double compensation by the same person for the same injury under two or more separate provisions of the Compensation Law. In addition, a successful litigant who has received damages in a pollution trial is ineligible to receive benefits under the Compensation Law. However, litigants may participate in health and welfare programs under the Compensation Law.

(vii) <u>Finances.</u> Fig. 6.2 and Table 6.10 together present the complete picture of the relevant institutions and the money flows between them. Prefectural and municipal governments with designated areas make the actual payment of disability benefits to victims and medical institutions treating victims. These local governments receive a subsidy from the national government for the administrative expenses incurred in connection with making such disbursements. This subsidy covers 50% of the total cost of the administrative expenses (Fig. 6.2, line D); the respective prefectural or municipal government covers the remaining 50%.

The Pollution-Related Health Damage Compensation Association is a quasi-governmental organization established to collect funds from pollutors. The association subcontracts the actual collection activity to local chambers of commerce, which charge a fee for their services. This fee and the association's other administrative expenses are paid by contributions from the national government and pollutors (Table 6.10, line 4). The association drafts its principal officers from industry, and industry (particularly Keidanren) manages its daily affairs under the guidance of the Environment Agency and the Ministry

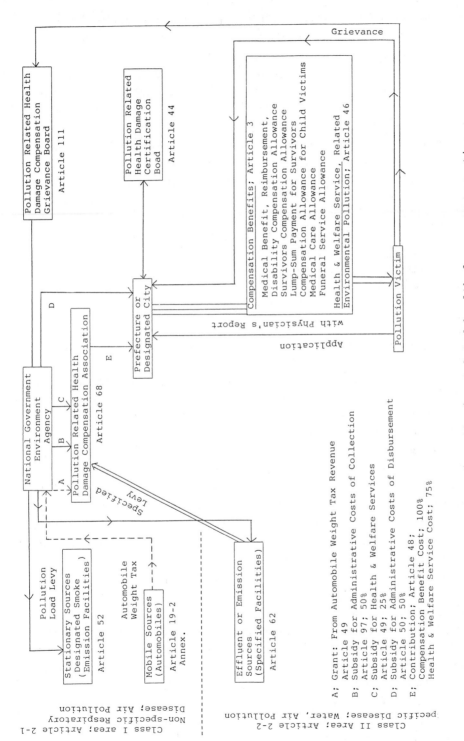

Fig. 6.2. Flowchart for the pollution-related health damage compensation.

TABLE 6.10

Source of finances under the pollution-related health damage compensation law

	Class I Areas Non-specific Respiratory Diseases		Class II Areas Specific Diseases	
Expenditures for Compensation Benefits	Pollution-Load Levy	80%	Specified Levy	100%
	Automobile Tonnage Tax	20%		
Expenditures for Pollution-Related Health & Welfare Programs	Pollution-Load Levy	40%	Specified Levy	50%
	Automobile Tonnage Tax	10%		
	National Government Prefectural or Municipal Government	25% 25%	National Government Prefectural or Municipal Government	25% 25%
Expenditures for Disbursement	National Government			50%
	Prefectural or Municipal Government			50%
Expenditures for Collection	Partial National Subsidy			
	Pollution-Load Levy and Specified Levy			

Source: Articles 47, 48, 49, 50 and 51 of the Pollution-Related Health Damage Conpensation Law, Automobile Tonnage Tax is based on Article 19-2 of the Pollution-Related Health Damage Compensation Law.

of International Trade and Industry.

The scheme, then, makes different institutions responsible for the functions of collection (the association) and disbursement (local governments). The architects of the Compensation Law felt that if one entity carried out both functions, a party dissatisfied with an aspect of disbursement (eg. the amount of benefits) might focus an attack on the collection apparatus, thereby under-mining the entity's operations.[64]

In fact the scheme has been a success: more than 99% of assessed levies have been collected.

Money flows for Class I (air pollution diseases) and Class II (water pollu-tion diseases) are kept distinct. Class II pollutors are readily identified; currently, there are only four--Chisso Corporation (Kumamoto Minamata disease), Showa Denko (Niigata Minamata disease), Mitsui Mining Company (Toyama itai-itai disease), and Sumitomo Kinzoku (Shimane and Miyazaki chronic arsenic poisoning). Each of these pollutors pays 100% of the cost of the benefit payments made to the victims of its pollution (Table 6.10, line 1). The

Environment Agency notifies each pollutor of the amount of the special levy, and the pollutors pay the victims directly. In addition, Class II pollutors pay 50% of the cost of the Class II health and welfare programs (Table 6.10, line 2). The national government and local government each pay 25% (Chart 6.2, line C; Table 6.10, line 3).

Class I payments are more complex. Stationary sources of air pollution (factories) pay 80% and mobile sources (vehicles) pay 20% of the total cost of the Class I benefit programs (Table 6.10, lines 1 and 2). The government amended the Compensation Law on 31 May 1974 to add the vehicle tonnage tax. Research indicated that about 20% of total sulfur oxides and nitrogen oxides emissions throughout Japan derived from automobiles (see Table 6.11). The vehicle tonnage tax is not levied by the association, but by the national government through the general budget. The government pays the association an amount equivalent to 20% of the budget for Class I benefits (Fig. 6.2, line A; Table 6.10, line 2) and 10% of the Class I health and welfare programs (Fig. 6.2, line A; Table 6.10, line 3). This amount represents only a small fraction of the total tonnage tax collected by the government.

Stationary pollution-emitting facilities pay the remaining 80% of the budget for Class I benefits (Table 6.10, line 1) and 40% of the Class I health and welfare programs (Table 6.10, line 2). This is done in the form of a pollution-load levy. The formula for calculating the amount of each facility's pollution-load levy is the adjusted unit levy (levy per cubic meter of sulfur

TABLE 6.11

Percentage of pollution emissions from stationary and mobile sources

Source Classification	SO_x	NO_x	Total
Stationary Sources; Mining, Manufacturing, Electric Power, Works, and Others	92.4%	64.3%	78.4%
Mobile Sources; Automobiles & Others	7.6%	35.7%	21.6%
Total	100.0%	100.0%	100.0%
Total Emissions	$750 \times 10^6 \ m^3$	$610 \times 10^6 \ m^3$	$136 \times 10^7 \ m^3$

Source: Environment Agency, Department of Environmental Health, 1974

Note: The ratio of emissions from stationary source to mobile sources is 8:2.

dioxide emitted) times the volume of sulfur dioxide emitted by the facility. Thus, a facility can decrease its pollution-load levy by reducing its sulfur dioxide emissions. Despite this effect, the Compensation Law is not meant to be a regulatory statute; other laws regulate the volume of pollution which facilities may emit.

Each fiscal year, the Environment Agency calculates the amount of the unit levy such that the total proceeds will cover the levy's share (80% and 40%, respectively) of Class I benefits and health and welfare programs. This is provisionally done by dividing the required budget by nationwide emissions. However, two other factors are then taken into account: the 9:1 differential for designated and non-designated areas, and the adjustment to balance revenues and disbursements.

First, some background on the 9:1 differential. The Compensation Law requires all stationary pollutors, whether in designated areas or elsewhere, to pay the pollution-load levy. The only exception is for small pollutors. Small pollutors are defined as facilities emitting less than 5000 cubic meters of sulfur dioxide per hour in designated areas and less than 10,000 cubic meters

TABLE 6.12

Comparison of class I unit levy in effect in FYs 1975, 1977, and 1985

Unit Levy = Yen/SO_x Nm^3

Area \ FY Item	1975 FY Unit Levy	1977 FY Block	Class	Unit Levy	Class	1985 FY Unit Levy
Designated Area	77.31 Yen	Osaka	A	536.63 Yen	A	3,318.94 Yen
		Tokyo			B	2,008.83 Yen
		Nagoya	B	383,31 Yen	C	1,834.85 Yen
		Yokkaichi			F	1,310.11 Yen
		Kobe			D	1,746.81 Yen
		Chiba	C	344.98 Yen		
		Fuji			E	1,397.45 Yen
		Fukuoka	D	306.65 Yen	G	1,222.77 Yen
		Okayama				
Non-Designated Area	8.59 Yen			42.59 Yen		194.09 Yen

Source: Guides for Pollution-Related Health Damage Compensation, 1985

per hour in non-designated areas. Small pollutors are excluded because the costs of collection exceed the proceeds. In any event, large pollutors account for more than 90% of sulfur dioxide emitted nationwide so there is a measure of fairness in this. By taxing all large pollutors, the Compensation Law extends the concept of collective responsibility drafted in the Yokkaichi decision. There were only six defendants in the Yokkaichi case, and the court relied on the joint tort statute to assign liability to all of them, even though the emissions of some of the defendants alone might not have been sufficient to cause the plaintiffs' injuries. The provision of the Compensation Law under discussion, however, assigns collective responsibility to thousands of pollu- tors.[65]

There were about 7,400 Class I pollutors in Japan in the mid-1970s.[66]

To appease those who opposed taxing industries in non-designated areas, a settlement was made whereby the unit levy for a facility within a designated area would be nine times the unit levy for a facility in a non-designated area. The 9:1 ratio is an approximation of the respective concentrations of sulfur dioxide between designated and non-designated areas. The theory is that two facilities--one in a designated area and one in a non-designated area--each emitting the same volume of sulfur dioxide, nevertheless are culpable to dif- ferent degrees. To release pollutants in an area where there is already a high concentration (annual average ppm of sulfur dioxide) of pollution causes more damage than to release the same volume of pollutants in an area of low pollu-

TABLE 6.13

The pollution-load levy in effect for class I areas in FY 1985

Area	Block	Grade	Factor	Levy Per Unit
Designated Area	Osaka	A	1.90	3,318.94 Yen/Nm^3
	Tokyo	B	1.15	2,008.83 Yen/Nm^3
	Nagoya	C	1.05	1,834.15 Yen/Nm^3
	Yokkaichi	F	0.75	1,310.11 Yen/Nm^3
	Kobe	D	1.00	1,746.81 Yen/Nm^3
	Chiba	D	1.00	same above
	Fuji	E	0.80	1,397.45 Yen/Nm^3
	Fukuoka	G	0.70	1,222.77 Yen/Nm^3
	Okayama	G	0.70	same above
Non-Designated Area				194.09 Yen/Nm^3

Source: Guides for Pollution-Related Health Damage Compensation, 1985

tion concentration.

In any event, the 9:1 differential was introduced in Fiscal Year 1974. Adjusted for the 9:1 differential, the unit levy was ¥15.84 per cubic meter in designated areas and ¥1.76 per cubic meter in non-designated areas. These rates were subsequently raised. FY 1975: ¥77.31/m^3 (designated), ¥8.59/m^3 (non-designated); FY 1976: ¥209.97/m^3 (designated), ¥23.33/m^3 (non-designated). In each case, the unit levy for designated areas is exactly nine times the unit levy for non-designated areas.

A further adjustment to the unit levy is made to balance revenues and disbursements within each designated area. After 1973, revenues and disbursements for each designated area were unbalanced. For example, in the City of Kawasaki, the ratio of revenues to disbursements in 1977 was 0.5:1, whereas in Kobe, the ratio was 2.4:1.[67]

To balance the budget in each designated area, the government transferred excess funds from one area to another where funds were deficient. In time, industry charged that this practice was inefficient, irrational, and unfair. Why, it was asked, should factories in Kobe pay for compensation payments and health and welfare programs in Kawasaki? To reduce interregional transfers, in 1977 the government introduced a system of gradation in the unit levy. A factor was assigned to each designated area ranging from 0.70 to 1.90, and the basic unit levy was multiplied by the area's factor to obtain the adjusted unit levy for that area. Table 6.12 compares the uniform levy in effect in Fiscal Year 1975 with the graduated levies in effect in Fiscal Years 1977 and 1985. Table 6.13 lists the factor and resultant pollution-load levy in effect for selected designated areas in Fiscal Year 1985. As can be calculated from Table 6.12, in Fiscal Year 1985, the Class A unit levy is 2.7 times the Class G unit levy. In Fiscal Year 1985, the unit levy in a Class A designated area is 17.1 times the unit levy in a non-designated area. Table 6.14 lists the relative contributions of the pollution-load levy for designated and non-designated areas in Fiscal Year 1984. The 1736 facilities in designated areas paid 35.9%

TABLE 6.14

The pollution-load levy in designated and non-designated areas in FY 1984

Designation Status	Number of Notification	Amount of Levy (Yen)	%
Designated Areas	1,736	25,156,123 x 10^3	35.9
Non-Designated Areas	6,846	44,903,180 x 10^3	64.1
Total	8,582	70,059,303 x 10^3	100.0

Source: Guides for Pollution-Related Health Damage Compensation, 1985

of total revenues; the 6846 facilities in non-designated areas paid 64.1% of total revenues.

(viii) Grievances. The Compensation Law established an administrative board to hear grievances relating to certification, benefits, or other matters. The Pollution-Related Health Damage Compensation Grievance Board consists of six members appointed by the prime minister with the consent of the Diet. The members should be persons of integrity with experience in law, medicine, or other fields related to compensation for health injury. The board's decision must be unanimous to overturn a previous ruling. A judicial review is available only after the board has issued its final decision. Before a pollutor may file an action in court, he must seek a review of the matter from the Environment Agency and the Ministry of International Trade and Industry.

A different grievance procedure was in effect for complaints under the 1969 Special Relief Law for Pollution-Related Health Hazards. That procedure, set forth in the Administrative Grievance Review Law of 1962, does not apply to grievances under the Compensation Law. Under the 1962 law, the Environment Agency is the body which reviews a decision of a prefectural governor challenged by a complainant. A number of grievances under the 1962 law are still pending. One case, filed by Minamata disease victims, concerns the review of certification decisions.

6.6 PERFORMANCE AND PROBLEMS

6.6.1 Trends in class I areas

Table 6.15 presents the trends in the number of Class I designated areas and certified patients from 1974 to 1984. The Table begins with 12 designated areas in September 1974 because, when the Compensation Law went into effect on 1 September 1974, the twelve areas designated under the 1969 Special Relief Law for Pollution-Related Health Hazards were transferred to the Compensation Law. Table 6.15 shows that the government has designated new areas four times, in November 1974, December 1975, January 1977, and June 1978. In March 1984, there were 49 designated areas in 41 cities, towns, or wards in 10 prefectures, with a total of 89,053 certified patients. On 31 December 1984, the number of certified patients was 91,665.

Table 6.15 shows that the number of active certified patients increased each fiscal year (measured at the end of March) due mostly to the addition of new designated areas. It took about three years for the number of certified patients to peak after the Compensation Law went into effect in 1974. The three-year lag can be attributed to the time it takes for patients, physicians, and others to become informed about the availability of compensation. At the end of March 1981, after a three-year period from the designation of three new areas in June 1978, the rate of annual increase of certified patients dropped

TABLE 6.15

Trends in class I designated areas and certified patients

Year Month	Designated Areas						Certified Patients	
	In number of Prefectures		In number of Cities, Towns, Wards		Designated Areas		Running Total	Annual % Increase
	New	Running Total	New	Running Total	New	Running Total		
1974 Sept.		7		12		12	14,355	
1974 Nov.	2	9	11	23	14	26		
1975 Mar.		9		23		26	19,281	
1975 Dec.	1	10	14	37	16	42		
1976 Mar.		10		37		42	34,184	77.3%
1977 Jan.		10	3	39	4	46		
1977 Mar.		10		39		46	53,414	56.3%
1978 Mar.		10		39		46	63,654	19.2%
1978 Jun.		10	2	41	3	49		
1979 Mar.		10		41		49	72,789	14.4%
1980 Mar.		10		41		49	77,493	6.5%
1981 Mar.		10		41		49	79,963	3.2%
1982 Mar.		10		41		49	83,211	4.1%
1983 Mar.		10		41		49	86,575	4.0%
1984 Mar.		10		41		49	89,053	2.9%

Source: Guides for Pollution-Related Health Damage Compensation; 1985

to 3.2%. From March 1983 to March 1984, the rate of annual increase in the number of certified patients dropped to 2.9%. Table 6.16 presents basic data on Class 1 areas.

TABLE 6.16

Basic data on class I areas

Item of Classification		Figures
Designation	Jurisdiction Area Population	40 Local Governments 1,283 km^2 12,697 x 10^3
Certification	Application Certification Rate (%)	123,002 113,284 92.1%
Total Number of Patient	Cured Died Active	21,681 8,431 83,211

Source: Department of Environmental Health, Environment Agency; (At the end of FY1981) 1982

TABLE 6.17

Trends in sulfur dioxide concentration AT five typical monitoring stations

(unit: ppb)

	Tokyo Chiyoda	Kawasaki Taishi	Yokohama Tsurumi	Yokkaichi Isozu	Osaka NASN
1967	66	100	60	81	91
1968	63	70	50	52	76
1969	54	60	50	51	60
1970	43	52	58	39	56
1971	35	49	45	47	51
1972	23	48	38	20	39
1973	29	40	32	21	26
1974	25	30	25	21	35
1975	27	27	30	10	26
1976	26	24	27	12	26
1977	21	16	22	13	24
1978	19	19	21	13	15
1979	18	16	15	11	14
1980	19	16	13	8	11
1981	16	14	12	10	14
1982	16	12	12	10	13
1983	13	12	13	8	12
1984	12	12	13	10	12

Source: Compiled from annual report of air monitoring results at general
(areal) air monitoring station; Ministry of Health & Welfare
(1967-1969). Environment Agency (1970-1984)

Table 6.17 shows the trends in air pollution levels measured by the average
concentration of sulfur dioxide at five typical monitoring stations in Japan.
It can be seen that pollution levels have decreased markedly in recent years.
This has been due to a rigorous enforcement program and desulfurization. The
government enacted the 1969 Special Relief Law for Pollution-Related Health
Hazards shortly after the worst period of air pollution, but it enacted the

TABLE 6.18

Trends in sulfur oxide emission

1976 = 100

FY Area	'76	'77	'78	'79	'80	'81	'82
Designated	100	74.5	56.6	39.0	35.6	31.6	26.4
Non-Designated	100	85.9	75.1	67.0	63.6	58.5	52.8
Total	100	84.4	72.5	63.2	59.8	54.8	48.8

Source: Department of Environmental Health, Environment Agency, 1982

TABLE 6.19

Classification of pollution-load levy by amount in FY 1984

Classification by Amount of Levy	Number of Notifications (Running Total)	Amount of Levy (Running Total)	% of Total Yen Amount
¥100 million and over	150	$45,099 \times 10^6$ Yen	64.4%
¥ 10 million to <¥100 million	542	$17,157 \times 10^6$ Yen	88.9%
¥ 1 million to <¥ 10 million	1,941	$6,317 \times 10^6$ Yen	98.0%
¥ 0 to <¥ 1 million	5,781	$1,430 \times 10^6$ Yen	100.0%

Source: Guides for pollution-Related Health Damage Compensation, 1985

Compensation Law at a time of considerable improvement in the level of air
pollution. Table 6.18 shows trends in the volume of sulfur oxides emissions by
designated and non-designated areas. Emissions decreased in both areas, but
much more in designated areas. The large increase in the pollution-load levy
after Fiscal Year 1979 apparently acted as an incentive to reduce emissions
because the air-pollution-control administration had already regulated
emissions in Fiscal Year 1979. Table 6.19 shows the distribution of the pollution-load levy among the range of small and large pollutors in Fiscal Year
1984. Of the 5781 facilities which received notifications for the pollution-
load levy, 150 facilities fell in the ¥100 million or more category, and
together the facilities in this category paid 64.4% of total revenues. Table
6.19 cumulatively includes this category in the next category (¥10 million to

TABLE 6.20

Trends in the age structure of class I certified patients

Year	0 – 14 Years Old	0 – 5 Years Old	15 – 59 Years Old	More Than 60 Years Old
31 March 1975	47.4%	(20.1%)	27.6%	24.7%
31 March 1976	47.4%	(17.2%)	28.2%	24.4%
31 March 1977	45.6%	(14.9%)	29.6%	24.8%
31 March 1978	44.6%	(13.1%)	30.1%	25.3%
31 March 1979	43.0%	(11.7%)	31.1%	25.9%
31 March 1980	41.7%	(9.9%)	31.8%	26.5%
31 March 1981	40.5%	(8.5%)	32.4%	27.1%
31 March 1982	39.8%	(7.3%)	32.8%	27.4%
31 March 1983	38.8%	(6.5%)	33.7%	27.5%
31 March 1984	37.6%	(6.0%)	34.6%	27.9%

Source: Guides for Pollution-Related Health Damage Compensation, 1985

TABLE 6.21

Trends in the disease structure of class I patients

Year	Chronic Bronchitis	Bronchial Asthma	Asthatic Bronchitis	Pulmanary Emphysema
31 March 1975	24.3%	43.4%	29.0%	3.3%
31 March 1976	22.1%	51.6%	22.5%	3.8%
31 March 1977	21.2%	60.2%	14.7%	4.0%
31 March 1978	20.5%	62.0%	13.6%	3.9%
31 March 1979	20.2%	64.2%	11.9%	3.7%
31 March 1980	19.9%	65.1%	11.4%	3.6%
31 March 1981	19.5%	68.8%	8.0%	3.7%
31 March 1982	19.1%	70.9%	6.5%	3.5%
31 March 1983	18.5%	73.2%	4.9%	3.4%
31 March 1984	18.1%	75.0%	3.5%	3.4%

Source: Guides for Pollution-Related Health Damage Compensation, 1985

less than ¥100 million). The 542 facilities in the top two categories, which comprise 11.97% of the total 5781 facilities, together paid 88.9% of total revenues. In Fiscal Year 1981, pollutors in the electric power, iron and steel, and chemical industries paid about 60% of the total pollution levy.

Table 6.20 represents the trends in the age structure of Class I certified patients from 1975 to 1984. The number of young patients (0-5 years old) has decreased while the number of older patients has increased. Table 6.21 sets forth the trends in the disease structure of Class I certified patients from 1975 to 1984. The incidence of chronic bronchitis has decreased slightly while bronchial asthma has increased. The incidence of asthmatic bronchitis

TABLE 6.22

Trends in the disability grade structure of class I certified patients

Year	Special Grade	First Grade	Second Grade	Third Grade	Others
31 March 1975	0.5%	4.8%	28.1%	44.3%	22.4%
31 March 1976	0.4%	4.2%	28.8%	45.9%	20.7%
31 March 1977	0.3%	3.4%	26.9%	47.9%	21.5%
31 March 1978	0.2%	2.9%	24.7%	48.9%	23.4%
31 March 1979	0.1%	2.3%	22.2%	50.2%	25.2%
31 March 1980	0.1%	1.8%	19.5%	51.2%	27.4%
31 March 1981	0.1%	1.4%	17.9%	52.0%	28.6%
31 March 1982	0.1%	1.2%	16.9%	51.9%	30.0%
31 March 1983	0.0%	1.1%	15.4%	52.3%	31.2%
31 March 1984	0.0%	0.9%	14.6%	52.4%	32.0%

Note: Special Grade (100%), First Grade (100%), Second Grade (50%),
        Third Grade (30%), Others (No significant disability)
Source: Guides for Pollution-Related Health Damage Compensation, 1985

decreased after March 1980 when medical experts introduced new criteria for certification. The incidence of pulmonary emphysema has remained constant. Table 6.22 presents the trends in the disability grade structure of Class I certified patients. The number of patients in the third grade has increased while the number of patients in the first and second grades has decreased. The number of patients deemed ineligible for the disability allowance due to a lack of disability has increased. However, these patients remain eligible for medical care benefits and the medical treatment allowance under another classification. In general, disease severity has declined and patients are improving.

Table 6.23 presents a comparison of expenditures under the Compensation Law

TABLE 6.23

Comparison of expenditures under the compensation law between FYs 1975 and 1985

unit: 10^6 Yen & %

Budget Item	1975 FY	1985 FY	Increase
I: Compensation Benefits	18,312	95,612	522.13%
1)Medical Care Allowance	6,653	43,607	655.45%
2)Disability Allowance	7,126	30,499	428.00%
3)Survivors Allowance	90	3,246	3606.67%
4)Lump-Sum Survivors Allowance	877	3,170	361.46%
5)Compensation Allowance for Child Victim	1,769	3,474	196.38%
6)Medical Treatment Allowance	1,646	11,121	675.64%
7)Funeral Allowance	151	495	327.81%
II:Pollution-Related Health & Welfare Programs	372	235	63.17%
III:Subtotal, Include Reserve	19,618	98,715	503.19%
IV:Administrative Costs of Collection	435	482	110.80%
Grand Total	20,053	99,197	494.67%

Source of Income	unit: 10^6 Yen & %		
I: Pollution-Load Levy	16,129	79,454	492.62%
1)80% of III	15,694	78,972	503.20%
2)IV	435	482	110.80%
II:Grant to the Association for for Pollution-Related Compensation (20% if III)	3,942	19,743	500.84%
Total	20,053	99,197	494.67%

Source: Complied from Report by Department of Environmental Health, Environment Agency 1982 & 1985

between Fiscal Years 1975 and 1985. All items have increased in absolute terms
due to the increase in the number of certified patients. However, the relative
share of each budget item to the total budget has also changed due to the
structural changes in the age, disease, and disability grades of certified
patients.

6.6.2 Trends in Class II areas

Table 6.24 presents the state of Class II areas. In Fiscal Year 1984, there
were 2067 certified patients in five Class II areas. This does not include the
567 deaths in Kumamoto, the 82 deaths in Kagoshima, and the 200 deaths in
Niigata; it does include the 86 deaths from itai-itai disease and the 48 deaths
from chronic arsenic poisoning. The five Class II areas in Table 6.24 fall
under the jurisdiction of six prefectures and one city. The government has not
designated a new Class II area since July 1974.

Under the present state of implementation of the Compensation Law, Class II
pollutors pay compensation benefits directly to victims. These are Chisso
Corporation (Kumamoto and Kagoshima Minamata disease), Showa Denko (Niigata
Minamata disease), Mitsui Mining Company (Toyama itai-itai disease), and
Sumitomo Kinzoku (Shimane and Miyazaki chronic arsenic poisoning). Payments are
made directly because the Minamata disease victims' organizations objected to
receiving payments via the Pollution-Related Health Damage Compensation
Association and local governments. Instead, they demanded that Chisso make a
lump-sum payment of between ¥16 million and ¥18 million to each victim at the
time of certification by the Pollution-Related Health Damage Compensation

TABLE 6.24

Status of class II areas

Designated Disease	Designated Area	Jurisdiction	Date	Number of Certified Patients
Minamata Disease	Agano River Basin	Niigata Prefecture Niigata City	1969 December	279 260
Itaiitai Disease	Jintsu River Basin	Toyama Prefecture	1969 December	32
Minamata Disease	Minamata Bay Area	Kumamoto Prefecture Kagoshima Prefecture	1969 December	1,086 299
Chronic Arsenic Poisoning	Sasagatani Area	Shimane Prefecture	1974 July	9
	Tohoku Area	Miyazaki Prefecture	1973 February	102
Total	5	7		2,067

Source: Annual Report of Environmental Quality, FY1984

Certification Board. Thus, statistics on the amount of payments made are difficult to acquire.

In addition to the lump-sum compensation payments, Class II pollutors make other direct payments to victims based on judicial awards and extrajudicial mediated settlements. In March 1973, just after the court issued its judgment on the Kumamoto Minamata disease case, T. Kawamoto, the leader of the victim's Self-Negotiation Group, and the president of Chisso had a heated argument, which finally resulted in a mediated settlement. In July 1974, the director general of the Environment Agency gave his support to the settlement.

Since then, there has been a sharp increase in the number of applications for certification of Minamata disease. However, applicants became dissatisfied and annoyed with the national and local governments because of the lack of medical personnel available to examine them. Also, victims complain of the limited capacity of Kumamoto prefecture's Pollution-Related Health Damage Certification Board. In 1974, the Environment Agency recruited medical experts from universities and hospitals to accelerate the medical examination of waiting patients at Minamata. However, victims' groups objected to the program due to difficulties in the doctor-patient relationships, and it collapsed. The situation has improved somewhat since 1977, but capacity remains far below demand. By August 1985, 10,752 people had applied for certification. Of these, the board had certified 1670 cases (15.5%), denied certification for 4030 cases (37.5%), and had postponed decisions on 5052 cases citing difficulty of judgment. Delays in certification procedures became a serious social, political, and administrative issue in Kumamoto prefecture. A number of dis-contented applicants have filed administrative grievances to challenge denials of certification or inaction due to delay of the certification procedure, and there have been ten civil actions with similar challenges against Kumamoto prefecture and the national government. In one case, a high court upheld part of a patient's claim in connection with a certification decision, and the case is on appeal in the Supreme Court. In addition to taking legal action, Minamata disease victims have engaged in a number of widely publicized instances of civil disobedience.

The judicial and extrajudicial payments which Chisso has made over the years, including expenditures for dredging toxic bottom sediment in Minamata Bay, have put a strain on its financial resources. By March 1984, Chisso had paid ¥71.6 billion to compensate Minamata disease victims and ¥7.4 billion for dredging operations. The company's accumulated deficits have exceeded total assets for more than three consecutive years, and it has failed to pay dividends to stockholders for more than five consecutive years.[68]

In 1979, the government responded to Chisso's near bankruptcy by providing a loan guaranteed in part by the national government. In addition, it established the Temporary Minamata Disease Certification Council to expedite the victims' compensation. However, only 98 people applied, and, of these, the Council certified 26 people and denied certification for 71 people.

Victims of chronic arsenic poisoning have also filed court actions. For victims in the Sasagatani area of Shimane prefecture, arranging for the financing of compensation payments proved difficult because of the liquidation of the mining enterprise which caused the injury.

With respect to victims of chronic arsenic poisoning, the Pollution-Related Health Damage Compensation Law has certified patients in the Sasagatani area of Shimane prefecture and the Toroku area of Miyazaki prefecture. Because the owners of the mine works at Sasagatani had liquidated the company prior to the enactment of the Compensation Law, Nihon Kogyo, another mining company, paid a special levy covering 10% of compensation benefits. This calculation was based on the contribution to arsenic pollution by Nihon Kogyo. The Pollution-Related Health Damage Compensation Association has paid the remaining 90% of the compensation benefits to the nine certified patients from the area. This program has been managed outside the usual procedures of the Compensation Law.

In Toroku, the prefectural governor negotiated a settlement between certified patients and the Sumitomo Mine Co. However, the patients were dissatisfied with the settlement. The case is in the High Court. The Pollution-Related Health Damage Compensation Association has collected a special levy in both cases only for the cost of the pollution-related health and welfare programs provided by the local governments.

6.6.3 Leap of faith: science vs. administrative expediency

A major theme in the debate surrounding the enactment of the Compensation Law was the conflict between the dire need to assist the victims of pollution and the need for scientific certainty in determining who would pay for the assistance. This theme can be traced through five issues raised in connection with the Class I aspect of the Compensation Law.

(i) Causation. Each of the four Class I diseases--chronic bronchitis, bronchial asthma, asthmatic bronchitis, and pulmonary emphysema--have multiple etiological factors, air pollution being just one of them. Yet, to have each patient seeking compensation to have to prove that his disease was caused by air pollution would place too great a burden on the victim. It took the plaintiffs in the Yokkaichi case thirteen years to prove their case in court successfully. Under the Compensation Law, victims are relieved of the burden of proving disease causation. This is not to suggest that the issue is ignored. Rather, the administrative practice under the Compensation Law has refined the basic approach to causation developed in the pollution trials into a general methodology for disease, area, term of exposure, and victim designation.[69]

(ii) <u>Area designation.</u> Perhaps more than any other issue, area designation
suggests the compromise between scientific uncertainty and administrative expediency. The criteria adopted were elevated sulfur oxides levels and a high
prevalence of designated pulmonary diseases as measured by the British Medical
Research Council (BMRC) health effects survey. Scientists also conducted a
morbidity study based on national health insurance records and a pulmonary
function test, but these did not provide consistent data. In formulating the
criteria for area designation, the government had the benefit of a number of
studies done prior to 1972, but the information was very incomplete. It also
drew on its administrative experience with area designation in connection with
the 1969 Special Relief Law for Pollution-Related Health Hazards. However, the
Special Relief Law did not provide any guidelines for district designation.

Even with elevated pollution levels and a high prevalence of disease, it
cannot be said with scientific certainty that the area's pollution caused the
disease. The best that can be said is that the pollution contributed to the
disease, or that it was a factor in the development of the disease. A related
problem is the arbitrary border of a designated area. Air flows freely over
the border, yet a person suffering from an air-pollution disease living just
outside a designated area is ineligible for compensation.

(iii) <u>Prevalence/incidence.</u> The BMRC measures the prevalence of pulmonary
diseases in an area at a given time, but it does not measure the incidence of
new cases of the diseases during a given period of time. Data providing a
correlation between pollution and incidence would have given more scientific
certainty to the process of area designation than merely pollution/prevalence
data. But incidence studies are expensive and time-consuming, and they were
dropped from the criteria used for area designation.

(iv) <u>Generalizing from Osaka and Yokkaichi.</u> The Mie Medical School, the
Osaka Adult Disease Center, prefectural health departments, and the Ministry of
Health and Welfare conducted extensive studies on air-pollution levels and
health effects in the cities of Osaka and Yokkaichi during the past decade. The
studies were valuable because they included epidemiological and clinical data.
A number of other epidemiological studies were available for Tokyo and
Kanagawa, but they were not continuous and systematic. Also, the air-
monitoring data was limited to sulfur dioxide concentration with only weak data
on particulates.

With the only good data from Osaka and Yokkaichi, the government used these
cities to formulate criteria for area designation applicable to the whole of
Japan. This was a case of administrative expediency. Even between Osaka and
Yokkaichi, the nature, composition, and pattern of the air pollution and the
area's geographical features were completely different. Also, there were
differences in the socioeconomic backgrounds of the exposed population. Yet,

it would have been very difficult to gather data and conduct studies in all polluted areas as was done in Osaka and Yokkaichi because a good study takes ten years. Also, retrospective studies were unfeasible.

(v) Transference from the 1969 Law to the 1973 Law. The twelve areas designated under the 1969 Special Relief Law were transferred to the 1973 Compensation Law when the latter became effective. But there was a wide variation in the levels of air pollution and the prevalence of chronic bronchitis in each of the twelve areas. Also, a number of the areas had been hurriedly designated in the milieu of social and political crisis. Some people queried whether a determination should be made to see if each of the 1969 areas met the criteria established under the Compensation Law. However, it was decided simply to transfer all the areas.

6.6.4 The future of area designation

In recent years, pollutors and victims have begun to push for conflicting proposals regarding the future of area designation. Pollutors wish to declassify areas with improved pollution levels while victims wish to add new areas, based on new criteria for nitrogen dioxide pollution.

In support of the proposal to declassify areas, the Keidanren (Federation of Economic Organizations) cites government studies showing that sulfur dioxide levels have declined since 1974 and especially since 1979. In fact, sulfur dioxide levels have declined more rapidly than even the air pollution control administration had expected. Nevertheless, the number of certified patients in absolute terms has continued to increase. The rate of increase did not slow down until 1979. In that year, the Keidanren began a campaign to declassify areas which show a clear improvement in air quality.[70]

The Keidanren does not object to continuing benefits for the group of currently certified patients; it objects to the certification of a new patient who is either born in or comes to a designated area where pollution levels have decreased. The Keidanren urges the revision of exposure requirements and designation criteria and the promulgation of standards for declassification.

Victims admit that sulfur dioxide levels have decreased, but they assert that nitrogen dioxide levels increased until about 1973 when they leveled off. Moreover, nitrogen dioxide levels in roadside areas are much higher than in other areas. In view of the results of experiments on animals regarding the damaging health effects of nitrogen dioxide, victims' groups have proposed that the government include nitrogen dioxide in the standards for Class I area designation. In 1977, the Environment Agency conducted a study on the health effects of nitrogen dioxide pollution in roadside zones, but the results did[71] not produce data sufficient to formulate new criteria for area designation.

However, in 1973, the Environment Agency developed an ambient air quality

standard for nitrogen dioxide, albeit based on scarce scientific information.
The agency set the standard at 0.02 ppm/24hrs. Economic and industrial organizations criticized this standard and pointed to the less strict U.S. Clean Air
Act in their defense. In 1978, the Central Advisory Council for Environmental
Pollution Control Measures issued new criteria and guides for air quality based
on three years of systematic data monitoring. The standards set were 0.02-0.03
ppm/year and 0.1-0.2 ppm/hr.[72]

In July 1978, the Environment Agency revised the ambient air-quality standard for nitrogen dioxide to 0.04-0.06 ppm/24hr. Economic and industrial
organizations objected that the revised standards were still too strict when
compared to U.S. standards.

Groups backed by the mass media have put political pressure on the Environment Agency to expand designation areas based on nitrogen dioxide pollution.
These include most of the political parties except for the Liberal Democratic
Party, the Bar Association's Committee Against Pollution, and the Environment
Conference, a group lead by Professors S. Tsuru and K. Miyamoto. The Environment Conference has requested the government to expand the number of designated
areas based on nitrogen dioxide pollution standards, and to improve the health-
and welfare-promotion programs.[73]

In this charged context, the Environment Agency has proceeded cautiously.
However, in 1983, it requested the Central Advisory Council for Environmental
Pollution Control Measures to reexamine proposals for new designation criteria
for Class 1 areas. Since this time, medical and public health personnel who
are expert in pollution matters have studied designation criteria based on
suspended particulates, sulfur dioxide, and nitrogen dioxide. In addition,
Professors I. Kato and A. Morishima have made a legal analysis of the Pollution-Related Health Damage Compensation Law, and the legal journal _Jurist_ has
published an article addressing critical issues in connection with the compensation system.[74]

6.6.5 The availability of judicial relief

In 1977, the Environment Committee of the Organisation for Economic Co-
Operation and Development published a report on the Compensation Law in which
it characterized the administrative system as a way to avoid conflict in court.
The report said, "In a country where the desire for mutual respect and trust is
so great, trials are socially disruptive, and it is not surprising that other
ways have been devised to settle conflicts, or rather to suppress them. Thus,
in passing the Pollution-Related Health Damage Compensation Law, the Government
was not trying to ensure that pollutees would be compensated more quickly, more
fully and more surely than they would have been by the courts; the Government
was also avoiding open conflicts."[75]

The OECD position is in error. Under the Compensation Law, a person is not barred from seeking judicial review of administrative determinations regarding certification, benefits, or other matters once administrative remedies are exhausted. In fact, from 1975 to 1983, a number of Class I certified patients have filed a total of five actions against private companies, quasi-government corporations, and the national government. Two cases involve industrial pollution--in Chiba in 1975 and in Okayama in 1983. Three cases involve industrial and automobile air pollution in areas adjacent to highways--in Hyogo prefecture in 1976, in Nishi-Yodogawa, Osaka in 1978, and in Kawasaki in 1982. All five cases are still pending. The plaintiffs are contesting an administrative determination of their ineligibility for certain compensation benefits.

Clearly, conflict-avoidance in the courts is not a goal of the Compensation Law because this option remains available and viable. It is true, however, that the Compensation Law may have a pacifying influence on the relationship between pollutors and victims. For example, the five lawsuits have proceeded in a climate of calm and dispassionate debate. The plaintiffs have continued to receive benefits under the Compensation Law, and the defendants have made all required payments and great efforts since 1974 to control their emissions. This is in contrast to the violent climate in which the pollution trials of the early 1970s were conducted.

6.6.6 The amount of benefits

In the 1970s, victims complained that the amount of the disability allowance was too small. This complaint can be attributed to an inappropriate comparison with the amount of damages awarded in the pollution trials.   In the trials, the courts did not directly make an award for loss of income because the plaintiffs did not ask for it. (Proving loss of income was too time-consuming and difficult.) Nevertheless, the courts made an award for loss of income under the rubric of mental suffering. The lump-sum awards were quite large compared to the small monthly disability benefit paid to a certified patient under the Compensation Law. However, in time, patients began to realize that, when cumulated, the disability benefits exceed the amount of the Yokkaichi award. Also, the disability benefit, which is based on average nationwide wages, has increased as wage levels have increased. In addition, the government has stressed the importance of the health and welfare programs, largely to counter another patient complaint--the lack of compensation for mental suffering. Although budgets for health and welfare programs have increased, local governments have always spent below budget. This is why the Fiscal Year 1985 budget for pollution-related health and welfare programs was 63.17% of the Fiscal Year 1975 budget. In any event, patients have decreased their complaints regarding the amount and scope of compensation.

In the evaluation of a patient's disability grade or cause of death, patients, families, physicians, and local Certification Councils have agonized over how to account for causes of disability or death unrelated to pollution. It is common knowledge that ageing and smoking are correlated with the incidence, prevalence, and aggravation of obstructive respiratory diseases. The government revised the diagnostic criteria for asthmatic bronchitis in May 1980 in order to exclude other causes of the disease. Since life expectancy is very long in Japan, the Keidanren has requested a review of compensation benefits, such as the survivor's allowance and the disability allowance mostly for people over 65 years of age.

6.6.7 The problems of physicians

In a study conducted under contract from the Environment Agency in March 1984, the Japan Medical Association reviewed the administration of the Compensation Law from the standpoint of the medical profession. There were two main issues: the fee scale for medical care and doctor-patient relations. The study found that doctors needed more time to consult with patients afflicted with pollution-related diseases than with other patients. This fact is seen as justifying the higher fee scale under the Compensation Law than applies under national health insurance. The government modified the fee scale for medical care in 1978 and 1984. From Fiscal Year 1975 to Fiscal Year 1985, total medical expenditures increased 6.5 times. This increase is greater than for other categories of compensation benefits. In addition, the Japan Medical Association report noted the need for a simpler and unified system of fee disbursement to cut down on the paperwork.[76]

The doctor-patient relationship issue centers on the fact that the doctor's diagnosis and recommendations affect the patient's eligibility and grade level for benefits. Doctors also make recommendations for the monthly medical treatment allowance and the survivor's benefit in cases where death is due to pollution-related causes. These are all related to the amount of compensation benefits the patient or his family will receive. These are sensitive issues, especially for members of local medical societies. In many cases the diagnosis is difficult because the symptoms are atypical or onset has been delayed.

6.6.8 The 80:20 ratio

The Keidanren and other industrial groups have attacked the cost allocation between stationary and mobile sources of air pollution. They charge that mobile sources should pay a greater proportion than they do now. Presently, stationary sources pay 80% and mobile sources pay 20% of the cost of providing benefits under the Compensation Law. Administrators arrived at the 80:20 ratio because that is the proportion in which stationary and mobile sources each contribute to total sulfur oxides and nitrogen oxides pollution. However, this formula assumes that a unit volume each of sulfur oxides and nitrogen oxides contribute to health injury in equal degrees. This has not been demonstrated to be true. In addition, mobile sources contribute more to the actual ground level concentration of nitrogen oxides. At present, the concentration of nitrogen oxides at monitoring stations is much higher than the concentration of sulfur oxides. In the past, the concentration of sulfur dioxide was higher than the concentration of nitrogen dioxide, but this shifted around 1972. In urban areas with many cars and few factories, automobile exhaust contributes about 70% to 80% of the ambient air concentration of nitrogen dioxide. However, there is no evidence to show that the present levels of the ambient air concentration of nitrogen dioxide cause harmful health effects.

Even if the law is changed so that automobile owners pay a greater proportion, there could be administrative problems. Unlike factories, automobile owners do not feel an obligation to pay for pollution damage. They have already been assessed for pollution damage through the automobile tonnage tax, which is a general government tax which existed before a part of it was allocated for compensation. If the tonnage tax is increased, some automobile owners may question their obligation to pay. This is in contrast to a factory which pays a levy based on the specific volume of sulfur dioxide emissions from its plant.

6.6.9 The high collection rate

The Pollution-Related Health Damage Compensation Association successfully collects 99.97% of payable levies. One reason for the high collection rate is that most pollutors are large, financially sound organizations. In Fiscal Year 1984, 8.2% of the notified pollutors from designated and non-designated areas paid 88.9% of the total levy collected. Five types of industries accounted for 78.3% of the total levy collected. These were the electric power, iron and steel, chemical, petroleum and coal products, and paper and pulp industries, in descending order of share. In short, big industries with a large volume of emission pay nearly 80% of the costs of the pollution-related health damage compensation system. Moreover, the association has kept its administrative costs down. In Fiscal Year 1985, it cost ¥482 million to collect ¥99,197 million, which is 0.49%. The cost of collection in Fiscal Year 1985 was only 1.1 times the cost in Fiscal Year 1975.

6.7 CONCLUSION

In general, the Pollution-Related Health Damage Compensation Law has achieved its primary goal of providing fair and timely compensation to victims of pollution. There have, of course, been many problems in the process, including the need to resort to a rebuttable presumption of causation. As the adminstration of the Compensation Law continues in its second decade, some old inequities have been eliminated but new ones have appeared in their place.

REFERENCES

1. Kogai Kenko Higai Hosho Ho, 1973 (1973, Law No.111).
2. 1950, Law No. 289.
3. Gresser, J., K. Fujikura and A. Morishima: Environmental Law in Japan, The MIT Press, Cambridge and London, 1981, 41.
4. Law 84 (1972) amending the Water Pollution Control Law, and Law 84 (1972) amending the Air Pollution Control Law.
5. Gresser, J., K. Fujikura and A. Morishima: Environmental Law in Japan, The MIT Press, Cambridge and London, 1981, 44.
6. Gresser, J., K. Fujikura, and A. Morishima: Environmental Law in Japan, The MIT Press, Cambridge and London, 1981, 305, citing data supplied by the Environment Agency.
7. Arima, S., et al. (Eds.): Minamata Disease (Chronological Table), 1979, 841-842.
8. MacAlpine, D. and Araki S. Lancet: 1958, 2, 629-631.
9. Gresser, J., K. Fujikura and A. Morishima: Environmental Law in Japan, The MIT Press, Cambridge and London, 1981, 29.
10. Gresser, J., K. Fujikura and A. Morishima: Environmental Law in Japan, The MIT Press, Cambridge and London, 1981, 87, 88, quoting Watanabe v. Chisso K.K., 696 Hanrei Jiho 15, Hanrei Kogaiho 1641 (Kumamoto Dist. Court, March 20th, 1973), the Kumamoto Minamata disease case.
11. Takeuchi, T., et al.: Kumamoto Medical Journal, 31 (Supplementary 2) (1957), 262 pp.
12. Kitamura, S., et al.: Kumamoto Medical Journal 34 (Supp. 3) (1960) 477 and H. Tokuomi et al., Kumamoto Medical Journal 34 (Supp. 3) (1960) 481.
13. Uchida, M., et al.: Kumamoto Medical Journal, 14(4), 1961, 171.
14. Irukayama, K., et al.: Nisshinigaku, 49(8) 1962, 536 and M. Fujiki, Kumamoto Medical Journal, 37(9), 1963, 494.
15. Shiraki: Science, 1964, 34, 8.
16. Kokyoyo Suiiki no Suishitsu no Hozen ni Kansuru Horitsu (1958, Law No. 181).
17. Harada, M.: Minamata Disease, 1979, 13.
18. Ui, J.: Politics of Environmental Pollution, (Kogai), 1968, 86.
19. Gresser, J., K. Fujikura and A. Morishima: Environmental Law in Japan, The MIT Press, Cambridge and London, 1981, 105 quoting the mimaikin contract.
20. Tsubaki, T.: Minamata Disease, 1979, 293-296.
21. Takizawa, Y., et al.: Journal of the Japan Hygiene Society, 42(10), 1967, 469.
22. Takizawa, Y., et al.: Journal of the Japan Hygiene Society, 42(10), 1967, 475.
23. Arima, S., et al. (Eds.): Minamata Disease, 1979, 868.
24. Arima, S., et al. (Eds.): Minamata Disease, 1979, 870 and T. Kitagawa, Investigation of the Cause of Methylmercury Pollution, 1981, 101-117.
25. Arima, S., et al. (Eds.): Minamata Disease, 1979, 875-876.
26. Kono, M., et al.: Clinical Nutrition, 18(4), 1952, 16-22.
27. Japan Public Health Association: The Report of the Contract Study under the Ministry of Health and Welfare; Environmental Pollution by Trace Heavy Metals, Fiscal Years 1965-1967, 1966-1968.
28. Yoshida, K., et al.: Arch. Env. Health, 13 (1966) 763-768.
29. Yoshida, K., et al.: Journal of the Japan Hygiene Society 22 (1967) 323-335.
30. Yoshida, K., et al.: Japan Journal of Public Health 11 (1964) 1-5.
31. Hashimoto, M.: Kankyo (Environment) 4(6) (1979) 42.

32. Yoshida, K.: 24th Assembly of the Japan Society of Air Pollution, 1983, 67.

33. Ono v. Showa Denko K.K.: 22 Kakyu Minshu (September) 1; Hanrei Jiho (NO. 642) 96; Hanrei Kogaiho 1379 (Niigata Dist. Court, September 29th, 1971); the Agano River-Niigata Minamata Disease case.

34. Watanabe v. Chisso K.K.: 696 Hanrei Jiho 15; Hanrei Kogaiho 1641 (Kumamoto Dist. Court, March 20th, 1973); the Kumamoto Minamata Disease case.

35. Shiono v. Showa Yokkaichi Sekiyu: 672 Hanrei Jiho 30, 280 Hanrei Taimuzu 100; Hanrei Kogaiho, 491 (Tsu Dist. Court, Yokkaichi Branch, July 24th, 1972); the Yokkaichi asthma case.

36. Komatsu v. Mitsui Kinzoku Kogyo K.K.: 22 Kakyu Minshu (Nos. 5 and 6) 1; 635 Hanrei Jiho 17; 264 Hanrei Taimuzu 103; Horitsu Jiho (July 1971) 336; Hanrei Kogaiho 1163 (Toyama Dist. Court, June 30th, 1971), affirmed on Koso appeal, 674 Hanrei Jiho 25; 280 Hanrei Taimuzu 182; Hanrei Kogaiho 1364 (Nagoya High Court., Kanazawa Branch, August 9, 1972); the Itai-Itai Disease case.

37. Gresser, J., K. Fujikura and A. Morishima: Environmental Law in Japan, The MIT Press, Cambridge and London, 1981, 124.

38. Ono v. Showa Denko K.K.: 22 Kakyu Minshu (September) 1; Hanrei Jiho (NO. 642) 96; Hanrei Kogaiho 1379 (Niigata Dist. Court, September 29th, 1971).

39. Gresser, J., K. Fujikura and A. Morishima: Environmental Law in Japan, The MIT Press, Cambridge and London, 1981, 92, quoting the Kumamoto Minamata disease case, Watanabe v. Chisso K.K., 696 Hanrei Jiho 15; Hanrei Kogaiho 1641 (Kumamoto Dist. Court, March 20th, 1973).

40. Yoshida, K.: Jurist 440 (1969) 104-108; K. Yoshida, Jurist (Special Edition) 84 (1972); A. Morishima, Commentary on the Important Court Judgment in 1972, 1973, 61.

41. Gresser, J., K. Fujikura and A. Morishima: Environmental Law in Japan, The MIT Press, Cambridge and London, 1981, 131.

42. Law No. 289, 1950.

43. Kogai Taisaku Kihon Ho (1967, Law No. 132); amended as Law No. 132, 1970; No. 88, 1971; No. 111, 1973; and No. 84, 1974.

44. Hashimoto, M.: Kankyo (Environment) 5(1) (1980) 49-53.

45. Hashimoto, M.: Thinking on Environmental Pollution (Nikkeishinsho 121) 1970, 146-157.

46. Hashimoto, M.: Kankyo (Environment) 5(1) (1980) 55-56.

47. Kogai Ni Kakaru Kenko Higai no Kyusai Ni Kansuru Tokubetsu Sochi Ho (1969, Law No. 90).

48. Government of Japan: White Paper on Environmental Pollution: 1970 Edition, 1971, 240-241.

49. Government of Japan: White Paper on Environmental Pollution: 1970 Edition, 1971, 237-240.

50. Hashimoto, M.: Kankyo (Environment) 5(1) (1980) 56.

51. Kido, K.: The Pollution-Related Health Damage Compensation Law, 1975, 4-6.

52. Kogai Kenko Higai Hosho Ho,1973 (1973, Law No.111).

53. Kido, K.: The Pollution-Related Health Damage Compensation Law, 1975, 422-423.

54. Kido, K.: The Pollution-Related Health Damage Compensation Law, 1975, 8-9.

55. Kido, K.: The Pollution-Related Health Damage Compensation Law, 1975, 424-427.

56. Kido, K.: The Pollution-Related Health Damage Compensation Law, 1975, 428-429.

57. Gresser, H, K. Fujikura and A. Morishima: Environmental Law in Japan, The MIT Press, Cambridge and London, 1981, 298.

58. Kido, K.: The Pollution-Related Health Damage Compensation Law, 1975, 435-436.

59. Kido, K.: The Pollution-Related Health Damage Compensation Law, 1975, 433-436.

60. Environment Agency: Pollution-Related Health Damage Compensation System Study Group, Compilation of Laws, Orders, Regulations, and Rules of the Pollution-Related Health Damage Compensation Law, 1985, 431-437.

61. Environment Agency: Pollution-Related Health Damage Compensation System Study Group, Compilation of Laws, Orders, Regulations, and Rules of the Pollution-Related Health Damage Compensation Law, 1985, 432-436.

62. Gresser, K. Fujikura, and A. Morishima, Environmental Law in Japan, The MIT Press, Cambridge and London, 1981, 297.

63. Kido, K.: The Pollution-Related Health Damage Compensation Law, 1975, 426-427.

64. Gresser, J., K. Fujikura and A. Morishima: Environmental Law in Japan, The MIT Press, Cambridge and London, 1981, 299.

65. Gresser, J., K. Fujikura and A. Morishima: Environmental Law in Japan, The MIT Press, Cambridge and London, 1981, 298.

66. Organization For Economic Co-Operation And Development: Environmental Policies in Japan, OECD, Paris, 1977, 47.

67. Gresser, J., K. Fujikura and A. Morishima: Environmental Law in Japan, The MIT Press, Cambridge and London, 1981, 312.

68. Gresser, J., K. Fujikura and A. Morishima: Environmental Law in Japan, The MIT Press, Cambridge and London, 1981, 317.

69. Gresser, J., K. Fujikura and A. Morishima: Environmental Law in Japan, The MIT Press, Cambridge and London, 1981, 290-292.

70. Keizai Dantai Rengokai (Federation of Economic Organizations): Thoughts on the Pollution-Related Health Damage Compensation System, 1979.

71. Environment Agency, Department of Environmental Health: Health Effect Study of Residents in Roadside Zones, 1977.

72. Environment Agency, Air Conservation Bureau: Criteria and Guides for Health Effect by Ambient NO_2 (Compilation of the Recommendations of the Central Advisory Council for Environmental Pollution Control Measures, 1978. The Report of the Expert Committee for Criteria and Guides of Ambient NO_2, March 1978.

73. Awaji, T., et al.: Proposal on the Pollution-Related Health Damage Compensation Law: Interim Report to the Fifth Nippon Kankyo Kaigi (Japan Environment Conference), 1984.

74. Kato, I., M. Hashimoto, A. Morishima and K. Yoshida: "The Problematic Issues of the Pollution-Related Health Damage Compensation Law (Record of Discussion)," Jurist, No.821, September 1984, 6-28.

75. Organisation for Economic Co-Operation and Development: Environmental Policies in Japan, 1977, 48-49.

76. Japan Medical Association: Interim Report of the Environmental Health Committee (Review of Pollution-Related Medical Care System), 1984.

SUBJECT INDEX